ELEMENTARY DIFFERENTIAL
EQUATIONS

ELEMENTARY DIFFERENTIAL EQUATIONS

By LYMAN M. KELLS, Ph.D.

Professor of Mathematics
at the U. S. Naval Academy

THIRD EDITION
THIRD IMPRESSION

New York and London
McGRAW-HILL BOOK COMPANY, INC.
1947

ELEMENTARY DIFFERENTIAL EQUATIONS

PREFACE TO THE THIRD EDITION

In this revision of "Elementary Differential Equations" better balance has been attempted by introducing theoretical discussions and expanded treatments all in keeping with the simplicity and strong intuitional appeal of the original text. Practically every article of the book has been revised to give maximum returns for study. While the main purpose of the book is to give general power of handling the differential equation tool effectively, a number of discussions point out the relation of the idealized situation dealt with by differential equations to the actual physical phenomena; also, the student is helped to understand many physical facts and processes from differential equations instead of memorizing them.

Early in the first chapter there is an illustrated geometrical discussion relating to solutions of differential equations. It is followed by a statement of simplified existence theorems with brief comments, the object being to give a broad point of view and a clear concept of a solution. Later these existence theorems are given in a more comprehensive form, illustrated with examples, and provided with comments and lists of problems to give penetration and detailed understanding.

The solutions of the practical problems of electricity furnish excellent illustrations of mathematical power. Accordingly the corresponding chapter has been considerably expanded. It interests a student to see how much information can be deduced from a few simple equations and to touch upon such important features of radio as resonance and frequency effects.

Operators are being used more and more in mathematics because of the brevity of their symbolism. Consequently this phase of the subject has been given more emphasis.

The importance of partial differential equations cannot be exaggerated. But its solutions are so general in nature that the student is likely to feel that they are meaningless. Accordingly boundary conditions leading to the determination of some arbitrary functions for a particular situation have been introduced at the start. Also new types have been considered and there is a separate chapter giving the outstanding applications of partial differential equations. This chapter is so designed that it may be studied without reference to the regular theoretical material.

Many of the ideas and problems in this revision have been contributed by users of the second edition and members of the Department of Mathematics at the United States Naval Academy. Profs. John Tyler and Alexander Dillingham and Dr. S. S. Saslaw have helped very materially with criticisms, suggestions, and problems.

LYMAN M. KELLS

ANNAPOLIS, Md.,
August, 1947.

PREFACE TO THE FIRST EDITION

The mathematician is generally interested in the purely formal processes and results of a mathematical investigation, independent of any particular interpretation. The physicist or engineer is likely to be interested in a result because of its meaning or interpretation when applied to some particular physical situation. The mathematical procedure, the particular interpretation, both are essential. In this book purely formal work and applications go hand in hand throughout the text.

Perhaps the most outstanding feature of the treatise is simple presentation of the fundamental types of differential equations together with illustrative examples and numerous carefully graded exercises. Although special emphasis is laid on the types most frequently used in applications, no important type is slighted. Some subjects, like simultaneous equations, are introduced in several places because they afford excellent practice and because they lend themselves to such treatment. Substitutions, integration by inspection, and use of integrating factors are stressed more than usual.

The object of the many applications is threefold, namely: to add life and interest to the subject, to give practice in formal work and interpretation, and to indicate the usefulness and power of differential equations in some important fields of knowledge. In making an application, a student must set up the appropriate differential equation, integrate it, and manipulate and interpret the result. This involves, in addition to formal procedure, understanding the general meanings of the symbols and perceiving in the result the relations existing between the quantities represented. This process is exceedingly instructive. Many applications concern the simple processes of everyday experience, many are geometrical in nature, and many others involve the laws of physics and mechanics. The lists of problems are so arranged that a student becomes familiar with necessary, fundamental ideas while solving simple problems near the beginning of a list and afterwards meets more difficult problems, some of which will tax the ingenuity of the best student.

It is a pleasure to express my appreciation of the valuable suggestions given by the members of the Department of Mathematics at the United States Naval Academy. I am especially indebted to Capt. L. B. McBride and to Profs. Paul Capron, L. T. Wilson, John Tyler, and J. B. Scarborough for various kinds of assistance.

LYMAN M. KELLS

ANNAPOLIS, MD.,
July, 1932.

CONTENTS

CHAPTER I

DEFINITIONS AND ELEMENTARY PROBLEMS

CHAPTER II

APPLICATIONS

Chapter VI

LINEAR DIFFERENTIAL EQUATIONS WITH CONSTANT COEFFICIENTS

Chapter VII

APPLICATIONS OF LINEAR EQUATIONS WITH CONSTANT COEFFICIENTS

Chapter VIII

MISCELLANEOUS DIFFERENTIAL EQUATIONS OF ORDER HIGHER THAN THE FIRST

Chapter IX

APPLICATIONS

Chapter X

DIFFERENTIAL EQUATIONS IN MORE THAN TWO VARIABLES. EXISTENCE THEOREMS

CHAPTER XI

SOLUTION BY SERIES AND BY METHODS INVOLVING SUCCESSIVE APPROXIMATIONS

ART.

CHAPTER XII

PARTIAL DIFFERENTIAL EQUATIONS OF THE FIRST ORDER

CHAPTER XIII

PARTIAL DIFFERENTIAL EQUATIONS OF ORDER HIGHER THAN THE FIRST

Chapter XIV

APPLICATIONS OF PARTIAL DIFFERENTIAL EQUATIONS

ELEMENTARY DIFFERENTIAL EQUATIONS

CHAPTER I

DEFINITIONS AND ELEMENTARY PROBLEMS

1. General remarks. Differential equations furnish a very powerful tool for solving a great many problems in pure mathematics. By them, problems involving relations between inclinations, slopes, curvatures, and other geometric quantities are often solved. The subject *differential geometry* considers a large variety of such problems. This book treats the main types of differential equations and gives some geometric applications; but the main applications are to problems of a physical nature.

Differential equations are of the greatest importance in solving many of the problems of engineering, physics, and science generally. A law is conceived and set forth as a system of differential equations; the solution of these equations tells a rather complete story of the states and motions to be expected of the materials obeying that law. For example, we assume the law, suggested by experiment, that radium disintegrates at a rate proportional to the amount present and express this in mathematical symbols by the equation

$$\frac{dQ}{dt} = kQ.$$

By solving this equation for a 100-gram lump and using facts found from experiment, the equation

$$Q = 100e^{-0.041t}$$

is easily derived. This tells approximately the amount of radium to be expected in the lump t centuries from now.

Newton conceived the law of gravitation and then solved the corresponding system of differential equations to show that the earth moves about the sun approximately in an ellipse with the sun at one focus. He made a large step forward in the development of celestial mechanics. About 1865, Maxwell conceived a relation between an electric current and the corresponding magnetic field, expressed the relation as a system of partial differential equations, solved them, and from the result predicted the waves of radio. Differential equations have played a prominent role in the development of the theories of radio, radar, and electricity generally. Similar remarks apply to nearly every great branch of science. The many applications in this book will show the great power of differential equations and give methods of using it.

2. Differential equation. Order. Degree. The student has already met differential equations of an elementary type in his study of the calculus. Thus,

$$\frac{dy}{dx} = x^2 + 3 \tag{1}$$

is a differential equation. In general, *an equation involving differentials or derivatives in its expression is a differential equation.* If the equation contains total differentials, total derivatives, or both, but does not contain partial derivatives, it is called an *ordinary differential equation;* if it contains partial derivatives, it is called a *partial differential equation.* Thus,

$$x^2\frac{d^2y}{dx^2} + 2x\frac{dy}{dx} + y = x^2 + 2, \tag{2}$$

$$\left(\frac{d^3y}{dx^3}\right)^2 + 2\frac{d^2y}{dx^2}\frac{dy}{dx} + x^2\left(\frac{dy}{dx}\right)^3 = 0, \tag{3}$$

$$\left[1 + \left(\frac{dy}{dx}\right)^2\right]^{\frac{3}{2}} = k\frac{d^2y}{dx^2}, \tag{4}$$

$$(x + y^2 - 3y)dx + (x^2 + 3x + y)dy = 0 \tag{5}$$

are ordinary differential equations; whereas

$$\frac{\partial z}{\partial x} = y, \tag{6}$$

$$\frac{\partial^2 u}{\partial x^2} + \frac{\partial^2 u}{\partial y^2} + \frac{\partial^2 u}{\partial z^2} = 0 \tag{7}$$

are partial differential equations.

The order of a differential equation is the order of the highest-ordered derivative involved in its expression. Thus, referring to the differential equations numbered (1) to (5), numbers (1) and (5) are of the first order, numbers (2) and (4) are of the second order, and number (3) is of the third order.

The degree of a differential equation is the degree that its highest-ordered derivative would have if the equation were rationalized and cleared of fractions with regard to all derivatives involved in it. Thus, equations (1), (2), (5), (6), and (7) are of the first degree; (3) and (4) are of the second degree. Equation (4) is of the second degree, for d^2y/dx^2 appears to the second degree in the equation resulting from clearing (4) of the radical represented by the 2 in the exponent $\frac{3}{2}$.

Exercises

1. Write the order and the degree of each differential equation:

(a) $\left(\frac{d^2y}{dx^2}\right)^2 = \left(\frac{dy}{dx}\right)^3 + 3$

(b) $\sqrt{\frac{d^3y}{dx^3}} = \frac{dy}{dx}$

(c) $\frac{d^2y}{dx^2} = \sqrt{3x + 4}$

(d) $\frac{d^2y}{dx^2} = \sqrt{1 + \left(\frac{dy}{dx}\right)^2}$

$$(e) \left(\frac{dy}{dx}\right)^3 - 4xy\,\frac{dy}{dx} = x^4\left(\frac{dy}{dx}\right)^2 \qquad (f)\ \frac{d^2y}{dx^2} = k\left[1 + \left(\frac{dy}{dx}\right)^2\right]^3$$

2. State the order and the degree of each differential equation in exercises 13 to 17 of §3.

3. Solution of a differential equation. *A solution, or integral, of an ordinary differential equation in two variables is a relation between the variables which satisfies the equation.* If, in particular, the solution has the form $y = f(x)$, then replacement of y and the derivatives of y with respect to x by $f(x)$ and its derivatives produces an identity. A few examples will make this clear.

Example 1. Prove that $y = Ae^x + Be^{-2x} + x^2 + x$, A and B constants, is a solution of $\dfrac{d^2y}{dx^2} + \dfrac{dy}{dx} - 2y = 3 - 2x^2$.

Proof. From $y = Ae^x + Be^{-2x} + x^2 + x$, we obtain

$$\frac{dy}{dx} = Ae^x - 2Be^{-2x} + 2x + 1, \frac{d^2y}{dx^2} = Ae^x + 4Be^{-2x} + 2.$$

Substituting these values in the differential equation, we get the identity

$$Ae^x + 4Be^{-2x} + 2 + Ae^x - 2Be^{-2x} + 2x +$$
$$1 - 2Ae^x - 2Be^{-2x} - 2x^2 - 2x = 3 - 2x^2.$$

Example 2. Prove that $\log y + x/y = c$ is a solution of $(y - x)dy + y\,dx = 0$.

Proof. The given differential equation may be written

$$(y - x)\frac{dy}{dx} + y = 0.. \qquad (a)$$

Using the regular process of differentiating an implicit function, we obtain from $\log y + x/y = c$

$$\frac{1}{y}\frac{dy}{dx} - \frac{x}{y^2}\frac{dy}{dx} + \frac{1}{y} = 0,$$

or, solving for dy/dx,

$$\frac{dy}{dx} = \frac{-y}{y - x}. \qquad (b)$$

Substituting in (a) the value of dy/dx from (b), we obtain

$$(y - x) \left(\frac{-y}{y - x} \right) + y = -y + y = 0.$$

Exercises

Prove that each equation is a solution of the differential equation written opposite it:

1. $y = x^3 + 2x^2 + 5x + c$ $\dfrac{dy}{dx} = 3x^2 + 4x + 5$

2. $y = A \sin x + B \cos x$ $\dfrac{d^2y}{dx^2} + y = 0$

3. $y = \dfrac{x^3}{4} + \dfrac{c}{x}$ $x \dfrac{dy}{dx} + y = x^3$

4. $2y = (x + 1)^4 + c(x + 1)^2$ $\dfrac{dy}{dx} - \dfrac{2y}{x + 1} = (x + 1)^3$

5. $y = (x + c)e^{-x}$ $\dfrac{dy}{dx} + y = e^{-x}$

6. $y = c_1 x + c_2 - \sin x$ $\dfrac{d^2y}{dx^2} = \sin x$

7. $y = c_1 \sin 3x + c_2 \cos 3x$ $\dfrac{d^2y}{dx^2} + 9y = 81x^2$
$+ 9x^2 - 2$

8. $y = c^2 + cx^{-1}$ $y + x \dfrac{dy}{dx} = x^4 \left(\dfrac{dy}{dx} \right)^2$

9. $y = c_1 e^{2x} + c_2 e^{-4x} + 2xe^{2x}$ $\dfrac{d^2y}{dx^2} + 2 \dfrac{dy}{dx} - 8y = 12e^{2x}$

10. $y = c(x - c)^2$ $\left(\dfrac{dy}{dx} \right)^3 - 4xy \dfrac{dy}{dx} + 8y^2 = 0$

11. $y^2 - cx + c^2 = 0$ $4y \left(\dfrac{dy}{dx} \right)^2 - 2x \dfrac{dy}{dx} + y = 0$

12. $\cos y = 1 + ce^{-\cos x}$ $\sin y \dfrac{dy}{dx} + \sin x \cos y = \sin x$

13. $y^{-3} = x^3 (3e^x + c)$ $x \dfrac{dy}{dx} + y + x^4 y^4 e^x = 0$

14. $x^2 + y^2 = x^2 y^2 + c$ $(x - y^2 x)dx + (1 - x^2)y \, dy = 0$

15. $\sin^{-1} \dfrac{y}{x} = c - x$ $x \dfrac{dy}{dx} - y + x\sqrt{x^2 - y^2} = 0$

16. $\log y = c_1 e^x + c_2 e^{-x} \ast$ $y \dfrac{d^2y}{dx^2} - \left(\dfrac{dy}{dx} \right)^2 = y^2 \log y$

17. $y = c_1 x^{c_2}$ $xy \dfrac{d^2y}{dx^2} + y \dfrac{dy}{dx} - x \left(\dfrac{dy}{dx} \right)^2 = 0$

$\ast$ The symbol log x, with no base specified, indicates throughout this text a logarithm to the base $e = 2.7183$ approximately.

4. Geometric considerations. Any differential equation of the first order and the first degree may be written in the form

$$\frac{dy}{dx} = f(x,y). \tag{8}$$

From the form of (8) we conclude that it associates to each point (x_0, y_0) a line whose slope is $(dy/dx)_0 = f(x_0, y_0)$, or, in

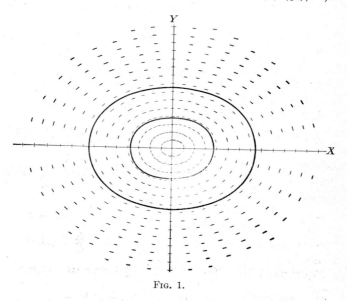

FIG. 1.

other words, it associates to each point in the plane a direction. Any curve satisfying (8) must have at each of its points the slope given by (8), that is, the tangent line to the curve at any point on it has the direction associated with this point by (8).

Figure 1 represents some points with a line through each to represent the direction associated with the point by

$$\frac{dy}{dx} = \frac{-x}{2y} .$$ (9)

The ellipses shown represent solutions of (9). Observe that at each point on an ellipse the curve is tangent to the associated direction line.

The solution of equation (9) is

$$x^2 + 2y^2 = c.$$ (10)

Here the constant of integration may be any number; hence equation (10) represents a family of ellipses. Any point $P(x_0,y_0)$ in the plane, except $(0,0)$, will lie on the ellipse represented by equation (10) with $c = x_0^2 + 2y_0^2$, and through each point, except $(0,0)$, will pass one and only one of these ellipses. The two arbitrary constants in the solution $x^2 + 2y^2 = x_0^2 + 2y_0^2$ are really equivalent to only one since all solutions could be obtained by taking $x_0 = 0$ and assigning values to y_0. The small ellipse is associated with the value $c = 1$ and the large one with $c = 2$.

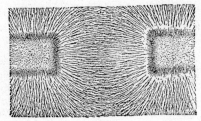

FIG. 2.

Figure 2, showing the distribution of iron filings under the influence of a magnet, exhibits the same type of relationship. The iron filings serve as direction lines, and their distribution is such that the curves to which they belong are suggested. A map indicating the directions of ocean currents and winds by means of barbed lines suggests the same situation.

5. Existence theorems. The existence theorems stated without proof in this article will be assumed throughout the text. For simplicity of statement the conditions given here are unnecessarily restrictive. More general theorems are stated in §83.

The relation indicated geometrically in §4 illustrates a case covered by the following theorem:

Theorem I. *A differential equation*

$$\frac{dy}{dx} = f(x,y) \tag{11}$$

has, in a region S, *a unique solution* y = φ (x) *satisfied by* (x_0, y_0) *provided that* (x_0, y_0) *is an interior point of* S *and that* f(x,y) *and* $\dfrac{\partial f(x,y)}{\partial y}$ *are real, single-valued, and continuous in* S.

Here x_0 and y_0 appear as two arbitrary constants. They are equivalent to only one for the reason suggested in §4.

When speaking of a region S in connection with several variables $x, y, y_1, \ldots$, we shall understand that each is restricted to a range of values defined by such expressions as

$$| x - x_0 | \leqq a, | y - y_0 | \leqq b, | y_1 - y_{10} | \leqq c, \cdots$$

Theorem II. *A system of differential equations*

$$\frac{d^n y}{dx^n} = f(x, y, y_1, y_2, \ldots, y_{n-1}),$$

$$\frac{dy}{dx} = y_1, \frac{d^2 y}{dx^2} = y_2, \ldots, \frac{d^{n-1} y}{dx^{n-1}} = y_{n-1} \tag{12}$$

has, in a region S, *a unique solution*

$$y = y(x), y_1 = y_1(x), \ldots, y_{n-1} = y_{n-1}(x) \tag{13}$$

satisfied by the values

$$x = x_0, y = b_0, y_1 = b_1, \ldots, y_{n-1} = b_{n-1},$$

provided $\quad x = x_0, y = b_0, \ldots, y_{n-1} = b_{n-1}$

lie in the region S, *and* $f, \dfrac{\partial f}{\partial y}, \dfrac{\partial f}{\partial y_1}, \ldots, \dfrac{\partial f}{\partial y_{n-1}}$ *are continuous and single-valued in* S.

Observe that (12) is equivalent to a differential equation of the nth order, that its solution is $y = y(x)$, and that it involves the arbitrary constants $b_0, b_1, \ldots, b_{n-1}$. The theorem may be stated roughly by saying that under certain restrictive conditions an nth order differential equation has a solution involving n arbitrary constants, or, more precisely, that it has a unique solution satisfying the conditions $y = b_0$, $\dfrac{dy}{dx} = b_1, \ldots, \dfrac{d^{n-1}y}{dx^{n-1}} = b_{n-1}$ when $x = x_0$. For more discussion of theorems I and II, see §83.

A differential equation may have a so-called *singular solution* that will not be represented by (13); geometrically this solution appears as an envelope of solution curves, and the restrictive conditions of the theorems are not all satisfied at its points. Singular solutions will be considered in Chapter V.

6. General solution. Primitive. *A particular solution* of a differential equation is any relation satisfying it. The general solution, also called the *complete solution* and the *complete primitive*, defines all, or nearly all, the solutions of the differential equation. The general solution for most of the elementary types considered in this book will contain a number of *arbitrary constants equal to the number expressing the order of the differential equation*. The student may observe that this relation held true for the equations and their solutions in §3; also the process of §7 will verify the relation. Particular solutions may be obtained from the general by replacing the arbitrary constants with definite numbers. The singular solution mentioned in §5 is not obtained in this way and is not considered as part of the general solution.

Take, for example, the differential equation $d^2y/dx^2 = 12x$. Let $y' = dy/dx$ and the equation becomes

$$\frac{dy'}{dx} = 12x, \text{ or } dy' = 12x \, dx. \qquad (a)$$

Obtain from this by integration

$$y' = 6x^2 + c_1.$$

Now replace y' by dy/dx, multiply through by dx, and integrate again to obtain

$$y = 2x^3 + c_1x + c_2. \tag{b}$$

Equation (b) is the complete solution of the given differential equation. Note that it contains two arbitrary constants c_1 and c_2 and that two is the order of the given differential equation. If c_1 and c_2 in (b) are replaced by 1 and 0, respectively, the particular solution $y = 2x^3 + x$ is obtained.

7. Finding differential equation from general solution.
Two problems arise: first, given a differential equation, to find a solution and the general solution if possible; second, given the general solution or primitive, to find the differential equation.

Generally, the complete solution cannot be found in finite form. Consequently much of our work will consist in dealing with important special cases. A very simple case is considered in §8. General methods by means of infinite series and approximation methods will be considered in Chapter XI.

To solve the converse problem, namely, that of *finding the differential equation when the general solution is given: differentiate the general solution, differentiate the derived equation, differentiate the second derived equation, etc., until the number of derived equations is equal to the number of independent arbitrary constants in the general solution; finally eliminate the constants from the general solution and the derived equations.* A few examples will illustrate the process.

Example 1. Find the differential equation whose general solution is $y = c \cos x$.

Solution. For convenience we shall use primes to indicate derivatives with respect to x. From the given general solution, obtain

$$y = c \cos x, \frac{dy}{dx} = y' = -c \sin x. \qquad (a)$$

Equate the values of c from the two equations in (a) to get

$$\frac{y}{\cos x} = \frac{-y'}{\sin x}, \text{ or } \mathbf{y' \cos x + y \sin x = 0.}^* \qquad (b)$$

Also, using determinants to eliminate c from (a), we obtain

$$\begin{vmatrix} y & \cos x \\ y' & -\sin x \end{vmatrix} = 0.$$

Example 2. Find the differential equation whose general solution is $y = c_1 e^{2x} + c_2 e^{-x} + x$.

Solution. The general solution and the first two derived equations are

$$y = c_1 e^{2x} + c_2 e^{-x} + x, \qquad (a)$$

$$\frac{dy}{dx} = y' = 2c_1 e^{2x} - c_2 e^{-x} + 1, \qquad (b)$$

$$\frac{d^2 y}{dx^2} = y'' = 4c_1 e^{2x} + c_2 e^{-x}. \qquad (c)$$

Eliminating c_2 from (a) and (b) and then from (b) and (c), we get

$$y' + y = 3c_1 e^{2x} + x + 1, \ y'' + y' = 6c_1 e^{2x} + 1. \qquad (d)$$

Multiplying the first equation of (d) by 2, subtracting the result from the second, and simplifying slightly, we get

$$\mathbf{y'' - y' - 2y = -2x - 1.}$$

Also by determinants we obtain from (a), (b), and (c):

$$\begin{vmatrix} y - x & e^{2x} & e^{-x} \\ y' - 1 & 2e^{2x} & -e^{-x} \\ y'' & 4e^{2x} & e^{-x} \end{vmatrix} = e^{2x} e^{-x} \begin{vmatrix} y - x & 1 & 1 \\ y' - 1 & 2 & -1 \\ y'' & 4 & 1 \end{vmatrix} = 0.$$

* Throughout the text answers to examples appear in boldface type.

Exercises

For each of the general solutions, numbered 1 to 16, find the corresponding differential equation:

1. $y = ce^x$
2. $y^2 = cx$
3. $y = c_1x^2 + c_2$
4. $y = c_1e^x + c_2e^{-2x}$
5. $y^2 = c_1x^2 + c_2$
6. $y = c_1x + c_2$
7. $y = c_1x^2 + c_2x + c_3$
8. $x^2 + y^2 = c^2$

9. $y = cx + 3c^2 - 4c$
10. $y = c_1 \sin 3x + c_2 \cos 3x$
11. $(x + y - 1)^3 = c(x - y + 3)$
12. $y = c_1e^{2x} + c_2e^{3x} + 2$
13. $y = x \tan (x + c)$
14. $y = c_1e^{c_2x}$
15. $(x - c_1)^2 + y^2 = c_2^2$
16. $(x - c_1)^2 + (y - c_2)^2 = 25$

17. Find the equation of the family of circles having unit radius and having their centers on the X-axis; (a) then obtain a differential equation whose general solution is the equation just found. Treat similarly the following plane families: (b) concentric circles with center at the origin; (c) straight lines through the origin; (d) all circles of radius four units; (e) confocal conics defined by $\dfrac{x^2}{2 + c} + \dfrac{y^2}{c - 2} = 1$; (f) all straight lines; (g) all circles.

18. Find the differential equation whose general solution represents the tangent lines of the parabola $y^2 = 4x$. Prove that $y^2 = 4x$ is a solution of this differential equation.

8. **Variables separable.** To illustrate the type of problem which calls for the general solution of a given differential equation, we shall consider a type of the first order and first degree, which can easily be reduced to the form

$$f_1(x)dx + f_2(y)dy = 0, \qquad (14)$$

where $f_1(x)$ is a function of x alone and $f_2(y)$ is a function of y alone. This type is referred to as *variables separable*. Direct integration of equation (14) gives the general solution

$$\int f_1(x)dx + \int f_2(y)dy = c, \qquad (15)$$

where c is an arbitrary constant. It is evident that equation (14) would result from differentiating equation (15), even if we should write any function of c instead of c. Hence, we may use $\log c$, $\tan^{-1} c$, or any other function of c instead of c, in order to obtain the simplest form of a solution.

Example 1. Find the equation of the curves for which

$$xy \, dy - \frac{1 + y^2}{1 + x^2} \, dx = 0. \qquad (a)$$

Also find the solution of (a) having a graph containing point $(1,-3)$.

Solution. Division of (a) by $x(1 + y^2)$ gives

$$\frac{y \, dy}{1 + y^2} - \frac{dx}{x(1 + x^2)} = 0. \qquad (b)$$

By integration we obtain from (b)

$$\int \frac{y \, dy}{1 + y^2} - \int \frac{dx}{x(1 + x^2)} = \text{constant},$$

or

$$\tfrac{1}{2} \log (1 + y^2) - \tfrac{1}{2} \log \frac{x^2}{1 + x^2} = \tfrac{1}{2} \log c. \qquad (c)$$

Canceling $\tfrac{1}{2}$ and using the laws of logarithms, we get

$$\log \frac{(1 + y^2)(1 + x^2)}{x^2} = \log c. \qquad (d)$$

Two numbers that have the same logarithm are equal. Hence

$$\frac{(1 + y^2)(1 + x^2)}{x^2} = c, \text{ or } (1 + y^2)(1 + x^2) = cx^2. \quad (e)$$

To find the equation of the curve through $(1,-3)$ substitute 1 for x and -3 for y in (e) to obtain $(1 + 9)(1 + 1) = c(1)^2$, or $c = 20$. Now replace c in (e) by 20 to obtain

$$(1 + y^2)(1 + x^2) = 20x^2.$$

Example 2. Find the general solution of $a\left(x\dfrac{dy}{dx} + 2y\right) = xy\dfrac{dy}{dx}$ and then find a particular solution in which $y = a$ when $x = 2a$.

Solution. Clearing of fractions and grouping the terms containing dx and those containing dy, we get

$$2ay\, dx + (ax-xy)dy = 0, \qquad (a)$$

or

$$2ay\, dx + x(a-y)dy = 0. \qquad (b)$$

Dividing through by xy and integrating, we obtain

$$2a\int\frac{dx}{x} + a\int\frac{dy}{y} - \int dy = \text{constant},$$

or

$$2a \log x + a \log y - y = a \log c. \qquad (c)$$

Dividing by a, replacing $2 \log x$ by $\log x^2$, and combining the logarithmic terms, we get

$$\log\frac{x^2 y}{c} = \frac{y}{a}.$$

Remembering that $e^{\log N} = N$, we obtain

$$e^{\log x^2 y/c} = e^{y/a}, \text{ or } \mathbf{x^2 y = ce^{y/a}}. \qquad (d)$$

To find c so that $y = a$ when $x = 2a$, substitute $2a$ for x and a for y in (d) and solve for c to obtain

$$4a^3 = ce^{a/a}, \text{ or } c = 4a^3 e^{-1}.$$

Substitute this value of c in (d) to obtain the required particular solution

$$\mathbf{x^2 y = 4a^3 e^{-1} e^{y/a}}.$$

Exercises

Find the general solutions of the differential equations 1 to 16.

1. $x\, dx + y\, dy = 0$

2. $x^2\, dy - y^2\, dx = 0$

3. $x\, dy - y\, dx = 0$

4. $x(1 + y^2)dx + 2y(1 + x^2)dy = 0$

5. $(1 + y)dx + (2 - x)dy = 0$

6. $\dfrac{d\rho}{d\theta} = \rho$

7. $L\dfrac{di}{dt} + Ri = 0$, L and R constants

8. $y\, dx - y^2\, dy = dy$

9. $y\, dx + \sqrt{1 + x^2}\, dy = 0$

10. $\sqrt{1 + y^2}\, dx = \sqrt{1 - x^2}\, dy$

11. $2x\, dy + y\, dx = x^2\, dy$

12. $xy\, dx - \sqrt{x^2 + a^2}\, dy = 0$

13. $x\,dy + y\,dx = x^3\,dy$ **15.** $e^{3x}e^{2y}dy - e^{-5y}dx = 0$

14. $y - x\dfrac{dy}{dx} = ay^2 + a\dfrac{dy}{dx}$ **16.** $\dfrac{dy}{dx} - y^2 = y$

Find the particular solution of each differential equation satisfied by the indicated values of the variables:

17. $x\,dx + y\,dy = 0$, $y = 3$ when $x = 2$

18. $x\,dy - y\,dx = 0$, $y = 12$ when $x = 2$

19. $\rho\,d\theta = d\rho$, $\rho = 2$ when $\theta = 0$

20. $(1 + x^2)dy = xy\,dx$, $y = -2$ when $x = 0$

21. $2x^2y\,dy - dx = x^2\,dx$, $y = 1$ when $x = 1$

22. $4\,dy + y\,dx = x^2\,dy$, $y = -1$ when $x = 4$

23. $y\sqrt{1 - x^2}\,dy + x\sqrt{1 - y^2}\,dx = 0$, $y = \frac{4}{5}$ when $x = \frac{3}{5}$

24. $2y\,dx + x^2dy = -dx$, $y = \frac{7}{2}$ when $x = \dfrac{1}{\log 2}$

25. $2x\,dy + dx = dy$, $y = 0$ when $x = 3$

26. $3e^x \tan y\,dx + (1 + e^x) \sec^2 y\,dy = 0$; $\left(\log_e 2, \dfrac{\pi}{4} \right)$

27. $\dfrac{dr}{r^2\,d\theta} = \sqrt{\dfrac{-1}{r^2} + \dfrac{3}{r} + 4}$, $r = \frac{2}{3}$ when $\theta = 0$. *Hint:* Let $z = \dfrac{1}{r}$.

CHAPTER II

APPLICATIONS

9. Problems involving slope. Many problems involving the slope of a curve, and therefore dy/dx in rectangular co-ordinates, can be solved by expressing the conditions of the problems in the form of differential equations and then integrating them. The following examples will illustrate the process.

Example 1. A curve passing through $(3, -4)$ has a slope at any point (x, y) on the curve equal to $2y/x$. Find its equation.

Solution.

$$\frac{dy}{dx} = \frac{2y}{x}, \text{ or } \frac{dy}{y} = 2\frac{dx}{x}. \tag{a}$$

Integrating (a), we obtain

$$\log y = 2 \log x + \log c = \log cx^2. \tag{b}$$

Hence

$$y = cx^2. \tag{c}$$

Since $(3, -4)$ lies on the curve, we substitute 3 for x and -4 for y in (c) to get

$$-4 = 9c, \text{ or } c = \frac{-4}{9}.$$

Hence

$$y = \frac{-4}{9}x^2, \text{ or } \mathbf{4x^2 + 9y = 0.}$$

Example 2. Find the most general kind of curve such that the normal at any point of it coincides in direction with the line connecting this point to the origin.

16

Solution. To solve a problem of this kind the student should first draw a figure representing the curve with any point (x,y) on it and showing the essential relations involved in the problem. Then he should try to find the value of the slope of the required curve or some expression containing the slope, form the equation, and integrate it.

Since the tangent at the point (x,y) and the normal at the same point are perpendicular to each other, the slope of one is the negative reciprocal of the slope of the other. From Fig. 1 it appears that the slope of the normal is y/x. Hence

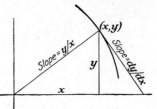

Slope of tangent $= \dfrac{dy}{dx} = \dfrac{-x}{y}$.

Integrating this, we obtain

Fig. 1.

$$\frac{x^2}{2} + \frac{y^2}{2} = \frac{c}{2}, \text{ or } \mathbf{x^2 + y^2 = c.}$$

This represents the family of circles with center at the origin.

Example 3. A curve which cuts every member of a family of curves at right angles is called an *orthogonal trajectory* of the family. Find the orthogonal trajectory through $(2,4)$ of the family of semicubical parabolas represented by

$$y^2 = cx^3. \tag{a}$$

Solution. Differentiating (a) and solving for dy/dx, we obtain

$$\frac{dy}{dx} = \frac{3x^2 c}{2y}. \tag{b}$$

Replacing c in (b) by its value from (a), we get

$$\frac{dy}{dx} = \frac{3x^2}{2y}\frac{y^2}{x^3} = \frac{3y}{2x}. \tag{c}$$

As the slope of the orthogonal trajectory is the negative reciprocal of the slope of the given curve, we have

$$\left(\frac{dy}{dx}\right)_{\text{orthog. traj.}} = \frac{-2x}{3y}. \qquad (d)$$

The solution of (d) is

$$2x^2 + 3y^2 = c_1. \qquad (e)$$

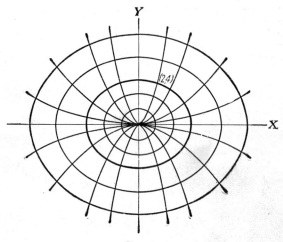

Fig. 2.

This represents a family of ellipses, but we want the curve through $(2,4)$. Substitution of 2 for x and 4 for y in (e) gives $c_1 = 56$. Hence

$$2x^2 + 3y^2 = 56.$$

A brief consideration of Fig. 2 will serve to clarify essential relations.

Problems

1. Find the equation of the system of curves and the equation of the particular curve that passes through point $(3,4)$, if the slope of the tangent at any point is $(a)\ 2x - 2$; $(b)\ 1/y^2$; $(c)\ y/x$; $(d)\ 9x/16y$; $(e)\ \dfrac{1+x}{1-y}$.

2. Prove that, if the slope of a plane curve is constant, the curve is a straight line.

3. Find the orthogonal trajectories of the system of curves (a) $y^2 = x^2 + c$; (b) $x^2 + y^2 = c^2$; (c) $y^2 = 2cx$; (d) $y = cx^5$; (e) $xy = cx - 1$.

4. In the solution of Example 3, the constant c was replaced by y^2/x^3. Why was this necessary? If we had not eliminated c but had integrated $dy/dx = -2y/3cx^2$, what would have been the relation between the original system of curves and the system obtained from the integration?

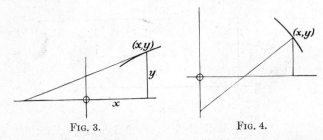

FIG. 3.   FIG. 4.

5. The segment of any tangent line to a curve between the point of contact and the X-axis is bisected by the Y-axis. Find the equation of the curve. If the segment of the tangent line just considered is cut in the ratio a/b by the Y-axis, find the equation of the curve (see Fig. 3).

6. A segment of the normal at any point of a curve is terminated by the point at one end and by the Y-axis at the other (see Fig. 4). Find the equation of the curve (a) if for every point of the curve the X-axis bisects this segment; (b) if the distance from the point to the intersection of the normal with the X-axis is to the length of the segment as a is to b.

7. Find the equation of the curve so drawn that every point on it is equidistant from the origin and the intersection of the X-axis with the normal to the curve at the point.

8. The ordinate of any point on a curve, the tangent to the curve at the point, and the X-axis bound an area of constant magnitude. Find the equation of the curve.

9. If the circle drawn tangent to a curve at any point (x,y) on the curve and passing through the point $(x,0)$ has a chord of constant length lying along the X-axis, find the equation of the curve.

10. Some review formulas. Many formulas can be conveniently recalled by means of figures suggesting important relations between the quantities involved. From Fig. 5 we read

$$\tan \theta = \frac{dy}{dx}, \; ds = \sqrt{dx^2 + dy^2} = \sqrt{1 + \left(\frac{dy}{dx}\right)^2} \, dx,$$

$$\sin \theta = \frac{dy}{ds}, \; \cos \theta = \frac{dx}{ds}, \ldots \tag{1}$$

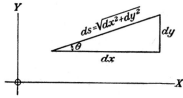

Fig. 5.

From Fig. 6 with indicated construction and definitions we read $TM/y = \cot \theta = dx/dy$, or

$$\text{Length of subtangent } TM = y\frac{dx}{dy}. \tag{2}$$

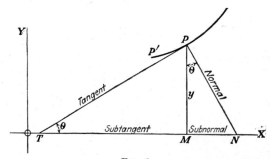

Fig. 6.

Also $MN/y = \tan \theta = dy/dx$, or

$$\text{Subnormal } MN = y\frac{dy}{dx} \tag{3}$$

Similarly, the student can easily obtain

$$PN = y\frac{ds}{dx}, \quad TP = y\frac{ds}{dy}. \tag{4}$$

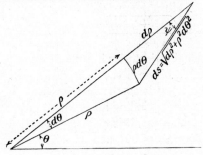

FIG. 7.

In Fig. 7, treat the small triangle as a right triangle and observe that ψ represents the angle between the radius vector at a point and the tangent line at the point. From Fig. 7 we read

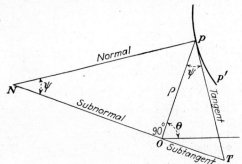

FIG. 8.

$$\tan\psi = \frac{\rho\, d\theta}{d\rho}, \quad ds = \sqrt{d\rho^2 + \rho^2\, d\theta^2} = \sqrt{\left(\frac{d\rho}{d\theta}\right)^2 + \rho^2}\, d\theta,$$

$$\cos\psi = \frac{d\rho}{ds}, \quad \sin\psi = \frac{\rho\, d\theta}{ds}, \cdots \tag{5}$$

From Fig. 8 with the indicated construction and definitions, we obtain

$$\text{Subtangent } OT = \rho^2 \frac{d\theta}{d\rho}, \text{ Subnormal } ON = \frac{d\rho}{d\theta},$$

$$PT = \frac{\rho\sqrt{d\rho^2 + \rho^2 \, d\theta^2}}{d\rho}, \quad PN = \frac{\sqrt{d\rho^2 + \rho^2 \, d\theta^2}}{d\theta}. \tag{6}$$

11. Orthogonal trajectories in polar coordinates. If ψ_c represents the angle between the radius vector to a point on a curve and the tangent to the curve at the point, and if ψ_o represents the corresponding angle for a perpendicular curve through the same point, it is evident that ψ_o and ψ_c differ by 90°. Hence $\psi_o = \psi_c \pm 90°$, and we have

$$\tan \psi_o = -\cot \psi_c = \frac{-1}{\tan \psi_c}. \tag{7}$$

The following example will illustrate the use of this formula.

Example. Find the orthogonal trajectories of the system of circles $\rho = c \cos \theta$.

Solution.

$$\tan \psi_c = \frac{\rho \, d\theta}{d\rho} = \frac{\rho}{d\rho/d\theta} = \frac{c \cos \theta}{-c \sin \theta}.$$

Therefore $\tan \psi_o = \sin \theta / \cos \theta$. Hence for the orthogonal trajectories $\rho(d\theta/d\rho) = \tan \theta$; therefore $\cot \theta \, d\theta = d\rho/\rho$, and

$$\log \rho = \log \sin \theta + \log c_1, \text{ or } \rho = c_1 \sin \theta.$$

Problems

1. Find the equation of the curve having (a) constant length of subnormal equal 5 and passing through (6,3); (b) constant length of subtangent equal 3 and passing through (0,10).

2. Find the curve whose subtangent equals n times the abscissa of the point of contact.

3. Find the curves in which the length of the subnormal is proportional to (a) the square of the ordinate; (b) the nth power of the abscissa.

4. Find the curve in which the polar subnormal is proportional to (a) the length of the radius vector; (b) the sine of the vectorial angle.

5. Find the curve in which the polar subtangent is proportional to (a) the length of the radius vector; (b) the length of the subnormal.

6. Find the orthogonal trajectories of the following curves:

(a) $\rho = c \sin \theta$ (b) $\rho = \tan \theta + c$ (c) $2\rho^2 = \theta^4 + c$

(d) $\sec \theta = c\rho^4$ (e) $\rho = c \sin (\theta/3)$ (f) $\rho = c(1 - \cos \theta)$

7. Find the equation of the curve through point $\rho = a$, $\theta = 0$ and cutting all lines through the pole at a constant angle α. *Hint:* $\tan \psi = \tan \alpha$.

8. Find the equation of the curve for which the angle between the radius vector to any point on it and the tangent to it at this same point is equal to (a) the vectorial angle of the point; (b) one third of the angle between the tangent line and the polar axis. *Hint to (b):* Use $\psi = \frac{1}{3}(\psi + \theta)$ and $180° - \psi = \frac{1}{3}(\psi + \theta)$.

9. The area bounded by a curve, the X-axis, a fixed ordinate, and a variable ordinate is proportional to the difference between the ordinates. Find the equation of the curve. *Hint:* $A = k(y - b)$, $dA = k \, dy$; that is, $y \, dx = k \, dy$.

10. The area bounded by the X-axis, a curve, a fixed ordinate, and a variable ordinate is revolved about the X-axis. If the volume of the solid generated is proportional to the difference between the radii of its bases, find the equation of the curve.

Hint: $\dfrac{d}{dx}\left[\int_a^x \pi y^2 \, dx\right] dx = \pi y^2 \, dx$

12. Higher-degree equations.

Many differential equations of the first order but of degree higher than the first can be integrated either (a) *by solving the equation for the first derivative and integrating each resulting equation separately,* or (b) *by factoring the equation, equating each factor to zero, and integrating the resulting equations.*

Example. Solve

$$\rho \frac{d\theta}{d\rho} - \frac{2}{\rho} \frac{d\rho}{d\theta} = 1.$$

Solution. Clearing of fractions and dividing by $d\theta^2$, we have

$$\rho^2 \frac{d\theta^2}{d\theta^2} - 2\frac{d\rho^2}{d\theta^2} = \frac{\rho \, d\rho \, d\theta}{d\theta^2}.$$

Hence

$$2\left(\frac{d\rho}{d\theta}\right)^2 + \rho\left(\frac{d\rho}{d\theta}\right) - \rho^2 = 0.$$

Solving for $d\rho/d\theta$, we find

$$\frac{d\rho}{d\theta} = \frac{-\rho \pm \sqrt{\rho^2 + 8\rho^2}}{4} = \frac{-\rho \pm 3\rho}{4} = -\rho, \frac{\rho}{2}.$$

Hence

$$\frac{d\rho}{d\theta} = -\rho, \frac{d\rho}{d\theta} = \frac{\rho}{2}.$$

The solutions of these equations are

$$\rho = ce^{-\theta}, \rho = ce^{\theta/2}.$$

All curves represented by the equations just written will also be represented by

$$(\rho - ce^{-\theta})(\rho - ce^{\theta/2}) = 0,$$

that is, by

$$\rho^2 - c\rho(e^{-\theta} + e^{\theta/2}) + c^2e^{-\theta/2} = 0.$$

Problems

1. Solve $y\dfrac{dx}{dy} + 2x = \dfrac{3x^2\,dy}{y\,dx}$

2. Solve $k\sqrt{dx^2 + dy^2} = dx$

3. Solve $\dfrac{\rho\,d\theta}{\sqrt{d\rho^2 + \rho^2\,d\theta^2}} = k$

4. Find two equations which satisfy

$$x\left(\frac{dy}{dx}\right)^2 - (2y + x^2)\frac{dy}{dx} + 2xy = 0$$

and which represent curves passing through $(-3,6)$.

5. Find the equation of the curve having (a) constant length of normal equal a and passing through $(0,a)$; (b) constant length of tangent equal a and passing through $(0,-a)$.

6. Show that, if any one of the four lengths, subnormal, subtangent, normal, tangent, in rectangular coordinates is proportional to any other one, the curve is a straight line. *Hint:* Prove that in each case the slope will be constant.

7. Find the equation of the curve through the point $\rho = a$, $\theta = 0$, with constant length a of (a) polar normal, (b) polar tangent.

8. The area of a surface of revolution between two planes perpendicular to its axis, one fixed the other variable, is proportional to the distance between the planes. Prove that the surface must be a sphere or a cylinder. *Hint:* $dS = 2\pi y\,ds = d[k(x - a)]$.

13. Use of limits.

In many cases it is convenient to use limits instead of determining the constant of integration and other constants. If we integrate a differential equation

$$f_1(x)dx + f_2(y)dy = 0, \tag{8}$$

we obtain

$$F_1(x) + F_2(y) = c, \tag{9}$$

where $F_1(x)$ and $F_2(y)$ are got by integrating $f_1(x)dx$ and $f_2(y)dy$, respectively. Suppose then that (a,b) and (l,m) are pairs of values satisfying (9) for a definite, but unknown, value of c. Then

$$F_1(a) + F_2(b) = c, \tag{10}$$
$$F_1(l) + F_2(m) = c. \tag{11}$$

Subtracting (11) from (10), we obtain

$$F_1(a) - F_1(l) + F_2(b) - F_2(m) = 0,$$

that is,

$$\int_l^a f_1(x)dx + \int_m^b f_2(y)dy = 0.$$

Again, subtracting (10) from (9), we obtain

$$F_1(x) - F_1(a) + F_2(y) - F_2(b) = 0,$$

that is,

$$\int_a^x f_1(x)dx + \int_b^y f_2(y)dy = 0.$$

It appears then, that in solving $f_1(x)dx + f_2(y)dy = 0$, *we may write*

$$\int_l^a f_1(x)dx + \int_m^b f_2(y)dy = 0, \int_a^x f_1(x)dx + \int_b^y f_2(y)dy = 0, \tag{12}$$

where (a,b), (l,m), (x,y) *represent corresponding pairs of values.*

The use of limits will be illustrated in the examples of §§ 15, 16, and 17.

14. Physical applications. Most situations in nature are so complicated that they cannot be dealt with exactly by mathematics. The regular procedure is to apply mathematics to an ideal situation having only important features of the actual one. The results are approximations having a practical importance which depends upon the closeness of approximation as verified by reasoning and experiment. Consider, for example, the procedure for the flight of a projectile. The forces of gravity and air resistance acting upon a large projectile rotating while moving forward are very complicated. If we assume that gravity is a constant vertical force and neglect both air resistance and rotary motion, a simple solution is easily obtained; it is practically worthless. If, as a better approximation, we assume that air resistance is proportional to velocity and acts opposite to the direction of motion, and if we get a good factor of proportionality based on experiment, the solution will give a better approximation to the actual motion and may be useful for some purposes. Finally if a group of mathematicians, physicists, and technicians are supplied with powerful computing machines and a proving ground permitting extensive experimentation, they can get results accurate enough for any practical purpose. They would investigate all forces involved, devise a theory, and then apply methods in the development of which differential equations would play a prominent role.

In this treatment the laws obtained by observation, experimentation, and reasoning are given. The student is required to express them in mathematical symbols, solve the resulting differential equations, and interpret the solutions.

15. Compound-interest law problems. Quantities which vary at a rate proportional to their size are said to obey the *compound-interest law* or the *snowball law*. Instances of such quantities are frequent in science.

The following example has reference to such a quantity.

Example. Radium decomposes at a rate proportional to the amount present.* If of 100 mg. set aside now there will be left 96 mg. 100 years hence, find how much will be left t centuries from the time when the radium was set aside and also how long a time will elapse before one-tenth of the radium has disappeared.

Solution. Let Q be the number of milligrams of radium left after t centuries. Then, since dQ/dt is the rate of decrease,

$$\frac{dQ}{dt} = kQ, \text{ or } \frac{dQ}{Q} = k \, dt. \qquad (a)$$

We have as pairs of corresponding values

$$\begin{array}{c|c|c|c} Q & 100 & 96 & 90 \\ \hline t & 0 & 1 & T \end{array}. \qquad (b)$$

From (a) and (b)

$$\int_{100}^{96} \frac{dQ}{Q} = k \int_0^1 dt, \int_{100}^{Q} \frac{dQ}{Q} = k \int_0^t dt, \int_{100}^{90} \frac{dQ}{Q} = k \int_0^T dt. \quad (c)$$

Evaluating the definite integrals, we have

$$\left. \begin{aligned} \log 96 - \log 100 = \log \frac{96}{100} = k, \; \log \frac{Q}{100} = kt, \\ \log \frac{90}{100} = kT. \end{aligned} \right\} \quad (d)$$

From the first equation of (d) we have

$$k = (\log 96 - \log 100) = (4.5644 - 4.6052) =$$
$$- 0.041 \text{ (approx.) } (e)$$

Substituting this value of k in the second equation of (d), we get

$$\log \frac{Q}{100} = -0.041t, \text{ or } \mathbf{Q = 100e^{-0.041t}.} \qquad (f)$$

* Radium does not disintegrate continuously as here indicated; very small particles radiate so that decrease of quantity takes place atom by atom, that is, discontinuously. However the results obtained by the method of the example are reliable when fairly large amounts of radium are considered. If the method were applied to a single atom of radium, the result would be absurd.

From (e) and the third equation of (d), we get

$$T = \frac{-1}{0.041} \log \frac{90}{100} = \textbf{2.6 centuries.}$$

Problems

1. If a body cools in moving air according to Newton's law, $d\theta/dt = -k\theta$, where t is the time and θ is the difference in temperature between the body and the air, find k if θ falls from 40°C. to 30°C. in 200 sec. Also find the time for the difference in temperature to fall from 30°C. to 20°C.

2. If a body cools according to Newton's law (see problem 1), and if the difference in temperature changes from 20°C. to 10°C. in 5 min., find k. How soon will the difference in temperature reach 5°C.?

3. When an amount of money invested increases at a rate proportional to its size, it is said to be compounded continuously. If an amount of money invested at continuously compounded interest doubles itself in 10 years, find an expression for the amount of money at the end of t years. How long will it take to triple itself?

4. What rate of simple interest will produce in one year from one dollar the same amount of money as one dollar compounded continuously at 6 per cent for one year?

5. When a simple electric circuit containing inductance and resistance but no condensers is cut off, the rate of decrease of current is proportional to the current. If the initial current is 30 amp., and it dies down to 11 amp. in 0.01 sec., find the current in terms of the time.

6. If at time t sec. q coulombs is the charge of electricity on a condenser of capacity C farads discharging through a resistance of R ohms, the equation

$$\frac{dq}{dt} + \frac{1}{RC}q = 0$$

applies. If $R = 100$ ohms, $C = 3 \times 10^{-4}$ farad, and initially $q = 0.5$ coulomb, in what time will the condenser lose half its initial charge?

7. A man has a certain sum of money drawing interest at the rate of 6 per cent per year compounded continuously. Assuming that he draws out the money continuously at the rate of $10 per day ($3650 per year), and exhausts the sum in 20 years, find the original sum.

8. Assume that the rate of change of air pressure with altitude (distance above the earth) is proportional to the air pressure.* If the

---

* The rate of change of pressure depends on air pressure, temperature of the air, and other conditions. Hence a formula neglecting all conditions except air pressure will give only rough approximations.

air pressure on the ground is 14.7 lb./in.², and if at an altitude of 10,000 ft., it is 10.1 lb./in.², find air pressure in terms of altitude, and find the air pressure at an altitude of 15,000 ft.

16. Acceleration. Velocity. Distance. If a particle of mass m moves in a straight line with acceleration a, under the influence of several applied forces whose resultant is F, then, in accordance with Newton's laws of motion, we have

$$F = ma, \tag{13}$$

where F, m, and a must be expressed in corresponding units. The set of units which we shall use in most problems is: force in *pounds*, mass in *slugs* (one slug = g lb. = 32.2 lb. nearly), distance in *feet*, and time in *seconds*. Velocity will then be represented in feet per second and acceleration in feet per second per second. Using the notation $t,s,v,$ and a for time, distance, velocity, and acceleration, respectively, we have from calculus

$$v = \frac{ds}{dt}, \ a = \frac{dv}{dt} = \frac{v\,dv}{ds}. \tag{14}$$

We may then write our equation of motion in the form

$$\mathbf{F(lb.)} = \frac{\mathbf{w(lb.)}}{\mathbf{32.2}} \frac{\mathbf{dv}}{\mathbf{dt}} = \frac{\mathbf{w}}{\mathbf{32.2}} \frac{\mathbf{v\,dv}}{\mathbf{ds}}. \tag{15}$$

Example. A coasting party weighing 1000 lb. coasts down a 5-deg. incline. The component of gravitational force parallel to the direction of motion is 87.2 lb. If the force of friction opposing the motion is 40 lb. and the air resistance in pounds is numerically equal to 1.5 times the speed in feet per second,* find an expression for the speed after t sec. from rest, the speed after 10 sec. from rest, and the limiting speed.

---

* The problem of finding the resistance of a fluid on a body moving through it is very complicated. It depends on speed, shape of the body, and properties of the fluid. Any such simple expression as $1.5v$ can represent it reasonably well for only a short period of time in most cases.

Solution. If downhill is chosen as the positive direction, we see from Fig. 9 that $F = 87.2 - 40 - 1.5v$. Therefore, the equation of motion is

$$47.2 - 1.5v = \frac{1000}{32.2}\frac{dv}{dt}.$$

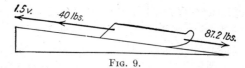

FIG. 9.

The initial conditions may be written

$$\frac{v \mid 0 \mid v_{10}}{t \mid 0 \mid 10}. \tag{b}$$

Separating the variables in (a) and integrating, we obtain

$$\int_0^{v_{10}} \frac{-1.5\,dv}{47.2 - 1.5v} = -\int_0^{10} 0.0483\,dt,$$

$$\int_0^{v} \frac{-1.5\,dv}{47.2 - 1.5v} = -0.0483\int_0^{t} dt. \tag{c}$$

From the first part of (c)

$$\Bigl[\log (47.2 - 1.5v)\Bigr]_0^{v_{10}} = \log \frac{47.2 - 1.5v_{10}}{47.2} = -0.483.$$

Then

$$\frac{47.2 - 1.5v_{10}}{47.2} = e^{-0.483} = 0.617, \text{ and } v_{10} = \mathbf{12.1\ ft./sec.} \tag{d}$$

From the second part of (c)

$$\log \frac{47.2 - 1.5v}{47.2} = -0.0483t, \text{ or } \frac{47.2 - 1.5v}{47.2} = e^{-0.0483t}. \tag{e}$$

Solving (e) for v, we obtain

$$\mathbf{v = 31.5(1 - e^{-0.0483t}).} \tag{f}$$

From (f) it appears that, as t increases without limit, $e^{-0.0483t}$ approaches zero as a limit and v approaches **31.5 ft./sec.**

This last result could have been found from the fact that as v approaches a limiting value, the rate of change of v, or dv/dt, approaches zero. Hence, from equation (a), $47.2 - 1.5v$ approaches zero, and v approaches 31.5 ft./sec.

Problems

1. If distance is expressed in feet and time in seconds, then a and $-0.3v^2$ for a certain rectilinear motion are expressed by the same number, that is $a = -0.3v^2$. If $v = 20$ ft./sec. when $t = 0$, find v in terms of t and find v when $t = 10$ sec. Also using $s = 0$ when $v = 20$ ft./sec. and $v\ dv/ds$ for a, find v in terms of s.

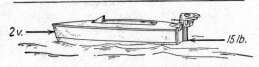

2v. ———→   ←——— 15 lb.

Fig. 10.

2. A force that increases uniformly at the rate of 6 lb./sec. from a value of 0 lb. when $t = 0$ acts on a 32.2-lb. body initially at rest. Find v in terms of t, then replace v by ds/dt and again integrate to find s in terms of t.

3. A man and boat together weigh 400 lb. (see Fig. 10). If the force exerted upon the boat by the oars in the direction of motion is equivalent to a constant force of 15 lb., if the resistance* (in pounds) to motion is equal numerically to twice the speed (in feet per second), that is, $2v$ lb., and if he starts from rest, find the speed (a) after t sec.; (b) after 10 sec.; (c) when $t = \infty$, that is, the limiting speed.

4. Work problem 3 under the assumption that the man in his boat was being towed 15 mi./hr. (22 ft./sec.), and that at the time $t = 0$ the towing line was suddenly severed and the man began to row.

5. Work problem 3 under the assumption that the boat is a scow so built that the resistance in pounds is four times the velocity in feet per second.

6. A freighter of 30,000 tons (1 ton = 2000 lb.) displacement starts from rest. Assuming that the resistance in pounds to motion is $6000v$, where v is the speed in feet per second, and that the force exerted on the ship by the propellers is 120,000 lb., find (a) the speed at any time;

* See footnote p. 29.

(b) the limiting speed; (c) the time taken to speed up to nine-tenths of the limiting speed.

7. Figure 11 represents a uniform ball E having the weight and radius of the earth pulling a w-lb. body toward it with a force inversely proportional to the square of the distance s from the center of E. By applying Newton's law of motion, we obtain the equation

$$\frac{w}{32.2} a = \frac{w}{32.2} \frac{v\,dv}{ds} = -\frac{wR^2}{s^2},$$

where $R = 4000 \times 5280$ ft., s is in feet, and t in seconds. Find the velocity attained by the body in falling from rest at a distance of $4R$

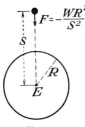

$$F = -\frac{WR^2}{S^2}$$

from the center of E to its surface. What velocity would correspond to a fall from an infinite distance?

8. A ship of w tons displacement is moved by a constant propeller force of p lb., its limiting speed being m ft./sec. If resistance to motion is proportional to the nth power of the speed, express in the form of a definite integral the time for the speed to change from $\frac{1}{2}m$ ft./sec. to $\frac{3}{4}m$ ft./sec.

Fig. 11.

17. Other rate problems. The idea of rate is basic in a great variety of problems, but only one more type will be illustrated at this point.

Example. A tank contains initially 100 gal. of brine holding 150 lb. of dissolved salt in solution. Salt water containing 1 lb. of salt per gallon enters the tank at the rate of 2 gal./ min., and the brine flows out at the same rate. If the mixture is kept uniform by stirring, find the amount of salt in the tank at the end of one hour.

Solution. If Q represents the amount of salt in the tank at the end of t min., we have

$$\frac{dQ}{dt} = \text{rate of gain} - \text{rate of loss}.$$

Evidently the rate of gain is 2 lb./min. and, as each gallon of brine in the tank contains $Q/100$ lb. of salt, the rate of loss is $2Q/100$ lb./min. Hence the equation is

$$\frac{dQ}{dt} = 2 - \frac{2Q}{100}, \text{ or } \frac{dQ}{Q - 100} = \frac{-2\,dt}{100}.$$

Corresponding values of Q and t are

Q	150	Q_{60}
t	0	60

Hence

$$\int_{150}^{Q_{60}} \frac{dQ}{Q - 100} = -0.02 \int_0^{60} dt.$$

From this we obtain

$$\log \frac{Q_{60} - 100}{150 - 100} = -(0.02)(60) = -1.2.$$

Hence

$$\frac{Q_{60} - 100}{50} = e^{-1.2} = 0.3012, \text{ and } \mathbf{Q}_{60} = \mathbf{115.1 \text{ lb.}}$$

Problems

1. Into a 100-gal. tank initially filled with fresh water flow 2 gal./min. of salt water containing 2 lb. of salt per gallon. The solution, kept uniform by stirring, flows out at the same rate. (a) How many pounds of salt will there be in the tank at the end of 1 hr. 40 min.? (b) What is the upper limit for the number of pounds of salt in the tank if the process keeps up indefinitely? (c) How much time will elapse while the quantity of salt in the tank is changing from 100 lb. to 150 lb.?

2. A 100-gal. tank initially filled with fresh water has a mixture of salt and insoluble material in its bottom. If the salt dissolves at a rate per minute equal to one-third of the difference between the concentration (number of pounds of salt per gallon) of the brine and the concentration of a saturated solution (3 lb./gal.), and if the concentration is kept uniform by stirring, find the number of pounds of salt dissolved in one hour.

3. A mass of inert material containing 15 lb. of salt in its pores is agitated with 10 gal. of water initially fresh. The salt dissolves at a rate which varies jointly as the number of pounds of undissolved salt and the difference between the concentration of the solution and that of a saturated solution (3 lb. of salt per gallon). If 9 lb. are dissolved in 10 min., when will 90 per cent be dissolved?

4. The differential equation expressing the generalized compound-interest law is

$$\frac{dy}{dx} = ay + b.$$

Show that its solution is $y = ce^{ax} - (b/a)$.

To apply this solution for solving problem 1, what values for a and b should you use?

5. Apply the solution of problem 4 to solve the following problem:

Air containing 20 per cent oxygen passes slowly into a 2-gal. flask initially filled with pure oxygen, and the mixture of air and oxygen, assumed uniform, passes out at the same rate. How much oxygen will the flask contain after 5 gal. of air have passed into it?

18. Miscellaneous Problems

Solve each of the differential equations numbered 1 to 4 subject to the initial conditions.

1. $\dfrac{dQ}{dt} = 3 - 0.02Q$; $Q = 50$ when $t = 0$

2. $\dfrac{dv}{dt} + 5v = 100$; $v = 15$ when $t = \log 2$

3. $L\dfrac{di}{dt} + Ri = E$; where L, R, and E are constants and $i = 0$ when $t = 0$

4. $x\,dx^2 - y(1 + 3x)dx\,dy + 3y^2\,dy^2 = 0$; $y = 5$ when $x = 3$. Give two answers.

5. When a gas expands without gain or loss of heat, the rate of change of pressure with volume varies directly as the pressure and inversely as the volume. Find the law connecting pressure and volume in this case.

6. Find the equation of the curve for which the area bounded by the tangent, the normal, and the Y-axis is proportional to the slope.

7. Determine the curves that have the following properties:

(*a*) Angle between the radius vector and tangent equals the angle between the radius vector and initial line. *Hint:* Use $\psi = \theta$ and $\psi = 180° - \theta$; therefore, $\tan \psi = \pm \tan \theta$.

(*b*) Perpendicular from the pole to a tangent is constant.

(*c*) Tangent is equally inclined to the radius vector and to the initial line. *Hint:* $\theta = 180° - 2\psi$, or $\psi = 90° - \frac{1}{2}\theta$.

(*d*) Radius vector is equally inclined to the normal and to the initial line.

(*e*) Area bounded by the radius vector, the tangent, and the initial line is proportional to ρ^2. *Hint:* To find the intercept of the tangent on the initial line, apply the law of sines to the triangle bounded by the tangent, the radius vector, and the initial line.

8. Consider a curve at each point of which the angle between the radius vector to the point and the tangent to the curve at the point is three times the vectorial angle. Then $\psi = 3\theta$ or $\psi = 3(180° - \theta)$. Find the orthogonal trajectories of each family.

9. A man and a parachute are falling (see Fig. 12) with a speed of 173 ft./sec. when the parachute opens, and the speed is reduced so as to approach the limiting value of 15 ft./sec. by air resistance proportional to the square of the speed. Show that

$$t = \frac{15}{g}\left(\coth \frac{v}{15} - \coth \frac{173}{15}\right).$$

Hint: When the speed is close to the limiting speed, the velocity is almost constant and the acceleration nearly zero. Hence $w - k15^2 = 0$

10. * Assuming that a man weighing w lb. falls from rest, that the resistance of the air is proportional to his speed v, and that his limiting speed is 173 ft./sec., find an expression for his speed at any time and find his speed at the end of the eleventh second.

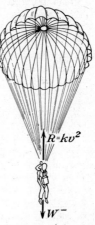

$\uparrow R = kv^2$

11. When heat is flowing through a wall at each point of which the temperature remains constant, but may be different at different points, which receives or loses no heat except through its faces, and whose faces are kept at constant temperature, the following equation is satisfied:

$$-kA\frac{dT}{dx} = Q, \qquad (\alpha)$$

where k is a constant found by experiment, A is the area of the face of the wall, x is the distance from one of its faces, T represents temperature and Q is a constant quantity of heat flowing through the wall

$\downarrow W^-$

By Newton's law $F = ma$,
$$W - kv^2 = \frac{W}{g}\frac{dv}{dt}$$

Fig. 12.

per unit of time. When c.g.s. (centimeter-gram-second) units are used, Q will be expressed in calories per second.

(*a*) Integrate equation (α) assuming A constant, and use your answer to find the number of calories of heat per day passing through the wall of an ice house having an area of 10^7 sq. cm., a thickness of

* According to the *Literary Digest*, dated Nov. 10, 1928, a 180-lb. man drops 1200 ft. in 11 sec. and then has a speed of 173 ft./sec., which remains constant or nearly so as the man continues to fall. The parachute, upon being opened, causes the speed to fall to about 15 ft./sec. in going 20 ft., and then this speed remains nearly constant.

30.5 cm., an inside temperature of 0°C., an outside temperature of 21.1°C., and a conductivity $k = 0.00023$.

(b) Find the heat lost per hour through 1 sq. m. of furnace wall, if this wall is 45.7 cm. thick, if k for its masonry is 0.0024, and if the faces of the wall are at 1000°C. and 120°C., respectively.

12. Equation (α) of exercise 11 applies to a protected cylindrical hot-water or steam pipe under the conditions of exercise 11, if x represents the distance from the axis of the pipe and A the lateral area of a cylinder of radius x and length equal to the length of the pipe considered, that is, if $A = 2\pi xl$.

Two steam pipes of 20 cm. diameter, protected with coverings 10 cm. thick of concrete ($k = 0.0022$) and magnesia ($k = 0.00017$), respectively, are run underneath the soil. If the outer surfaces are at 30°C. and the pipes themselves are at 160°C., compute the losses per hour per meter length of pipe in the two cases. Also find the heat lost per hour per meter length of pipe from one of those pipes, if it is protected with a covering 5 cm. thick of magnesia and, over this, a covering of concrete 5 cm. thick.

13. When water is forced by its own weight to issue from an open tank through a small orifice h units below the surface of the water, the rate of flow is given by

$$\frac{dv}{dt} = -0.6b\sqrt{2gh} = -a\,dh, \tag{β}$$

where v represents volume of water in the tank, b the area of the orifice, a the area of the cross section of the tank at water level, t the time, and g the acceleration of gravity. A consistent set of units is: h in feet, a and b in square feet, v in cubic feet, t in seconds, and $g = 32.2$ ft./sec.[2].

Use equation (β) to find the time to empty a cylindrical tank 2 ft. in diameter and 3 ft. high, through a hole 2 in. in diameter in the bottom of the tank. The tank is initially full of water and its axis is (a) vertical; (b) horizontal.

14. Use equation (β) of exercise 13, properly modified, to find the time required to fill a cubical tank whose edge is 3 ft., if there is a round hole 1 in. in diameter in the bottom of the tank and if water is poured into the tank at the rate of π cu. ft./min.

15. A cubical tank of edge 4 ft. is full of water which runs out a vertical slit $\frac{1}{8}$ in. wide and extending from the top to the bottom of the tank. If the quantity of water per second issuing from a small part of the slit of area a situated at distance x from the surface of the water is $0.6a\sqrt{2gx}$, find the time for the surface of the water to fall 3 ft. *Hint:* First, find the number of cubic feet per minute of water issuing from the slit when the water is h ft. deep.

CHAPTER III

DIFFERENTIAL EQUATIONS OF THE FIRST ORDER AND THE FIRST DEGREE

19. Simple substitutions. Many problems may be reduced to the case of variables separable by simple substitutions. Thus, to solve

$$(x + y - 3)dx + (x + y + 4)dy = 0, \qquad (a)$$

let us try the substitution

$$z = x + y. \qquad (b)$$

Then

$$dz = dx + dy. \qquad (c)$$

The next step is to eliminate either y or x from (a) by using (b) and (c). From (b), $y = z - x$; and from (c), $dy = dz - dx$. Substituting these values in (a), we obtain

$$(z - 3)dx + (z + 4)(dz - dx) = 0,$$

or

$$-7dx + (z + 4)dz = 0.$$

Here the variables are separated and, solving, we find

$$14x - z^2 - 8z = -c.$$

Replacing z by its equal $x + y$, we find

$$14x - (x + y)^2 - 8(x + y) = -c,$$

or

$$\mathbf{x^2 + 2xy + y^2 - 6x + 8y = c.}$$

If the form of an equation indicates that two expressions play a prominent role, it may be well to introduce two new variables. Thus, in considering the equation

$$4(x^2 + y^2)(x\,dx + y\,dy) = \frac{y}{x}(x\,dy - y\,dx), \qquad (d)$$

37

we note that $x^2 + y^2$ and y/x stand out. This suggests the substitution

$$w = x^2 + y^2, \; z = \frac{y}{x}. \qquad (e)$$

Taking differentials of both equations, and also solving for x^2, we find

$$dw = 2x \, dx + 2y \, dy, \; dz = \frac{x \, dy - y \, dx}{x^2}, \; x^2 = \frac{w}{1 + z^2}. \qquad (f)$$

Substituting from (e) and (f) in (d), we obtain

$$2w \, dw = \frac{zw}{1 + z^2} dz. \qquad (g)$$

The solution of (g) is
$$4w = \log c(1 + z^2),$$
or, replacing w and z by their values from (e),

$$\mathbf{4x^2 + 4y^2 = \log c \left(1 + \frac{y^2}{x^2} \right).}$$

Substitution involves: (a) *writing the substitution equations;* (b) *differentiating the substitution equations;* (c) *eliminating all but two of the unknowns between the differential equation and the results of* (a) *and* (b); (d) *solving the result from* (c); (e) *replacing the new variables in terms of the old in the result of* (d) *and simplifying.*

No general rule for finding the substitution equation can be given; the form of the differential equation must suggest the substitution to be tried. However, any outstanding expression may be made the basis of a substitution. From time to time substitutions effective for certain classes of equations will be given.

Exercises

1. $(x + y)dx + (x + y - 2)dy = 0$; let $z = x + y$
2. $xy(x \, dy + y \, dx) = 6y^3 \, dy$; let $z = xy$
3. $x^2(x \, dx + y \, dy) = (x^2 + y^2)^2 \, dx$; let $z = x^2 + y^2$
4. $(st + 1)t \, ds + (2st - 1)s \, dt = 0$; let $z = st$

5. $(x - 2y + 5)dx - [2(x - 2y) + 9]dy = 0$

6. $(2x + y + 9)dx + (2x + y + 6)dy = 0$

7. $(x^2 + 3)(x + y)dy + [3x + (x^2 + 3)(x + y) - x(x + y)^2]dx = 0$; let $z = x + y$

8. $(t^2 + s^2)dt = ts \, ds$; let $s = zt$

9. $3\theta \dfrac{d\rho}{d\theta} + 3\rho = \rho^4\theta^4 e^\theta$; let $z = \rho\theta$

10. $\theta^3 \dfrac{d\rho}{d\theta} = \sin(\rho\theta^2) - 2\rho\theta^2$

11. $x\dfrac{dy}{dx} + 3y = 8x^5$; let $z = x^3y$

12. $dx + dy = (x + y)\left(\dfrac{y}{x} + 1\right)^2 (x \, dy - y \, dx)$; let $z = x + y$, $w = \dfrac{y}{x}$

13. $(x^2 + y^2)(x \, dy + y \, dx) = xy(x \, dx + y \, dy)$; let $z = x^2 + y^2$, $w = xy$

14. $(\rho + \theta)^2 \, d\rho = m^2 \, d\theta$

20. Homogeneous equations. A homogeneous expression of the nth degree in x and y is an expression such that if x and y are replaced by tx and ty, the result will be the original expression multiplied by t^n, or, analytically expressed,

$$f(tx, ty) = t^n f(x, y). \tag{1}$$

Thus, $x^2 + y^2$ is homogeneous in x and y for $(tx)^2 + (ty)^2 = t^2(x^2 + y^2)$. In fact, *any polynomial all terms of which are of the same degree in* x *and* y *is homogeneous.* It appears also that such an expression as $\sqrt{x^2 + y^2} + y \tan^{-1}(y^2/x^2)$ is homogeneous, since

$$\sqrt{(tx)^2 + (ty)^2} + ty \tan^{-1}\frac{(ty)^2}{(tx)^2} = t\left[\sqrt{x^2 + y^2} + y \tan^{-1}\frac{y^2}{x^2}\right].$$

A useful relation is obtained by letting $t = 1/x$ in the definition expressed by (1). This gives for a homogeneous expression of the nth degree

$$\frac{1}{x^n}f(x, y) = f\left(\frac{x}{x}, \frac{y}{x}\right) = \varphi\left(\frac{y}{x}\right),$$

or

$$f(x,y) = x^n f\left(1, \frac{y}{x}\right) = x^n \varphi\left(\frac{y}{x}\right). \qquad (2)$$

A differential equation

$$M\,dx + N\,dy = 0 \qquad (3)$$

is homogeneous in x *and* y *if* M *and* N *are homogeneous functions of the same degree in* x *and* y.

Either of the substitutions, y = vx, *or* x = vy, *will reduce any homogeneous differential equation of the first order and first degree to the type of variables separable.* To prove this for the substitution $y = vx$, let n be the degree of the homogeneous differential equation and write in accordance with (2),

$$M\,dx + N\,dy = x^n \varphi_1\left(\frac{y}{x}\right)dx + x^n \varphi_2\left(\frac{y}{x}\right)dy = 0. \qquad (4)$$

Make the substitution

$$y = vx, \quad dy = v\,dx + x\,dv \qquad (5)$$

in (4) and obtain

$$x^n \varphi_1(v)dx + x^n \varphi_2(v)(v\,dx + x\,dv) = 0. \qquad (6)$$

Dividing (6) by x^n and collecting the terms involving dx and those involving dy, we have

$$[\varphi_1(v) + v\varphi_2(v)]dx + x\varphi_2(v)dv = 0,$$

or

$$\frac{dx}{x} + \frac{\varphi_2(v)dv}{\varphi_1(v) + v\varphi_2(v)} = 0, \qquad (7)$$

and the variables are separated.

Example. Solve $(x^2 + y^2)dx - 2xy\,dy = 0$.

Solution. Since the equation is homogeneous, write

$$y = vx, \quad dy = v\,dx + x\,dv.$$

Substituting these values for y and dy in the equation, we get

$$(x^2 + v^2x^2)dx - 2vx^2(v\,dx + x\,dv) = 0.$$

Collecting coefficients of dx and dv, we obtain

$$(x^2 + v^2x^2 - 2v^2x^2)dx - 2vx^3\,dv = 0,$$

or
$$x^2(1 - v^2)dx - 2vx^3\,dv = 0.$$

Division by $x^3(1 - v^2)$ gives
$$\frac{dx}{x} - \frac{2v\,dv}{1 - v^2} = 0.$$

Integrating this, we obtain
$$\log x + \log (1 - v^2) = \log c, \text{ or } x(1 - v^2) = c.$$

Replacing v by its equal y/x, we have
$$x\left(1 - \frac{y^2}{x^2}\right) = c, \text{ or } \mathbf{x^2 - y^2 = cx.}$$

Exercises

1. Show that each expression is homogeneous: (a) $x^2 + 8xy - 10y^2$.

(b) $x^3 + y^3 - 3x^2y$. (c) $x^n + 3x^{n-k}\,y^k + y^n$. (d) $x^2 \sin \dfrac{y}{x} + y^2 \, \cos \, \dfrac{y}{x} +$

$xy \log \dfrac{x + y}{x - y}$.

2. If $x^m + y^n + x^l y^{2k}$ is homogeneous, what relations must exist between l, m, n, and k?

3. $(x + y)dx + (x - y)dy = 0$

4. $(x^2 + y^2)dx + 2xy\,dy = 0$

5. $(x + y)dx + x\,dy = 0$

6. $(5x^2 - 7y^2)dx - 14xy\,dy = 0$

7. $(\theta + \rho)d\theta + (\theta - \rho)d\rho = 0$

8. $(2x + y)dx + (x + y)dy = 0$

9. $x\,dy - y\,dx = \sqrt{x^2 + y^2}\,dx$

10. $xy^2\,dy = (x^3 + y^3)dx$

11. $(2\sqrt{xy} - x)dy + y\,dx = 0$

12. $x \cos \dfrac{y}{x} \dfrac{dy}{dx} = y \cos \dfrac{y}{x} - x$

13. $\left(x \sin \dfrac{y}{x} - y \cos \dfrac{y}{x}\right)dx + x \cos \dfrac{y}{x} dy = 0$

14. $\left(x + y \cos \dfrac{y}{x}\right)dx - x \cos \dfrac{y}{x} dy = 0$

15. Solve $x\,dy - y\,dx = 3x(x^2 + y^2)^{\frac{3}{2}}\,dx$ by making the substitution $y = rx$.

16. Show that a straight line through the origin intersects at a constant angle all integral curves of a homogeneous differential equation.

17. Find the orthogonal trajectories of the circles $x^2 + y^2 + 2cx = 0$.

18. Find the equation of all curves that cut the circles $x^2 + y^2 = r^2$ at an angle of 45 deg.

19. If the area bounded by the X-axis, the Y-axis, a certain curve, and the ordinate of any point (x,y) on the curve be revolved about the X-axis, the volume generated will be equal to the volume of a circular cylinder having the abscissa of the variable point as radius of base and one-half the variable ordinate as altitude. Find the equation of the curve.

21. Equations of the form $(ax + by + c)dx + (\alpha x + \beta y + \gamma)dy = 0$. To solve this type of equation make the substitution

$$x = x' + h, \; y = y' + k, \; dx = dx', \; dy = dy', \quad (8)$$

to obtain

$(ax' + by' + ah + bk + c)dx' +$
$$(\alpha x' + \beta y' + \alpha h + \beta k + \gamma)dy' = 0. \quad (9)$$

If we now choose h and k so that

$$ah + bk + c = 0, \; \alpha h + \beta k + \gamma = 0, \quad (10)$$

the equation (9) in x' and y' becomes homogeneous. We then apply the method for solving homogeneous equations and replace, in the resulting solution, the new variables in terms of the old.

The method just described breaks down if $a/b = \alpha/\beta$. In this case the substitution $z = ax + by$, or $z = \alpha x + \beta y$, will give rise to an equation in which the variables are separable.

Example. Solve

$$(2x - 3y + 4)dx + (3x - 2y + 1)dy = 0.$$

Solution. Substituting $x = x' + h, \; y = y' + k$ in the given equation, we obtain

$(2x' - 3y' + 2h - 3k + 4)dx' +$
$$(3x' - 2y' + 3h - 2k + 1)dy' = 0. \quad (a)$$

Let $2h - 3k + 4 = 0$, and $3h - 2k + 1 = 0$.

Then $h = 1$ and $k = 2$, and the equation (a) reduces to

$$(2x' - 3y')dx' + (3x' - 2y')dy' = 0. \qquad (b)$$

Solving this homogeneous equation and simplifying, we get

$$(y' + x')^5 = c(y' - x'). \qquad (c)$$

Since $x = x' + h = x' + 1$, $y = y' + k = y' + 2$, we have

$$x' = x - 1, \ y' = y - 2. \qquad (d)$$

Substituting the values of x' and y' from (d) in (c), we obtain

$$\mathbf{(x + y - 3)^5 = c(y - x - 1).}$$

Exercises

1. $(x - 2y + 5)dx + (2x - y + 4)dy = 0$
2. $(2x + 3y)dx + (y + 2)dy = 0$
3. $(2x - 2y)dx + (y - 1)dy = 0$
4. $(x + y + 3)dy = (y - 4x - 2)dx$
5. $(2x + y)dx - (4x + 2y - 1)dy = 0$
6. $(2x - y + 2)dx + (4x - 2y - 1)dy = 0$

22. Exact differential equation.

The formula for the total differential of a function $f(x,y)$ is

$$df(x,y) = \frac{\partial f}{\partial x}dx + \frac{\partial f}{\partial y}dy. \qquad (11)$$

Any expression that is exactly the total differential of some function of x *and* y *is called an exact differential, and such an expression equated to zero is an exact differential equation.* For example, in accordance with (11),

$$d(x^2 + 8x^2y - 10y^3) = (2x + 16xy)dx + (8x^2 - 30y^2)dy$$

is an exact differential and

$$(2x + 16xy)dx + (8x^2 - 30y^2)dy = 0$$

is an exact differential equation.

Exercises

1. Find the total differential of each expression:

(a) $x^3 - xy^2 - 4x^2y$.   (b) $5 \log (xy) + 12$.   (c) $x^4y^4 + \sin x$.

2. Form an exact differential equation from each of the following expressions by equating its total differential to zero:

(a) $x^3y - y^2$.   (b) $x^2 - y^2 - \log y^3$.   (c) $ax^2 + bxy$.

3. If M represents the coefficient of dx and N that of dy in each of the answers to exercise 2, show that $\partial M/\partial y = \partial N/\partial x$ in each case.

4. Each of the following expressions is an exact differential. In each case find a function of x and y which has the given expression as its total derivative:

(a) $(2x + y)dx + (x - 2y)dy$
(b) $(2x + y)dx + (x - 3y^2 - 3)dy$
(c) $(3x^2 - 2xy)dx + (4y^3 - x^2 + 3)dy$
(d) $(2x + \tan y)dx + (x \sec^2 y - 3y^2)dy$

23. Condition that a differential be exact.

From (11) it appears that an expression

$$M\,dx + N\,dy \tag{12}$$

is exact, if there exists a function $f(x,y)$ such that

$$M = \frac{\partial f}{\partial x}, \; N = \frac{\partial f}{\partial y}.* \tag{13}$$

From (13) we obtain

$$\frac{\partial M}{\partial y} = \frac{\partial^2 f}{\partial y\,\partial x}, \; \frac{\partial N}{\partial x} = \frac{\partial^2 f}{\partial x\,\partial y}.$$

Since $\dfrac{\partial^2 f}{\partial y\,\partial x} = \dfrac{\partial^2 f}{\partial x\,\partial y}$, it appears that

$$\frac{\partial \mathbf{M}}{\partial \mathbf{y}} = \frac{\partial \mathbf{N}}{\partial \mathbf{x}} \tag{14}$$

is a necessary condition that (12) *be an exact differential.*

Conversely, we shall show that *if* (14) *holds, then* (12) *must be an exact differential*, by finding a function $f(x,y)$ whose differential is $M\,dx + N\,dy$, that is, a function f such that

$$\frac{\partial f}{\partial x} = M, \frac{\partial f}{\partial y} = N. \tag{15}$$

---

* It is assumed that M, N, and their partial derivatives of the first and second orders are continuous.

If the first equation of (15) holds,

$$f = \int^x M \, dx + \varphi(y) \tag{16}$$

where $\varphi(y)$ does not contain x and the superscript x means that y is to be held constant during the integration. Substituting the value of f from (16) in the second part of (15), we obtain

$$\frac{\partial f}{\partial y} = \frac{\partial}{\partial y} \int^x M \, dx + \frac{d\varphi}{dy} = N, \tag{17}$$

or

$$\frac{d\varphi}{dy} = N - \frac{\partial}{\partial y} \int^x M \, dx. \tag{18}$$

Since the partial derivative with respect to x of the right member of (18) is $\dfrac{\partial N}{\partial x} - \dfrac{\partial M}{\partial y}$, it is zero because of (14). Therefore the right member of (18) does not contain x. Hence we find, by integrating (18), that

$$\varphi = \int \left[N - \frac{\partial}{\partial y} \int^x M \, dx \right] dy. \tag{19}$$

Substituting φ from (19) in (16), we have

$$f(x,y) = \int^x M \, dx + \int \left[N - \frac{\partial}{\partial y} \int^x M \, dx \right] dy. \tag{20}$$

This value of f satisfies (15) provided (14) is true.

24. Solution of exact differential equations. From §23, it appears that an equation

$$M \, dx + N \, dy = 0 \tag{21}$$

is exact if

$$\frac{\partial M}{\partial y} = \frac{\partial N}{\partial x}, \tag{22}$$

and a general solution of (21) is

$$f(x,y) = \int^x M\ dx + \int\left[N - \frac{\partial}{\partial y}\int^x M\ dx\right]dy = c, \quad (23)$$

where the superscript x indicates that y is to be considered constant in the integration.

An exact differential equation can be solved by substituting for M and N in (23) their values from the given equation and carrying out the integrations. The second integral in (23) often consists of the sum of the integrals of those terms in N which do not contain x. This will always be true when M and N are polynomials. The following procedure is effective.

To integrate a differential equation M dx + N dy = 0 *for which* $\partial M/\partial y = \partial N/\partial x$, *equate to a constant the sum of the integral of* M *with respect to* x *and the integrals of the terms in* N dy *which do not contain* x; *if the derivative of the result does not give* M dx + N dy = 0, *use* (23).

Example 1. Solve $(2x + y^{-1})dx + (y^{-1} - xy^{-2})dy = 0$.

Solution. Here $M = 2x + y^{-1}$, $N = y^{-1} - xy^{-2}$ and

$$\frac{\partial M}{\partial y} = -y^{-2}, \frac{\partial N}{\partial x} = -y^{-2}, \text{ that is, } \frac{\partial M}{\partial y} = \frac{\partial N}{\partial x},$$

and the equation is exact. In accordance with the rule the solution is

$$\int^x (2x + y^{-1})dx + \int y^{-1}\ dy = c$$

or

$$x^2 + xy^{-1} + \log y = c. \qquad (a)$$

From this we obtain by differentiation the original equation and therefore (a) is the required solution.

Example 2. Solve

$$(3x^2 + 2y \sin 2x)dx + (2 \sin^2 x + 3y^2)dy = 0.$$

Solution. Here $\partial M/\partial y = \partial N/\partial x = 2 \sin 2x$. Hence the equation is exact. The first part of the italicized statement does not yield a correct answer. Hence use (23). Substituting M and N from the given equation in (23) and noting that $\int^x (3x^2 + 2y \sin 2x)dx = x^3 - y \cos 2x$, obtain

$$x^3 - y \cos 2x + \int \left[2 \sin^2 x + 3y^2 - \frac{\partial}{\partial y}(x^3 - y \cos 2x) \right] dy = c. \quad (a)$$

The integral in (a) gives $y^3 + y$. Substitute $y^3 + y$ for the integral in (a) to obtain

$$\mathbf{x^3 - y \cos 2x + y^3 + y = c.}$$

Exercises

1. $(x - y + 5)dx + (y - x)dy = 0$
2. $(\tan y + x)dx + (x \sec^2 y - 3y)dy = 0$
3. $(x^2 + y^2)dx + (2xy + 3y - 1)dy = 0$
4. $(\sec x \tan x - y)dx + (\sec y \tan y - x + 2)dy = 0$
5. $(a^2 - 2xy - y^2)dx - (x + y)^2 dy = 0$
6. $(2ax + by + g)dx + (2cy + bx + e)dy = 0$
7. $\dfrac{2xy + 1}{y}dx + \dfrac{y - x}{y^2}dy = 0$
8. $(2xy + y^2)dx + \dfrac{x^2 y + 2xy^2 + 1}{y}dy = 0$
9. $\dfrac{x\, dy - y\, dx}{y^2} = x^3\, dx$
10. $\dfrac{dx}{\sqrt{x^2 + y^2}} + \left(\dfrac{1}{y} - \dfrac{x}{y\sqrt{x^2 + y^2}}\right)dy = 0$
11. $\dfrac{y^2 - 2x^2}{xy^2 - x^3}dx + \dfrac{2y^2 - x^2}{y^3 - x^2 y}dy = 0$
12. $\dfrac{x^{n+1}}{y^{n+2}}dy - \dfrac{x^n}{y^{n+1}}dx + x^m\, dx = 0$
13. $\sin 2x \cos^2 y\, dx + \cos^2 x \sin 2y\, dy = 0$
14. Prove exact

$$[f(x) + \varphi(y)]dx + \left[x\frac{d\varphi}{dy} + \psi(y)\right]dy = 0,$$

where f, φ, and ψ are continuous and possess continuous derivatives but are, in other respects, arbitrary functions of the indicated variables.

25. Integrating factors. If, when a differential equation is multiplied through by an expression, the result is an exact differential equation, then the expression is said to be an integrating factor of the differential equation.

Integrating factors of many differential equations may be found by recognizing certain groups as differentials of known expressions. Since $d\left(\dfrac{y}{x}\right) = \dfrac{xdy - ydx}{x^2}$, it appears that $1/x^2$ is an integrating factor of

$$x \, dy - y \, dx + f(x)dx = 0,$$

and the solution is

$$\frac{y}{x} + \int \frac{f(x)}{x^2} dx = c.$$

Similarly $1/y^2$ is an integrating factor of

$$x \, dy - y \, dx + f(y)dy = 0,$$

and its solution is

$$-\frac{x}{y} + \int \frac{f(y)dy}{y^2} = c.$$

In fact, division of $x \, dy - y \, dx$ by x^2, y^2, $x^2 + y^2$, or $x^2 - y^2$ gives an exact differential, as may be seen by inspection or by applying test (14) of §23. Other simple exact differentials are $x \, dy + y \, dx = d(xy)$ and $x \, dx + y \, dy = d\left(\dfrac{x^2 + y^2}{2}\right)$.

Hence the group $x \, dy - y \, dx$ suggests as integrating factors $\dfrac{1}{x^2}, \dfrac{1}{y^2}, \dfrac{1}{xy}, \dfrac{1}{x^2 \pm y^2}$, the group $x \, dy + y \, dx$ suggests some function of xy, and the group $x \, dx + y \, dy$ suggests a function of $x^2 + y^2$.

From time to time, integrating factors applying to special cases will be given.

It is worthy of note that the differential expressions here

considered suggest substitutions; thus, $x\,dy - y\,dx$ suggests the substitution $z = y/x$, $x\,dx + y\,dy$ suggests $z = x^2 + y^2$, etc.

Example 1. Solve $x\,dy + y\,dx = x^2y\,dy$.

Solution. $1/x^2y^2$ is observed to be an integrating factor. Multiplying the equation through by this, we have

$$\frac{x\,dy + y\,dx}{(xy)^2} = \frac{x^2y\,dy}{x^2y^2}.$$

As this equation is exact, we can solve it as such, or we may write it

$$\frac{d(xy)}{(xy)^2} = \frac{dy}{y}.$$

Integrating this, we have

$$\frac{-1}{xy} = \log cy, \text{ or } \mathbf{xy \log cy + 1 = 0.}$$

Example 2. Solve $(x^2y + x)dy + (xy^2 - y)dx = 0$.

Solution. This equation may be written

$$x\,dy - y\,dx + xy(x\,dy + y\,dx) = 0.$$

Hence $1/xy$ is an integrating factor, and the solution is

$$\mathbf{\log y - \log x + xy = c.}$$

Example 3. Solve $y\,dx - x\,dy = x^3\sqrt{x^2 - y^2}dx$.

Solution. If we write this in the form

$$y\,dx - x\,dy = x^4\sqrt{1 - \left(\frac{y}{x}\right)^2}dx,$$

it appears that $1 \div x^2\sqrt{1 - \left(\dfrac{y}{x}\right)^2}$ is an integrating factor. Multiplying by this, we get

$$\frac{\dfrac{y\,dx - x\,dy}{x^2}}{\sqrt{1 - (y/x)^2}} = \frac{-d\left(\dfrac{y}{x}\right)}{\sqrt{1 - (y/x)^2}} = x^2\,dx.$$

Therefore

$$-\sin^{-1}\frac{y}{x} = \frac{x^3}{3} - \frac{c}{3}, \text{ or } \mathbf{y} = \mathbf{x}\sin\left(\frac{\mathbf{c} - \mathbf{x^3}}{3}\right).$$

Exercises

1. Find an integrating factor and solve $x\,dy - y\,dx = (x^2 - 3)dx$.

2. Find an integrating factor and solve $x\,dy + y\,dx = 3x^3y\,dx$.

3. Find an integrating factor and solve

$$x\,dx + y\,dy = 3(x^2 + y^2)y^2\,dy.$$

4. Prove that $1/(x^ny^n)$ is an integrating factor of $x\,dy + y\,dx = x^ny^m\,dy$ and solve.

5. Prove that x^2 is an integrating factor of $x\dfrac{dy}{dx} + 3y = x$ and solve.

6. Prove that x^{-4} is an integrating factor of

$$(x^3 + y^3)dx - xy^2\,dy = 0$$

and solve.

7. Solve $x\,dy - y\,dx = x\,dx + y\,dy$.

8. Solve $x\,dy - y\,dx = (x^2 + y^2)^2(x\,dx + y\,dy)$.

9. If the differential equation $M\,dx + N\,dy = 0$ is homogeneous, then $\dfrac{1}{xM + yN}$ is an integrating factor. Use this fact to solve equations

(a) $(y^2 - xy)dx + x^2\,dy = 0$

(b) $(x^3 - y^3)dx + xy^2\,dy = 0$

(c) $(x^2 - xy + y^2)dx + (x^2 - xy)dy = 0$

10. $d(x^my^n) = mx^{m-1}y^n\,dx + nx^my^{n-1}\,dy = x^{m-1}y^{n-1}(my\,dx + nx\,dy)$. Hence an expression $mx\,dy + ny\,dx$ occurring in a differential equation suggests the substitution $z = x^my^n$. For example, to solve equation (a) below, make the substitution $z = x^3y^2$, and eliminate y (or x) to obtain an equation in z and x (or y) of the type variables separable. Solve the following differential equations:

(a) $3y\,dx + 2x\,dy = xy\,dx$ (c) $5y\,dx + 3x\,dy = x^4y^7\,dx$

(b) $3y\,dx + 2x\,dy = x^4y^4\,dy$ (d) $3yx^2\,dx - 4x^3\,dy = 7y\,dy$

11. Read exercise 10 and then solve exercises 1 and 2 by means of substitutions. Also solve 7 and 8 by means of the substitution $z = xy^{-1}$, $w = x^2 + y^2$.

12. Two functions $f(x,y)$ and $\varphi(x,y)$, one of which is a function of the other, say $f(x,y) = F(\varphi(x,y))$, are said to be dependent. The condition for this is,

$$\begin{vmatrix} \dfrac{\partial f}{\partial x} & \dfrac{\partial f}{\partial y} \\[2mm] \dfrac{\partial \varphi}{\partial x} & \dfrac{\partial \varphi}{\partial y} \end{vmatrix} \equiv 0,^*$$

or in words, that their Jacobian be indentically zero.

Show that if $f(x,y) = c_1$ and $\varphi(x,y) = c_2$ are two solutions of $M\,dx + N\,dy = 0$, then $f(x,y)$ and $\varphi(x,y)$ are dependent. *Hint:* Along curve $\psi(x,y) = C$, $\dfrac{dy}{dx} = -\dfrac{\partial \psi}{\partial x}\Big/\dfrac{\partial \psi}{\partial y}$, and along a solution of $M\,dx + N\,dy = 0$, $\dfrac{dy}{dx} = -\dfrac{M}{N}$.

13. (a) Prove that x^k is an integrating factor of $M\,dx + N\,dy = 0$, when $\dfrac{\partial M}{\partial y} - \dfrac{\partial N}{\partial x} = N\dfrac{k}{x}$.

(b) Show that the equation $(y^4 + x^3)dx + 8xy^3\,dy = 0$ satisfies the condition of (a) for a certain value of k and solve the equation.

14. (a) Prove that $e^{\int f(x)dx}$ is an integrating factor of $M\,dx + N\,dy = 0$, if $\dfrac{\partial M}{\partial y} - \dfrac{\partial N}{\partial x} = Nf(x)$.

(b) Show that the equation $(xy^2 + x^2y^2 + 3)dx + x^2y\,dy = 0$ satisfies the condition expressed in (a) and solve the equation.

15. (a) Prove that $e^{\int f(y)dy}$ is an integrating factor of $M\,dx + N\,dy = 0$, if $\dfrac{\partial M}{\partial y} - \dfrac{\partial N}{\partial x} = -Mf(y)$.

(b) Show that the equation $x^2y^2\,dx + (x^3y + y + 3)dy = 0$ satisfies the condition expressed in (a) and solve the equation.

16. It can be shown that every equation of the form
$$yf_1(xy)dx + xf_2(xy)dy = 0$$
has $1 \div xy[f_1(xy) - f_2(xy)]$ as an integrating factor.

Make use of this fact to solve

(a) $(1 + x^2y^2)x\,dy + (x^2y^2 - 1)y\,dx = 0$

(b) $x^3y^4\,dx - (x^2y - x^4y^3)dy = 0$

(c) $y(xy + 2x^2y^2)dx + x(xy - x^2y^2)dy = 0$

17. Prove the statement made in problem 16 by test (14) of §23.

26. Linear differential equation. *A differential equation of any order is said to be* linear, *when it is of the first degree in the*

---

* See SOKOLNIKOFF, I. S., "Advanced Calculus," p. 422.

dependent variable and its derivatives. It follows that a general type of linear differential equation of the *first order* is

$$\frac{dy}{dx} + Py = Q, \tag{24}$$

where P and Q are functions of x only.*

To find an integrating factor of (24), let us solve

$$\frac{dy}{dx} + Py = 0, \text{ or } \frac{dy}{y} = -P\,dx. \tag{25}$$

Here the variables are separated, and the solution is

$$y = ce^{-\int P\,dx}, \text{ or } ye^{\int P\,dx} = c. \tag{26}$$

The differential of the left-hand member of (26) is $e^{\int P\,dx}(dy + Py\,dx)$. It appears then that, if (24) be multiplied by $e^{\int P\,dx}\,dx$, the left-hand member will be an exact differential and the right-hand member will contain x only. Hence, multiplying (24) by $e^{\int P\,dx}\,dx$, we obtain the exact equation

$$e^{\int P\,dx}(dy + Py\,dx) = Qe^{\int P\,dx}\,dx. \tag{27}$$

The solution of (27), and therefore of (24), is

$$ye^{\int P\,dx} = \int Qe^{\int P\,dx}\,dx + c. \tag{28}$$

Hence, to solve an equation having the form (24), either substitute in form (28), or multiply by $e^{\int P\,dx}$ and integrate the result as an exact differential equation.

Example 1. Solve $x\dfrac{dy}{dx} + 2y = x^3$.

Solution. Division by x gives

$$\frac{dy}{dx} + \frac{2}{x}y = x^2.$$

This has the form (24) and

$$Q = x^2, \; P = \frac{2}{x}, \; e^{\int P\,dx} = e^{2\int dx/x} = e^{\log x^2} = x^2.$$

* This equation is involved in many useful applications.

Substituting these values in (28), we obtain

$$yx^2 = \int x^2 \cdot x^2 \, dx + \frac{c}{5} = \frac{x^5}{5} + \frac{c}{5},$$

or

$$5yx^2 = x^5 + c.$$

Example 2. Solve $\dfrac{dy}{dx} + y \cot x = \csc x$.

Solution. Multiplying by the integrating factor $e^{\int P dx} = e^{\int \cot x \, dx} = e^{\log \sin x} = \sin x$, we obtain

$$\sin x \frac{dy}{dx} + y \cos x = 1.$$

Since this is exact, we write the answer by the method of §24,

$$y \sin x = x + c.$$

Exercises

Solve each of the following differential equations and, when initial conditions are indicated, find the particular solution satisfied by them:

1. $\dfrac{dy}{dx} + \dfrac{1}{x}y = x^3 - 3$

2. $\dfrac{dy}{dx} + \dfrac{2}{x}y = x^2 + 2$

3. $x\dfrac{dy}{dx} - 2y = x^2 + x$; $y = 1$ when $x = 1$

4. $\dfrac{dy}{dx} - y \tan x = 3e^{-\sin x}$; $y = 4$ when $x = 0$

5. $x^2 \, dy - \sin 2x \, dx + 3xy \, dx = 0$

6. $\dfrac{dx}{dy} - \dfrac{4x}{y} = y^5$; $y = 1$ when $x = 4$

7. $\dfrac{dy}{dx} - xy = xe^{x^2}$; $y = 5$ when $x = 0$

8. $(x + 2y)dx + dy = 0$; $y = -1$ when $x = 0$

9. $(1 + x^2)dy - a \, dx = xy \, dx$; $y = 2a$ when $x = 0$

10. $x(1 - x^2)dy - ax^3 \, dx = (2x^2 - 1)y \, dx$

11. $(\sin 2\theta - 2\rho \cos \theta)d\theta = 2 \, d\rho$

12. $x^2\dfrac{dy}{dx} = x^2 + 2xy - y$

13. $(1 + x^2)dy = (xy + a)dx$

14. $L\dfrac{di}{dt} + Ri = E \sin \omega t$; R, L, E, ω are constants, $i = 0$ when $t = 0$

15. $R\dfrac{di}{dt} + \dfrac{1}{C}i = E\omega \cos \omega t$; R, C, E, ω are constants, $i = 0$ when $t = 0$

27. Equations reducible to linear form. The equation

$$\frac{dy}{dx} + Py = Qy^n, \tag{29}$$

where P and Q are functions of x only, is named *Bernoulli's equation*, after James Bernoulli, who studied it in 1695. To solve it,* we first divide by y^n and obtain

$$y^{-n}\frac{dy}{dx} + Py^{1-n} = Q. \tag{30}$$

This form suggests the substitution

$$v = y^{1-n}, \frac{dv}{dx} = (1 - n)y^{-n}\frac{dy}{dx}. \tag{31}$$

Substituting from (31) in (30), we get

$$\frac{1}{1 - n}\frac{dv}{dx} + Pv = Q, \tag{32}$$

a linear equation. *Hence, to solve an equation of type* (29), *make the substitution* (31) *and then proceed as in the case of the linear equation.*

Example. Solve $\dfrac{dy}{dx} - \dfrac{2}{x}y = y^4$.

Solution. Multiplying by $-3y^{-4}$, we get

$$-3y^{-4}\frac{dy}{dx} + \frac{6}{x}y^{-3} = -3.$$

Substituting $v = y^{-3}, \dfrac{dv}{dx} = -3y^{-4}\dfrac{dy}{dx}$, we obtain

---

* Also the equation is readily solved by the method indicated in exercise 11 of this article.

$$\frac{dv}{dx} + \frac{6}{x}v = -3.$$

The solution of this equation by means of (28) is

$$ve^{6 \log x} = vx^6 = \int -3x^6 \, dx + c = -\tfrac{3}{7}x^7 + c.$$

Simplifying and replacing v by y^{-3}, we get

$$\mathbf{y^{-3} = -\frac{3}{7}x + cx^{-6}}.$$

Exercises

Solve each of the following differential equations and determine the constant of integration when initial conditions are given:

1. $2\dfrac{dy}{dx} - \dfrac{y}{x} = 5x^3 y^3$

2. $3\dfrac{dy}{dx} + \dfrac{3}{x}y = 2x^4 y^4$

3. $\dfrac{dy}{dx} + y = 12e^{2x} y^2$

4. $3\dfrac{dy}{dx} + \dfrac{1}{x+1}y = 3(x+1)y^{-2}$

5. $\dfrac{dy}{dx} - 4xy = 16xe^{3x^2}\sqrt{y}$

6. $\dfrac{dy}{dx} + y^2 = \dfrac{y}{x}$; $y = 1$ when $x = 1$

7. $x\dfrac{dy}{dx} + y = y^2 x \log x$; $y = 2$ when $x = 1$

8. $y - \cos x \dfrac{dy}{dx} = y^2 \cos x \,(1 - \sin x)$; $y = 2$ when $x = 0$

9. $\dfrac{dx}{dy} - xy = x^2 y^3$; $y = 0$ when $x = 1$

10. $(x + myx^3)dy = dx$

11. The substitution $y = uv$ leads to a solution of (29). To illustrate the method substitute $y = uv$ in

$$\frac{dy}{dx} + \frac{y}{2x} = \tfrac{1}{2}x^2 y^5.$$

to obtain

$$u \, dv + v \, du + \frac{uv}{2x} \, dx = \tfrac{1}{2}x^2 u^5 v^5 \, dx \qquad (a)$$

Evidently either u or v may be chosen as any desired function. Hence choose u so that $v \, du + \tfrac{1}{2}(uv/x)dx = 0$. Then $u = x^{-\frac{1}{2}}$. Substituting this in (a) for u and integrating the resulting equation we obtain $v = (c - 2x)^{-\frac{1}{2}}$. Hence the solution is

$$y = uv = x^{-\frac{1}{2}}(c - 2x)^{-\frac{1}{2}}, \text{ or } \mathbf{y}^{-4} = \mathbf{x}^2(\mathbf{c} - 2\mathbf{x}).$$

Use this method to solve exercises 1, 2, and 3 of this article and exercises 1, 2, and 3 of §26.

28. Simultaneous equations. Two differential equations in three variables often arise in applications. Only pairs of equations that can be solved by means of the theory already developed will be considered at this time. Two equations,

$$\left. \begin{array}{l} A_1\, dx + A_2\, dy + A_3\, dt = 0, \\ B_1\, dx + B_2\, dy + B_3\, dt = 0, \end{array} \right\} \qquad (33)$$

where the A's and B's represent functions of x, y, and t, have solutions consisting of two relations of the form

$$f_1(x,y,t,c_1,c_2) = 0, \, f_2(x,y,t,c_1,c_2) = 0. \qquad (34)$$

One relation is generally found by eliminating one of the variables from the given equations and solving the resulting equation in two unknowns by methods already considered. When one relation has been found, it may be used with the given differential equations to find others. Of course, if an equation contains all three variables but separated so that no term contains more than one variable or, if an equation is exact, it may be integrated directly to obtain one of the required equations.

Example 1. Solve

$$\frac{dx}{dt} + y = x, \, \frac{dy}{dt} = 3y \qquad (a)$$

Solution. Since there are only two variables in the second equation, we solve it to obtain

$$y = c_1 e^{3t}. \qquad (b)$$

Substituting y from (b) in the first of (a), we obtain

$$\frac{dx}{dt} + c_1 e^{3t} = x. \qquad (c)$$

Since (c) is a linear equation in two variables, we solve it by §26 to find

$$xe^{-t} = \frac{-c_1}{2}e^{2t} + c_2. \tag{d}$$

Rewriting equations (b) and (d) slightly simplified, we have

$$\mathbf{y = c_1 e^{3t}, \; x = -\tfrac{1}{2}c_1 e^{3t} + c_2 e^t.}$$

Example 2. Solve

$$\frac{dx}{dt} + t\frac{dy}{dt} = 2t, \; t\frac{dx}{dt} - \frac{dy}{dt} = -x \tag{a}$$

Solution. To eliminate y we multiply the second equation of (a) by t and add the result to the first and obtain

$$(1 + t^2)\frac{dx}{dt} = -tx + 2t. \tag{b}$$

Equation (b) may be solved by separating the variables. The solution is

$$\log (x - 2) = \log c_1(1 + t^2)^{-\frac{1}{2}}$$

or

$$\mathbf{x = 2 + c_1(1 + t^2)^{-\frac{1}{2}}.} \tag{c}$$

Substituting x from (c) in the first of (a), we get

$$-c_1 t(1 + t^2)^{-\frac{3}{2}} + t\frac{dy}{dt} = 2t. \tag{d}$$

Separating the variables in (d) and integrating, we find

$$\mathbf{y = 2t + \frac{c_1 t}{\sqrt{1 + t^2}} + c_2.} \tag{e}$$

Equations (c) and (e) constitute the solution.

Exercises

1. $\dfrac{dx}{dt} - 2t = 0, \; \dfrac{dy}{dt} - x + t^2 = 0$

2. $\dfrac{dy}{dt} + y = e^{-t}, \; \dfrac{dx}{dt} + y = te^{-t}$

3. $\dfrac{dx}{dt} = 1000, \; \dfrac{dy}{dt} = 0.5\dfrac{dx}{dt} - 16t$

4. $\dfrac{d\rho}{dt} + \rho = e^t, \dfrac{d\theta}{dt} = \rho$

5. $(t - 1)\dfrac{dx}{dt} + \dfrac{dy}{dt} = 6t^2, \dfrac{dx}{dt} - \dfrac{dy}{dt} = x$

6. $x\,dt + t\,dx = 2t\,dt, \dfrac{dx}{dt} + \dfrac{dy}{dt} = x - t$

7. $(x^2 + t^2)dt - xt\,dx = 0, t\dfrac{dy}{dt} = x^2 t + y$

8. $t\dfrac{dx}{dt} + \dfrac{dy}{dt} = 4(t^2 + 1)e^t, \dfrac{dx}{dt} - t\dfrac{dy}{dt} = 4(t^2 + 1)e^{2t}$

9. $\dfrac{d\rho}{\rho} = \dfrac{d\theta}{\rho + \theta + t} = \dfrac{dt}{t}$

10. $dx + ay\,dt = 0, dy - ax\,dt = 0$

11. Show that the expression $P\,dx + Q\,dy + R\,dt$, where P, Q, and R represent functions of x, y, and t, is the total differential of some expression in x, y, and t, provided that

$$\frac{\partial Q}{\partial x} = \frac{\partial P}{\partial y}, \quad \frac{\partial R}{\partial y} = \frac{\partial Q}{\partial t}, \quad \frac{\partial P}{\partial t} = \frac{\partial R}{\partial x}.$$

Hint: Read §§22 and 23.

29. Summary. In solving a differential equation of the form $M\,dx + N\,dy = 0$, the student will often find it helpful to proceed, until a method of solution is found, as follows:

I. Consider whether the equation comes under the case of

(*a*) Variables separable (§8).

(*b*) M and N homogeneous and of the same degree (§20).

(*c*) Linear equation (§26).

(*d*) Reducible to linear equation (§27).

(*e*) Exact differential equation (§23).

(*f*) M and N linear but not homogeneous (§21).

II. Search for an integrating factor (§25 exercises 9 to 16).

III. Make a substitution and consider the result under headings I and II (§19).

At present we have studied a few important special types of the differential equation having the form $M\,dx + N\,dy = 0$. It may be of interest to consider what remains to be done with this form. The result of multiplying this equation by $\mu(x,y)$ will be exact, provided $\dfrac{\partial}{\partial y}(\mu M) = \dfrac{\partial}{\partial x}(\mu N)$.

In Chapter XII, §97, we shall learn how to solve this partial differential equation for μ in terms of x and y. Not only will this furnish a general method of attack, but also it will enable us to make up types of equations that are readily solvable. In Chapter XI, two of the many methods of approximating a particular solution of a differential equation are explained. And also, in Chapter XI the method of integration in infinite series is considered. This method may be applied to solve a great variety of differential equations.

Exercises

Solve each of the following differential equations and determine the constant of integration when initial conditions are given:

1. $x^2\, dy + y^2\, dx = x^2 y\, dy - xy^2\, dx$

2. $(x^2 + 3)\dfrac{dy}{dx} + 2xy + 5x^2 = 0$

3. $(5x^2 + y^2)dx + 2x^2\, dy = 0$

4. $(y + x)^2\,\dfrac{dy}{dx} = 2(y + x)^2 - 3$

5. $\cos x\, dy + 3y \sin x\, dx - 2\cos^2 x\, dx = 0$

6. $(xy^2 + y)dx - x\, dy = 0$

7. $(3x^2 + 2xy)dx + (x^2 + \cos y)dy = 0;\ y = \dfrac{\pi}{2}$ when $x = 0$

8. $y^2 + x^2\dfrac{dy}{dx} = xy\dfrac{dy}{dx};\ y = 1$ when $x = 1$

9. $y\, dx + x\, dy = xy(dx + dy)$

10. $x^2\, dy^2 - y^4\, dx^2 = 0$

11. $xy\left(\dfrac{dy}{dx}\right)^2 - (2x^2 + y^2)\dfrac{dy}{dx} + 2xy = 0.$ *Hint:* Solve for $\dfrac{dy}{dx}$

12. $2x^3 y\, dx + x^2 y^2\, dy = y\, dx + x^2\, dy;\ y = 1$ when $x = 1$

13. $(xy + 1)(x\, dy - y\, dx) = y^2(x\, dy + y\, dx);\ y = 2$ when $x = 1$

14. $y^2\, dx + y\, dy = 2\cos x\, dx;\ y = 0$ when $x = \dfrac{\pi}{2}$

15. $x\, dy = (xy^2 - 3y)dx;\ y = 2$ when $x = 2$

16. $(2x + 3y - 1)dx = (5 - 2x - 3y)dy$

17. $(x^2 y + y^3)dx - 2x^3 dy = 0$; $y = 3$ when $x = 2$

18. $(x^3 - x)\dfrac{dy}{dx} = (x^2 + 1)y + 12x(x^2 - 1)^3$; $y = 9$ when $x = 2$

19. $[6x(x + 2y) + a^2]dy + (12xy + 6y^2 + b^2)dx = 0$

20. $\left(\dfrac{1}{x} + \dfrac{2y}{x^2 - 1}\right)dx + \left(\log \dfrac{x - 1}{x + 1} + \dfrac{1}{y}\right)dy = 0$

21. $(x + y - 3)dx + (x + y + 5) dy = 0$; $y = 0$ when $x = 1$.

22. $(5x + 4y + 4)dx + (4x + 3y + 1)dy = 0$

23. $4(x^2 - y)^3 (2x\, dx - dy) = 3(x^2 - y^2)^{-\frac{1}{4}} (x\, dx - y\, dy)$

24. Using the principles of exercises 14 and 15 in §25, solve the following differential equations:

   (a) $(2x - y)dx + (x^2y - y^2x - x)dy = 0$

   (b) $(6xy + 6x^2y + 2x)dx + 3x^2\, dy = 0$

   (c) $(2xy + 1)dx + x(x + xy + 1)dy = 0$

   (d) $(6x^2y + 2xy + 3y^2)dx + (x^2 + y)dy = 0$

25. $(x^2 - y^2)(x\, dy + y\, dx) = 2xy(x\, dy - y\, dx)$

26. $(4x - 3y)^2\, dy = 2(4x - 3y)dy + 4\, dx$

27. $\dfrac{dy}{dx} - xy = xy^2 - 2xy^3$; $y = 2$ when $x = 0$

28. $(3x^2 + 4y^2 - 5)x\, dx = (6 - 3x^2 - 4y^2)y\, dy$; let $u = x^2$, $v = y^2$

29. $\cos x \dfrac{dy}{dx} + \sin x = 1 - y$

30. $2x^3y^2\, dx + 2x^2y^3\, dy = x\, dy + y\, dx$; $y = -1$ when $x = 1$

31. $(x - y^2)dx + 2xy\, dy = 0$; $y = -2$ when $x = 1$

32. $x(x + y)dx + y(y\, dx - x\, dy) = 0$; $y = 2$ when $x = 2$

33. $(x - 2y)dx + (2x - y - 3)dy = 0$; $y = -1$ when $x = -1$

34. $(y^2 + 4xy + 3x^2)dx + (x^2 - y^2)dy = 0$

35. $(\rho + \sin \theta \cos \theta)d\theta + (\theta - \rho^2)d\rho = 0$

36. $x^2(x + y)^2 (dx + dy) = m(x\, dy - y\, dx)$

37. $(x + y)^2 (x\, dy - y\, dx) + [y^2 - 2x^2(x + y)^2] (dx + dy) = 0$;

let $v = x + y$, $w = \dfrac{y}{x}$

38. $2(x^2 + y^2 + x)(x\, dx + y\, dy) - xy\, dy + y^2\, dx = 0$; let $z = x^2 + y^2$ and eliminate y

39. $(x^2 + y^2)(x\, dy + y\, dx) + 2xy(x - y)(dx - dy) = 0$

40. Prove that the substitution $z = xy$ may be used to transform the equation $\varphi(xy)y\, dx + \psi(xy)x\, dy = 0$ to the type of variables separable. Solve

   (a) $(x^2y^2 - 1)x\, dy + (x^2y^2 + xy - 2)y\, dx = 0$

   (b) $[xy \cos (xy) + n \sin (xy)]y\, dx + xy \cos (xy)x\, dy = 0$

41. Transform $\varphi(x^m y^n)y\,dx + \psi(x^m y^n)x\,dy = 0$ to the type variables separable by the substitution $z = x^m y^n$. Solve

(a) $(2 + 4x^2\sqrt{y})y\,dx + x^3\sqrt{y}\,dy = 0$

(b) $2\left[x \sin\left(\dfrac{\sqrt{y}}{x}\right) - \sqrt{y}\cos\left(\dfrac{\sqrt{y}}{x}\right)\right]\sqrt{y}\,dx +$

$$\left[\cos\left(\dfrac{\sqrt{y}}{x}\right) + 1\right]x\,dy = 0$$

42. The equation

$$x^\alpha y^\beta(my\,dx + nx\,dy) + x^\rho y^\sigma(ay\,dx + bx\,dy) = 0$$

where α, β, m, n, ρ, σ, a, and b are constants, has an integrating factor of the form $x^p y^q$. Solve

(a) $xy^2(3y\,dx + 2x\,dy) + \sqrt{xy}(10y\,dx + 2x\,dy) = 0$

(b) $x^3(5y\,dx + 3x\,dy) + y(y\,dx + 2x\,dy) = 0$

Hint: Multiply by $x^p y^q$, apply equation (22), equate coefficients of like terms, and solve the results for p and q.

43. The equation $(3xy^2 + 7x^3)dx + (4x^2y + 3\sqrt{xy})dy = 0$ has an integrating factor of the form x^k. Determine k and solve the equation.

44. Prove the statement made in exercise 42.

45. Prove that $(xy)^{-1}$ is an integrating factor of

$$\varphi(x^m y^n)(my\,dx + nx\,dy) = \psi(x^q y^r)(qy\,dx + rx\,dy).$$

46. In the equation $(P + Rx^{k+1})dy = (Q + Ryx^k)dx$, P, Q, and R are homogeneous functions of x and y, P and Q are of the same degree, and k is a constant. Transform the given equation to the type considered in §27 by the substitution $y = vx$. Solve

$$[x^2 + y^2 + (y + 2x)x^{-1}]dy = [2(x^2 + y^2) + (y + 2x)x^{-2}y]dx.$$

47. $\dfrac{dx}{dt} - 3x = e^{3t}$, $dx - dy + x\,dt = 0$

48. $dx - dy = dt$, $x\,dt + y\,dx = 0$

49. $x\,dy + y\,dx = 2t\,dt$, $(xy + t^2)(dx + dy) = 4t\,dt$

50. $\left(\dfrac{dx}{dt}\right)^2 + \left(\dfrac{dy}{dt}\right)^2 = 25$, $y\dfrac{dy}{dx} = 1$

CHAPTER IV

APPLICATIONS INVOLVING DIFFERENTIAL EQUATIONS OF THE FIRST ORDER

30. Miscellaneous elementary applications. The solutions of the following problems involve various types of first-order differential equations. Inasmuch as no new knowledge nor new methods are needed in finding and solving the appropriate differential equations, no introductory illustrative examples will be given.

Problems

1. A curve passing through $(3, -2)$ has a slope given by $(x^2 + y^2)/(y^3 - 2xy)$. Find the equation of the curve.

2. Find the equation of the curve for which the abscissa x of the point of contact and the perpendicular from the origin to the tangent have equal lengths.

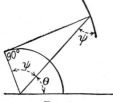

3. Find the orthogonal trajectories of the system of tangent lines to the circle $\rho = a$. From Fig. 1 $\sin \psi = a/\rho$.

4. Find the equation of the orthogonal trajectories (examples 3, §9) of all circles $x^2 + y^2 - 2my = 0$ tangent to the X-axis at the origin.

Fig. 1.

5. A point (x,y) moves, relative to a set of rectangular axes, in such a way that the area of the triangle bounded by the normal at (x,y), the ordinate of (x,y), and the X-axis is proportional to the difference of the cubes of x and y. Show that

$$y^3 = 6ke^{-6kx}\left(\int x^3 e^{6kx} dx + C\right).$$

6. Suppose that amounts a and b, respectively, of two substances are involved in a chemical reaction in which the velocity of transformation dx/dt is proportional to the product $(a - x)(b - x)$ of the amounts remaining untransformed. Integrate on the suppositions that,

62

when $t = 0$, $x = 0$ and that $a \neq b$. Also find t in terms of x, if $a = 0.6$, $b = 0.4$, and if $x = 0.2$ when $t = 300$ sec.

7. Integrate the equation of problem 6 if $a = b$.

8. In problem 2 replace "origin" by $(x,0)$ and solve the resulting problem.

9. Find the equation of the orthogonal trajectories (§11) of the system of circles $\rho = c \cos \theta + 6 \sin \theta$.

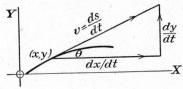

FIG. 2.

31. Applications involving simultaneous equations.

Let $x, y, s, v,$ and t represent abscissa, ordinate, arc length, velocity, and time, respectively, for a point moving in a plane, and let dots denote derivatives with respect to the time. Then the quantities

$$v = \frac{ds}{dt} = \dot{s}, \; \dot{x} = \frac{dx}{dt}, \; \dot{y} = \frac{dy}{dt} \tag{1}$$

have the relations indicated in Fig. 2. From the triangle we read, for example,

$$\frac{dy}{dx} = \tan \theta, \; \dot{x} = v \cos \theta, \; \dot{y} = v \sin \theta, \tag{2}$$

$$|v| = \sqrt{\dot{x}^2 + \dot{y}^2}. \tag{3}$$

$\dot{x}$ is called the component of velocity along the X-axis, and $\dot{y}$ the component along the Y-axis. A number of the problems in this article refer to plane motion.

Some problems will refer to substances in solution. In these a pertinent equation will often be obtained by using the expression

$$\begin{cases} \text{Rate of change of sub-} \\ \text{stance in a region} \end{cases} = \begin{cases} \text{rate of} \\ \text{entrance} \end{cases} - \begin{cases} \text{rate of} \\ \text{exit.} \end{cases} \tag{4}$$

Example 1. A particle moves on the curve $y = \frac{2}{3}x^{\frac{3}{2}}$ with a constant velocity of $\frac{2}{3}$ unit/sec. Find x and y in terms of t if $\dot{x}$ is positive and $x = 0$ when $t = 1$.

Solution. Two equations for the motion are

$$y = \tfrac{2}{3}x^{\frac{3}{2}}, \quad \dot{x}^2 + \dot{y}^2 = \tfrac{4}{9}. \tag{a}$$

Differentiating the first equation of (a) with respect to t and substituting $\dot{y}$ thus obtained in the second equation, we get

$$\dot{y} = \sqrt{x}\,\dot{x}, \quad \dot{x}^2 + x\dot{x}^2 = \tfrac{4}{9}. \tag{b}$$

From the second equation of (b), we get

$$(1 + x)^{\frac{1}{2}}dx = \tfrac{2}{3}dt, \quad \tfrac{2}{3}(1 + x)^{\frac{3}{2}} = \tfrac{2}{3}t + c.$$

Since $x = 0$ when $t = 1$, $c = 0$. Hence

$$(1 + x)^{\frac{3}{2}} = t, \text{ or } \mathbf{x} = \mathbf{t^{\frac{2}{3}} - 1}.$$

Since $y = \frac{2}{3}x^{\frac{3}{2}}$ from (a), we have

$$\mathbf{x = t^{\frac{2}{3}} - 1, \; y = \tfrac{2}{3}\,(t^{\frac{2}{3}} - 1)^{\frac{3}{2}}.}$$

Example 2. Initially tank I and tank II (see Fig. 3) each contain 100 gal. of brine, tank I having 200 lb. of salt and tank II 50 lb. of salt in solution. Brine runs at 2 gal./min. from tank I to tank II through one pipe and at 3 gal./min. from tank II to tank I through another pipe. The brine is kept well stirred. How much salt will the second tank contain at the end of 50 min.?

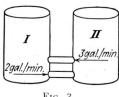

Fig. 3.

Solution. Let Q_1 and Q_2 represent the respective amounts of salt in tanks I and II at time t. Then using (4), we obtain

$$\dot{Q}_1 = \frac{3Q_2}{100 - t} - \frac{2Q_1}{100 + t}, \tag{a}$$

$$\dot{Q}_2 = \frac{2Q_1}{100 + t} - \frac{3Q_2}{100 - t} \tag{b}$$

Addition of these equations gives

$$\dot{Q}_1 + \dot{Q}_2 = 0, \text{ or } dQ_1 + dQ_2 = 0,$$

Hence $Q_1 + Q_2$ = constant and, since $Q_1 + Q_2 = 250$ initially,

$$Q_1 + Q_2 = 250 \qquad\qquad (c)$$

at all times. Substituting Q_1 from (c) in (b), we get

$$\frac{dQ_2}{dt} = \frac{500 - 2Q_2}{100 + t} - \frac{3Q_2}{100 - t} = \frac{-(500 + t)Q_2}{100^2 - t^2} + \frac{500}{100 + t}.$$

The general solution of this linear equation is

$$Q_2 = \frac{500}{(100 + t)^2}[100(100 - t) - (100 - t)^2 + c(100 - t)^3]. \quad (d)$$

Using the fact that $Q_2 = 50$ when $t = 0$, we get $C = 0.001$. Then replacing t by 50, we get $(Q_2)_{t=50} = \mathbf{58\frac{1}{3}\ lb.}$

Problems

1. A particle moves on parabola $y^2 = 4x$ with a velocity such that $\dot{x} = 2t + 2$ at all times. Find x and y in terms of t if the particle passes through (4,4) at time $t = 1$ with positive y-component.

2. A particle moves on the catenary $y = \cosh x$ with a velocity of constant magnitude 2 ft./sec. It passes through (0,1) at time $t = 0$. Show that $x = \pm \sinh^{-1}(2t)$, $y = \sqrt{1 + 4t^2}$.

3. A particle moves on curve $y = x^2 - \frac{1}{8}\log x$ with a velocity of constant magnitude 10. If it passes through (1,1) with positive x-component of velocity at time $t = 0$, show that $8x^2 + \log x = 80t + 8$.

4. Under certain conditions the motion of a projectile is given approximately by the equations

$$\dot{x} + 0.032x = 1600, \qquad\qquad \dot{y} + 0.032y = 1600 - 32t.$$

If $x = 0$ and $y = 0$ when $t = 0$, find x and y in terms of t.

5. Brine from a first tank runs into a second tank at 2 gal./min. and brine from the second tank runs into the first at 1 gal./min. Initially there are 100 gal. of brine containing 200 lb. of salt in the first tank and 100 gal. of fresh water in the second tank. How much salt will the first tank contain after 50 min.? Assume that the brine in each tank is kept uniform by stirring.

6. Brine containing 2 lb. of salt per gallon runs into a first tank at 4 gal./min., brine from the first tank runs into a second tank at 3 gal./min. and brine runs out of the second tank at 2 gal./min. Initially the first tank contains 100 gal. of brine with 300 lb. of salt in solution and the second tank 100 gal. of fresh water. Assuming uniform concentration in each tank, find the quantity of salt in the second tank at the end of 50 min.

7. If the brine running from the second tank in problem 6 should run into the first tank instead of escaping, how much salt would the second tank contain after 50 min.?

8. Differential equations of the type $\dfrac{d^2s}{dt^2} + a\dfrac{ds}{dt} + bs = 0$ are involved in the investigation of important vibratory motions. In the equation

$$\frac{d^2s}{dt^2} + 2\frac{ds}{dt} - 3s = 0$$

make the substitution

$$\frac{ds}{dt} = v, \quad \frac{d^2s}{dt^2} = \frac{dv}{dt} = \frac{ds}{dt}\frac{dv}{ds} = \frac{v\,dv}{ds} \tag{A}$$

and solve the result to obtain $(v + 3s)^3 (v - s) = C$.

9. A point moves in a plane curve through $(1,1)$ so that its components $\dot{x}$ and $\dot{y}$ are given by

$$\dot{x} = -2x + 6y, \quad \dot{y} = 2x + 2y.$$

Prove that it must move either on the line $x = y$ or on the line $x + 3y = 0$ and find x and y in terms of t for its motion on the line $x = y$. *Hint:* Divide the second equation by the first member by member.

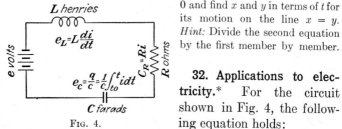

L henries

$e_L = L\dfrac{di}{dt}$

$C_R = Ri$

R ohms

e volts

$e_c = \dfrac{q}{c} = \dfrac{1}{c}\displaystyle\int_{t_0}^{t} i\,dt$

C farads

Fig. 4.

32. Applications to electricity.* For the circuit shown in Fig. 4, the following equation holds:

$$L\frac{di}{dt} + Ri + \frac{1}{C}\int_{t_0}^{t} i\,dt = e, \tag{5}$$

where i represents current, e represents electromotive force, and L, R, and C are constants. Electromotive force e is analogous to force, i to the rate of flow, L to inertia, and R to friction. The term $\dfrac{1}{C}\displaystyle\int_{t_0}^{t} i\,dt$ has reference to a condenser;

* Some fundamental laws of electricity are treated in §§61 to 65. Only a few applications of the basic equation are given at this time.

C represents its capacity and the integral represents the charge q of electricity on it.   Hence

$$q = \int_{t_0}^{t} i \, dt, \text{ or } \frac{dq}{dt} = i. \tag{6}$$

Substituting the value of i from (6) in (5), we get

$$L\frac{d^2q}{dt^2} + R\frac{dq}{dt} + \frac{q}{C} = e. \tag{7}$$

If there is no condenser in a circuit, the terms q/C and $\frac{1}{C}\int_{t_0}^{t} i \, dt$ should be omitted from (5) and (7).   Also if $L = 0$ or $R = 0$, the corresponding term disappears.

A set of units in common use are quantity q in *coulombs*, current i in *amperes*, electromotive force e in *volts*, inductance L in *henrys*, resistance R in *ohms*, and capacity C in *farads*.

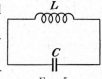

Fig. 5.

Problems

1. (*a*) Solve equations (6) and (7) for i and q in terms of t taking $L = 0$ and $e = E$, a constant, if $q = q_0$ when $t = 0$.   (*b*) What are the limiting values of i and q as t increases without limit?

2. (*a*) Solve equations (6) and (7) if $L = 0$, and $i = I_0$ when $t = 0$. (*b*) Would the conditions $i = 0$, $q = 0$, when $t = 0$ be possible if $L = 0$, and R, C, and E are all different from zero?

3. By solving equations (6) and (7) for q and i in terms of t when $L = 0$, $R = 10$ ohms, $C = 250 \times 10^{-6}$ farad, $e = 110 \sin 300t$, show that q rapidly approaches $11(4 \sin 300t - 3 \cos 300t)/2500$ and i rapidly approaches $1.32(4 \cos 300t + 3 \sin 300t)$.

4. Solve equation (5) for a circuit in which there is no condenser if $e = E$ and (*a*) $i = I_0$ when $t = 0$, (*b*) if $i = 0$ when $t = 0$.   Show that i approaches E/R as t increases.

5. If there is no condenser in a circuit of the type shown in Fig. 4 and $L = 0.1$ henry, $R = 10$ ohms, and $e = 100 \sin 200t$, show that the current i is given (nearly) by $i = 2 \sin 200t - 4 \cos 200t$ after a very short time.

6. Use equations (6) and (7) with $R = 0$ and $e = 0$ (see Fig. 5) to find i and q for the discharge of a condenser through an inductance L. Assume as initial conditions $q = q_0$, $i = 0$, when $t = 0$.

Hint: To solve $L\dfrac{d^2q}{dt^2} + \dfrac{q}{C} = 0$, first let $i = \dfrac{dq}{dt}$ and $\dfrac{d^2q}{dt^2} = \dfrac{di}{dq}\dfrac{dq}{dt}$

$= \dfrac{i\,di}{dq}$. After solving for i, replace i by $\dfrac{dq}{dt}$ and solve for q.

33. Air pressure. The concept of pressure and that of density are very important. Everywhere we meet with processes involving pressure and density of liquids and gases.

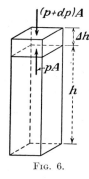

Fig. 6.

Consider a plane area at right angles to which a distributed force is acting. If P is the total force acting on a region of this plane surrounding a fixed point B and containing A square units, then $\bar{p} = P/A$ is the average pressure per square unit on this region, and the limit p of P/A as the dimensions of the region approach zero is called the pressure at point B. Again, consider a space containing material, and in this space a region of volume v surrounding a point B and containing a mass m of the material; then $\bar{\rho} = m/v$ is the average density of the material in the region, and the limit ρ of m/v as the dimensions of the region approach zero is the density at point B.

To obtain an expression for air pressure at height h above the earth, consider a vertical column of air (see Fig. 6) having a small square cross section of area A and extending from the ground upward indefinitely. An element of this column bounded above and below by two horizontal planes at heights h ft. and $h + \Delta h$ ft., respectively, from the ground is subjected to an upward force on its lower side of p lb./in.², a downward force on its upper side of $p + \Delta p$ lb./in.², the weight of the element, and horizontal forces. Since the element is in equilibrium, the vertical forces balance. Equating the algebraic sum of the vertical forces to zero, we have

$$pA - (p + \Delta p)A - \bar{\rho}A \; \Delta h = 0, \qquad (8)$$

where $\bar{\rho}$ represents the average density of the element of air. Canceling A, dividing by Δh, and finding the limit approached as Δh approaches zero, we obtain

$$dp + \rho \; dh = 0. \qquad (9)$$

If the air obeys Boyle's law for perfect gases,

$$\rho = kp.^* \qquad (10)$$

Solving (9) and (10) as simultaneous equations, we obtain

$$p = ce^{-kh}, \; \rho = kce^{-kh}.$$

Problems

1. Assuming that the atmosphere obeys Boyle's law, find the air pressure at a height of 70,000 ft. Assume that the pressure at the surface of the earth is 14.7 lb./in.^{2}, and that it is 10.08 lb./in.^{2} at an altitude of 10,000 ft.

2. Find air pressure at an altitude h, if air obeys the adiabatic law $p = k\rho^{1\cdot4}$. Show that in this case the pressure would become zero at a finite height. Find this height in terms of k and the pressure p_0 at the surface of the earth.

3. Compute the theoretical height of an atmosphere which obeys the adiabatic law $p = k\rho^{1\cdot4}$, assuming that pressure at height zero is 14.7 lb./in.^{2} and pressure at a height of 10,000 ft. is 10.08 lb./in.^{2}.

34. Miscellaneous Problems

1. Find the equation of the curve so constructed that the area swept out by the radius vector in turning from $\theta = 0$ to any position is proportional to the nth power of the radius vector of that position.

2. A tank contains 100 gal. of fresh water. If water containing

---

* A good approximation to air pressure is not to be expected by assuming Boyle's law or the law of adiabatic expansion because the density of a gas depends on its temperature. In fact for a perfect gas

$$p = RT\rho,$$

where p is the pressure per square unit, ρ the density, T the absolute temperature, and R a constant. Evidently this relation is equivalent to Boyle's law when T is constant.

2 lb. of salt per gallon runs into the tank at the rate of 2 gal./min., and if the mixture runs out at the rate of 3 gal./min., find how much salt will be in the tank at the end of one hour. Assume that the solution is kept uniform by stirring.

3. Find the equation of the curve for which the intercept of the tangent on the X-axis is proportional to the second power of the radius vector for every point on the curve.

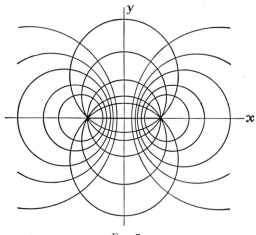

Fig. 7.

4. Find the orthogonal trajectories of the family of circles $x^2 + y^2 - 2cx - 9 = 0$. Observe that the given circles all pass through the points $(0,3)$ and $(0,-3)$ (see Fig. 7).

5. Find the equation of a system of curves that cut the circles $x^2 + y^2 = C$ at $\tan^{-1} 2$. *Hint:* If y_r' and y_g' represent the respective slopes of the required curve and the given curve, then $\pm 2 = \dfrac{y_r' - y_g'}{1 + y_r' y_g'}$.

6. In the chemical process called *fractional precipitation* the equations

$$\frac{dx}{dt} = k_1(a - x)(c - z), \quad \frac{dy}{dt} = k_2(b - y)(c - z)$$

apply. Given that $x = 0$ when $y = 0$, prove that

$$k_1 : k_2 = \log \frac{a}{a - x} : \log \frac{b}{b - x}.$$

7. On a rough circular cylinder with horizontal axis and radius a, and in a plane perpendicular to the axis of the cylinder, lies a thin,

uniform, flexible, inextensible chain with one end resting on the cylinder
and the other hanging down to a distance l below the axis. If the chain
is on the point of slipping, the tension T at any
point of the chain and the angle φ (see Fig. 8)
for this same point satisfy, approximately, the
differential equation

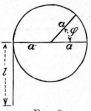

$$\frac{dT}{d\varphi} - \mu T = \rho a(\cos \varphi + \mu \sin \varphi)$$

where ρ is the weight per unit length of the
chain and μ is the coefficient of friction.   (a)
Find the general solution of the equation.

FIG. 8.

(b) If one end of the chain is at the level of the axis of the cylinder
and the other hanging down to a distance l below the axis, show that

$$l = \frac{2\mu a}{1 + \mu^2}(1 + e^{\pi\mu}).$$ (c) If one end of the chain is at the highest

point of the cylinder and $l = 0$, show that $e^{\frac{\pi}{2}\mu}(1 - \mu^2) = 2\mu$. Hint:
Obtain initial conditions by finding T and φ at the ends of the part of
the chain in contact with the cylinder.

8. Find the equation of the curve for which the area bounded by
the curve, any two ordinates, and the X-axis is equal to the average of
these two ordinates multiplied by the distance between them.

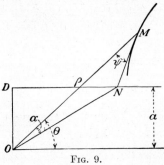

9. Given a point O and a
straight line D, find a curve such
that the portion of the tangent
MN included between the point of
contact M and the point of intersection N of the tangent and the
line D subtends a constant angle
at O (see Fig. 9). Hint: Use the
law of sines to obtain

$$\frac{ON}{\sin \varphi} = \frac{\rho}{\sin (\psi + \alpha)}$$

FIG. 9.   Also $ON = a \csc (\theta - \alpha)$

10. If in problem 9, the angle MON, instead of being constant is
equal to angle OMN, show that the differential equation of the curve
is either $d\theta = 0$ or $(2a - \rho \sin \theta)d\rho + \rho^2 \cos \theta \, d\theta = 0$. Prove that
$1/\rho^3$ is an integrating factor of this latter equation and find its solution.

11. Assuming that the weight of a cubic foot of sea water under
a pressure of P lb./ft.^{2} is $64(1 + 2P \times 10^{-8})$ lb., find the weight per
cubic foot of the water at the bottom of an ocean 5 mi. deep.

12. A mass of $4\pi \times 10^9$ lb. has the form of a sphere of radius R ft. The pressure, P lb./ft.^{2}, is directed toward the center, is the same for all points at the same distance from the center, and is 1000 lb./ft.^{2} at the surface. The density, ρ lb./ft.^{3}, at the surface is unity, and at a distance r ft. from the center of the sphere it is $\rho = cP/r$, where c is a constant. Find R if $dP = -\rho\ dr$.

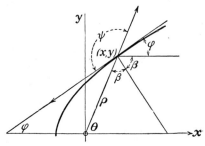

Fig. 10.

13. A point (x,y) referred to a set of rectangular axes moves so that the x-component of its velocity is proportional to y and the y-component is proportional to x. If it passes through point $(1,1)$ with velocity 10 ft./sec. in a direction inclined $\tan^{-1} \frac{3}{4}$ to the X-axis, find its position at any time. *Hint:* Initial conditions are $x = 1$, $y = 1$, $\dfrac{dx}{dt} = 8$, $\dfrac{dy}{dt} = 6$, all when $t = 0$.

14. Referred to a set of rectangular axes, the path of a moving particle is given by $x^2 - y^2 = 25$ and the components $\dot{x}$ and $\dot{y}$ of its velocity satisfy $\dot{x} + \dot{y} = 1$. Find the position of the particle at time t, if $x = 5$ when $t = 5$.

15. One end of an inextensible string, of length l, is fastened to a weight which rests on a rough horizontal table. The other end is carried slowly along a straight line in the table. Find the path of the weight. Assume that the string is always tangent to the curve described by the weight.

16. A light situated at a point in a plane sends out beams in every direction. The beams in the plane meet a curve and are all reflected parallel to a fixed straight line in the plane. If the angle of incidence with the normal to the curve at the point of incidence is equal to the angle of reflection, find the equation of the curve. Solve by using polar coordinates and also by using rectangular coordinates (see Fig. 10).

CHAPTER V

FIRST-ORDER EQUATIONS OF DEGREE HIGHER THAN THE FIRST. SINGULAR SOLUTIONS

35. Foreword. Differential equations of the first order but higher degree than the first have general solutions, and also, in some cases, a particular solution called a *singular solution*. Since the graph of the singular solution is an envelope of the curves defined by the general solution, a treatment of envelopes will be given.

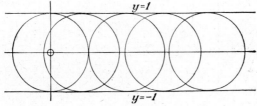

Fig. 1.

36. Envelopes. *Any curve which is tangent to an infinite number of members of a singly infinite family of curves, and which is tangent at each of its points to a finite number of these curves, is either a part or the whole of the envelope of the family.* For example, a curve may be considered as the envelope of its tangent lines or of its osculating circles. In Fig. 1 the circles $(x - c)^2 + y^2 = 1$ are represented with their envelope $y = \pm 1$. Figure 2 shows a curve as the envelope of its tangent lines.

Let the equation

$$f(x,y,c) = 0 \qquad\qquad (1)$$

73

represent the family of curves which are tangent to some curve. The coordinates of the intersection of this latter curve with a curve of (1) is determined by a value of c, that is, x and y of this curve are functions of c and may be written in the form

$$x = \varphi_1(c),\ y = \varphi_2(c). \tag{2}$$

For convenience, partial derivatives will be denoted by subscripts. Thus

$$\frac{\partial f(x,y,c)}{\partial x} = f_x(x,y,c),\ \frac{\partial^2 f(x,y,c)}{\partial c^2} = f_{cc}(x,y,c),\ \text{etc.}$$

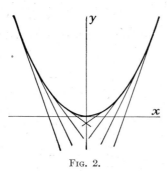

FIG. 2.

The slope of (1) is given by

$$f_x + f_y\frac{dy}{dx} = 0. \tag{3}$$

Since x and y of (2) satisfy (1), we take the total derivative of (1) with respect to c to obtain

$$f_x\frac{dx}{dc} + f_y\frac{dy}{dc} + f_c = 0 \tag{4}$$

for the points of curve (2). It therefore appears from (3) and (4) that the curves (1) and (2) will have the same slope at intersection points, if

$$f_c = 0. \tag{5}$$

In other words, if (2) represents the envelope of family (1), it must satisfy both (1) and (5). Hence, if an equation (1) has an envelope, it will be represented in the result of eliminating c between (1) and (5). Referring to this eliminant as the *c-discriminant*, we may say, *if a family of curves has an envelope and its equation a c-discriminant, the envelope will be a part or all of the graph of the c-discriminant.*

Along a locus of singular points of (1) we have

$$f_x = 0, f_y = 0. \tag{6}$$

If (2) represents such a locus, then (1) and therefore (4) are true for its points. Hence, from (4) and (6) we have $\partial f/\partial c = 0$, and it appears that *the c-discriminant contains any locus of singular points that* (1) *may have.* A locus of singular points generally does not form part of the envelope. The following examples illustrate the theory:

For the circles $(x - c)^2 + y^2 = 1$, we have

$$f(x,y,c) = (x - c)^2 + y^2 - 1 = 0, f_c = 2(x - c) = 0.$$

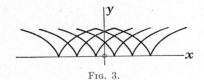

FIG. 3.

The solution of these equations for x and y in terms of c is

$$x = c, y = \pm 1. \tag{7}$$

Thus the envelope is $y = \pm 1$, and each circle $(x - c)^2 + y^2 = 1$ touches the envelope at $(c, \pm 1)$ as indicated in Fig. 1.

The family of straight lines represented by $3y - 2cx + c^2 = 0$ has an envelope defined by

$$f = 3y - 2cx + c^2 = 0, f_c = -2x + 2c = 0.$$

Eliminating c from these equations, we obtain

$$3y = x^2. \tag{8}$$

Figure 2 shows $3y = x^2$ as the envelope of its tangent lines $3y - 2cx + c^2 = 0$.

For the family of semicubical parabolas $y^3 = (x - c)^2$ equations (1), (5), and (2) have the respective forms

$$f = y^3 - (x - c)^2 = 0, f_c = 2(x - c) = 0, x = c, y = 0. \tag{9}$$

Since $f_x = -2(x - c)$ and $f_y = 3y^2$ are both zero on (9), it appears that (9) is a locus of singular points. It is the locus of the cusps $(c,0)$ of the curves $y^3 = (x - c)^2$ as indicated in Fig. 3. The family has no envelope.

37. Sufficient conditions for an envelope. A family of curves may not have an envelope. Illustrations of such families are the parallel lines $x + y - c = 0$ and the concentric circles $x^2 + y^2 - c^2 = 0$. The following theorem expresses sufficient, but not necessary, conditions for the existence of an envelope.

THEOREM. *Each curve of the family* $f(x,y,c) = 0$ *for a value of c near* c_0 *is tangent to a curve defined by*

$$f(x,y,c) = 0, \ f_c(x,y,c) = 0 \tag{10}$$

provided that $f(x_0,y_0,c_0) = 0$, $f_c(x_0,y_0,c_0) = 0$, *that* f, f_x, f_y, f_{xc}, f_{yc}, f_{cc} *are continuous in the neighborhood of* x_0, y_0, c_0, *and that*

$$f_{cc}(x_0,y_0,c_0) \neq 0, \quad \begin{vmatrix} f_x(x_0,y_0,c_0) & f_y(x_0,y_0,c_0) \\ f_{xc}(x_0,y_0,c_0) & f_{yc}(x_0,y_0,c_0) \end{vmatrix} \neq 0. \tag{11}$$

The proof of this theorem has been omitted since it is more a theorem of calculus than of differential equations and is proved in books on advanced calculus.* Equations (11) are the conditions that (10) be solvable for x and y in terms of c.

The student may note that the conditions of the theorem are satisfied for $f(x,y,c) = y - 2cx + c^2 = 0$, and that there is an envelope. He may also note that one or both of conditions (11) are not satisfied for $f(x,y,c) = x + y + c = 0$, $f(x,y,c) = x^2 + y^2 - c^2 = 0$, or $f(x,y,c) = y^3 - (x - c)^2 = 0$, and that the corresponding families do not have envelopes. On the other hand, the conditions (11) are not satisfied at the point $x = c$, $y = 0$ when $f(x,y,c) = y - x (x - c)^4 = 0$; nevertheless $y = 0$ is an envelope of this family. We conclude that there may be an envelope even though the conditions of the theorem are not satisfied.

Exercises

1. Find the envelope of each family of curves:

(a) $cy - c^2x = 4$

(b) $y^2 = 3cx - c^3$

(c) $x \sin c + y \cos c = 3$

(d) $x \tan c - y \sec c = 3$

* See, FITE, W. B., "Advanced Calculus," pp. 324–326.

2. Find in parametric form the equations of the envelope of

(a) $y = cx - c - c^3$ (b) $x \sin \alpha + y \cos \alpha = \alpha$

3. The evolute of a curve is the envelope of its family of normals (see Fig. 4). Show that the evolute of $xy = 1$ is represented by

$$x = \frac{1 + 3c^4}{2c^3}, \; y = \frac{3 + c^4}{2c}$$

where c is the abscissa of any point on the given curve.

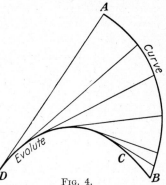

4. Show that the evolute of the curve $x = a \cos \theta + a \theta \sin \theta$, $y = a \sin \theta - a \theta \cos \theta$, is the circle $x^2 + y^2 = a^2$.

5. Show that the family $c \log x + c \sin cy = \pi$ has an envelope in the neighborhood of $x = e^\pi$, $y = \pi$, $c = 1$.

6. Show that for the family

Fig. 4.

$$f(x,y,c) = (y - c)(y - 2x + c) = y^2 - 2xy + 2cx - c^2 = 0 \quad (A)$$

the equations $f = 0$, $f_c = 0$ define the line $x = c$, $y = c$, or $x - y = 0$. Show that along this line $f_x = 0$ and $f_y = 0$. How is the line related to the family (A)?

38. Envelope from differential equation.

In this chapter dy/dx is represented by p,

$$p = \frac{dy}{dx}.$$

Consider a differential equation

$$\psi(x,y,p) = 0, \tag{12}$$

having $F(x,y,c) = 0$ as general solution. Substitution of (x_0, y_0) in $F(x,y,c) = 0$ gives $F(x_0, y_0, c) = 0$, an equation in c having, let us suppose, n roots. Since a curve is associated with each of these n values of c, we conclude that, in general, n curves of the family $f(x,y,c) = 0$ pass through (x_0, y_0). If now $f_c(x_0, y_0, c_0) = 0$, then c_0 is a multiple root of $f(x_0, y_0, c) = 0$, and therefore a fewer number of curves than usual pass through (x_0, y_0). This condition may be described by saying that *a smaller number of curves than usual pass through a point on the envelope of the solution.* Since the slopes of curves of the general solution through a point (x_0, y_0) on its envelope are given by $\psi(x_0, y_0, p) = 0$ and there are fewer than usual, $\psi(x_0, y_0, p) = 0$ must have a multiple root, p_0. Therefore $\psi_p(x_0, y_0, p_0) = 0$. Hence along the envelope of $F(x, y, c) = 0$ we have

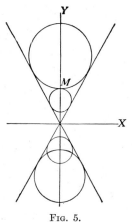

$$\psi(x, y, p) = 0, \ \psi_p(x, y, p) = 0. \quad (13)$$

The result of eliminating p from (13), called the *p-discriminant,* contains the equation of the envelope. In general *this equation of the envelope satisfies the differential equation* because the slope of the envelope at each of its points is the same as that of a curve belonging to the general solution; it is called the *singular solution.* A part of an envelope defined by $x = c$, a constant, would not ordinarily satisfy the differential equation since along such a curve, p does not exist.

Fig. 5.

The name *tac-locus* is given to a locus of points at each of which two or more curves of a family have the same tangent. In Fig. 1 of §36, $y = 0$ is a tac-locus for the system of circles. Since, at a point on the tac-locus, two of the values of p associated to the point by the differential equation are equal, the coordinates of the point must satisfy the p-discriminant, that is, *the graph of the* p-*discriminant must contain the tac-locus.* Also, at a cusp, the values of p for each of two branches are equal. Hence *the graph of the* p-*discriminant contains any locus of cusps belonging to the corresponding family.*

Example 1. Find the envelope belonging to the solution of

$$(4x^2 - y^2)p^2 - 2xyp + 3x^2 = 0. \qquad (a)$$

Solution. Differentiate (a) with respect to p to obtain

$$2p(4x^2 - y^2) - 2xy = 0. \qquad (b)$$

Eliminate p between (a) and (b) to get

$$4x^2(3x^2 - y^2) = 0, \text{ or } x = 0, y = \pm\sqrt{3}\,x. \qquad (c)$$

Since $y = \pm\sqrt{3}\,x$ satisfies (a), it represents an envelope. The solution of (a) is $x^2 + (y - 2c)^2 = c^2$, a family of circles. Figure 5 represents this family having as envelope the lines $y = \pm\sqrt{3}\,x$. Note that $x = 0$ in (c) represents the tac-locus of such points as M.

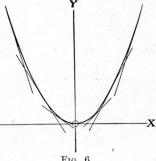

Example 2. Find the singular solution of

$$y = px - p^2. \qquad (a)$$

Solution. Equations (13) for (a) are

$$y = px - p^2, x - 2p = 0. \quad (b)$$

Fig. 6.

Eliminating p from (b), we obtain

$$y = \frac{x^2}{2} - \frac{x^2}{4}, \text{ or } x^2 = 4y. \qquad (c)$$

Since (c) satisfies (a), it is the singular solution. Figure 6 represents the solution. The parabola represents the singular solution, and the tangent lines represent the general solution which is $y = cx - c^2$.

Example 3. Find the singular solution of

$$4y = (3y - a)^2 p^2. \qquad (a)$$

Solution. The partial derivative of (a) with respect to p is

$$2p(3y - a)^2 = 0. \qquad (b)$$

This is satisfied, if
$$p = 0, \text{ or if } 3y - a = 0. \tag{c}$$
Eliminating p between (a) and (c), we have
$$3y - a = 0, \text{ and } y = 0. \tag{d}$$
The equation $\mathbf{y} = \mathbf{0}$ satisfies equation (a) and represents the envelope. $3y - a = 0$ represents the tac-locus shown by the line $y = a/3$ in Fig. 7.

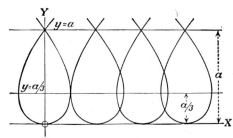

FIG. 7.

The general solution of (a) is
$$(x + c)^2 = y(y - a)^2.$$
From this, the c-discriminant is found to be
$$y(y - a)^2 = 0. \tag{e}$$
As $\mathbf{y} = \mathbf{0}$ satisfies (a), it is the equation of the envelope. $y = a$ is a nodal locus (see Fig. 7).

Exercises

1. Show that the envelope of the solution of $4y = 4px - 3p^{\frac{4}{3}}$ is $4y = x^4$.

2. Show that $x - y = 1$ is the envelope of the solution of $y - x + 2p = p^2$.

3. Show that the envelope of the solution of $3(y - x + p^2) = 2p^3$ is $3x - 3y = 1$. $y - x = 0$ is part of the p-discriminant. It represents the cuspidal locus of the general solution which is $9(y - c)^2 = 4(x - c)^3$.

4. Show that the envelope of the solution of $4y^2(1 + p^2) = 4x - 1 + 4yp$ is $y^2 = x$. Part of the p-discriminant is $y = 0$. It represents a tac-locus of the general solution $(x - 0.5 - c)^2 + y^2 = c + 0.25$. Figure 8 indicates the relations.

5. Find the singular solution of $y = 2p^3x + 3p^2x^2 + 1$.

39. Equations solvable for dy/dx. A method of solving an equation of the first order and higher degree, when the equation can be resolved into factors linear in dy/dx, has already been considered in §12. We shall consider this type more completely at this point.

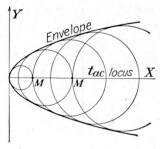

Fig. 8.

Writing $dy/dx = p$, we see that an equation of the nth degree in p, which may be reduced to the form

$$(p - A_1)(p - A_2) \cdots (p - A_n) = 0, \qquad (14)$$

where the $A_1, A_2, \ldots, A_n$ represent functions of x and y, may be solved by equating each factor to zero and integrating the resulting equations. The solutions thus obtained,

$$\varphi_1(x,y,c_1) = 0, \quad \varphi_2(x,y,c_2) = 0, \cdots, \quad \varphi_n(x,y,c_n) = 0, \qquad (15)$$

may be regarded as the result required, or we may write

$$\varphi_1(x,y,c) \cdot \varphi_2(x,y,c) \cdots \varphi_n(x,y,c) = 0 \qquad (16)$$

as the general solution, since equations (15) represent all the curves defined by (16) and no others.

The solution (16) indicates that a curve to be a solution of (14) must satisfy the equation obtained by equating only one factor of (14) to zero. Evidently any continuous curve possessing a derivative at each of its points and satisfying (14) represents a solution of (14) even though a certain factor of (14) should be zero over parts of its range, a second factor zero over another part, and so on. Since such a curve consists of parts each of which is included in (16), we shall consider (16) as a general solution.

Take for example the differential equation

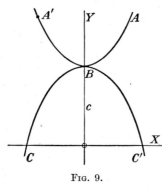

Fig. 9.

$$p^2 - 9x^4 = 0. \qquad (a)$$

From this we write $p - 3x^2 = 0$, $p + 3x^2 = 0$, and solve to get

$$y = x^3 + c_1, \ y = -x^3 + c_2, \ (b)$$

as the general solution of (a).

Figure 9 represents a pair of curves ABC and $A'BC'$ of the solution. Observe however that the curve ABA', having equations

$$y = x^3 + c, \ x \geqq 0; \ y = -x^3 + c, \ x < 0$$

and curve CBC' are also solutions. However, the parts of these curves are represented by (b).

Exercises

1. $x^2p^2 + 3xyp + 2y^2 = 0$, $p = \dfrac{dy}{dx}$

2. $p^2 + py = x^2 + xy$

3. $(p - x^2)(p - xy)(p - y^2) = 0$

4. $(a^2 - x^2)p^3 + bx(a^2 - x^2)p^2 - p - bx = 0$

5. $xp^2 - 2yp - x = 0$

6. $(x + 2y)p^3 + 3(x + y)p^2 + (y + 2x)p = 0$

7. $p^3 - 2p^2 - p + 2 = 0$

8. If, from the equation $x^2p^2 + 5xyp + 6y^2 = 0$, we form a new equation by replacing p by $-1/p$, what will be the relation between the systems of curves represented by the solutions of the two equations?

40. Equations solvable for y. When a first-order differential equation is solvable for y, it may be written in the form

$$y = f(x,p). \qquad (17)$$

Taking the total derivative of this equation with respect to x, we get

$$\frac{dy}{dx} = p = \frac{\partial f}{\partial x} + \frac{\partial f}{\partial p}\frac{dp}{dx}. \tag{18}$$

This equation, since y does not appear in it, may be solved as an equation in x and p to get

$$\psi(x,p,c) = 0. \tag{19}$$

Equations (17) and (19) may be thought of as the parametric equations (p being the parameter) of a system of curves and therefore as the general solution of (17). If we eliminate p between equations (17) and (19), we get the general solution as an equation in x and y involving an arbitrary constant. If one suspects that the eliminant contains, as it may, extraneous factors that do not represent solutions, he should check by substituting in the differential equation.

Example. Solve $y = 2xp + 4xp^2$. $\qquad\qquad$ (a)

Solution. By differentiating with respect to x we obtain from (a)

$$p = 2p + 4p^2 + (2x + 8xp)\frac{dp}{dx}, \tag{b}$$

or, rearranged,

$$2x(1 + 4p)\frac{dp}{dx} + p(1 + 4p) = 0. \tag{c}$$

Equation (c) will be satisfied if either of the equations

$$2x\frac{dp}{dx} + p = 0, \; 1 + 4p = 0, \tag{d}$$

holds true. From the first of (d), we get by integration

$$p^2x = c, \text{ or } x = cp^{-2}. \tag{e}$$

Parametric equations of the solution obtained by solving (a) and (e) for x and y in terms of p are

$$x = cp^{-2}, y = 2cp^{-1} + 4c. \tag{f}$$

To get the solution in terms of x and y, eliminate p between (a) and (e). Writing (a) in the form $(y - 4xp^2)^2 = 4x^2p^2$, replacing p^2 in this by c/x from (e), and simplifying, we obtain

$$(y - 4c)^2 = 4cx. \qquad (g)$$

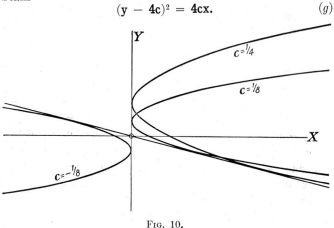

Fig. 10.

A particular solution, called a *singular solution*, is obtained by eliminating p between the second equation of (d) and (a). This gives

$$4y + x = 0.$$

Observe that the p-discriminant of (a) is $x = 0$, $4y + x = 0$, and the c-discriminant of (g) is the same thing. Figure 10 shows a few curves of the solution. Note that $x = 0$ is a part of the envelope. Strictly speaking $x = 0$ does not satisfy (a); but if (a) be multiplied through by dx/dy to obtain

$$y\left(\frac{dx}{dy}\right)^2 = 2x\frac{dx}{dy} + 4x,$$

$x = 0$ satisfies the result.

Exercises

1. Solve each equation by the method of this article. Also in each case equate to zero the factor that may be canceled from the equation in

x, p, and dp/dx and eliminate p between the result and the original equation to obtain a singular solution. Compare the singular solution thus obtained with the c-discriminant and with the p-discriminant.

(a) $2yp = 3x + xp^2$;   (b) $y = x^4p^2 - xp$

2. Find solutions of the following equations in parametric form:

(a) $y = 2xp - 3p^2$;   (b) $2y + px = 6p^2$

3. Solve $x^2(y - px) = yp^2$. Show that it does not have a singular solution.

4. Solve $p^2 - 4px + 6y = 0$. Find the p-discriminant and show that it is not a solution of the given differential equation. Show that $y = 0$ is a solution of the given equation although it is not a special case of the general solution nor the equation of an envelope of the general solution.

41. Equations solvable for x. A first-order differential equation which is solvable for x may be written in the form

$$x = f(y,p). \qquad (20)$$

Taking the total derivative of this equation with respect to y, we get

$$\frac{dx}{dy} = \frac{1}{p} = \frac{\partial f}{\partial y} + \frac{\partial f}{\partial p}\frac{dp}{dy}. \qquad (21)$$

This equation may be solved as an equation in y and p to obtain

$$\psi(y,p,c) = 0. \qquad (22)$$

Equations (20) and (22) may be considered as the general solution in parametric form, or we may eliminate p between (20) and (22) to obtain the solution as a relation between x, y, and a constant of integration.

Example. Solve $y = 2px + y^2p^3$.   (a)

Solution. Solving for x, we get

$$x = \frac{y}{2p} - \frac{y^2p^2}{2}. \qquad (b)$$

The derivative of (b) with respect to y is

$$\frac{dx}{dy} = \frac{1}{p} = \frac{1}{2p} - yp^2 - \left(\frac{y}{2p^2} + y^2p\right)\frac{dp}{dy}, \qquad (c)$$

or, simplified,

$$\frac{1}{2p} + yp^2 = -\frac{y}{p}\left(\frac{1}{2p} + yp^2\right)\frac{dp}{dy}. \tag{d}$$

Dividing out $\frac{1}{2p} + yp^2$ and integrating, we obtain

$$py = c, \text{ or } y = \frac{c}{p}. \tag{e}$$

Substituting y from (e) in (b), we get

$$x = \frac{c}{2p^2} - \frac{c^2}{2}. \tag{f}$$

Equations (e) and (f) give, in parametric form, the general solution required. Eliminating p between (e) and (f), we find the solution in rectangular form to be

$$x = \frac{y^2}{2c} - \frac{c^2}{2}, \text{ or } \mathbf{y^2 = 2cx + c^3}.$$

Equation (d) is satisfied if $(1/2p) + yp^2 = 0$. Eliminating p between this equation and (a), we obtain the singular solution,

$$\mathbf{27y^4 = -32x^3}.$$

Exercises

1. Integrate the following equations by the method of this article:

(a) $x = y + \log p$;   (b) $y - 2px - p^2y = 0$;
                    (c) $xp^2 - 2yp + x + 2y = 0$

2. Find the solutions of the following equations in parametric form:

(a) $x = y + p^2$;   (b) $4px = y + a^2p^2y$

3. Solve each equation by the method of this article. Also in each case equate to zero the factor that may be canceled from the equation in y, p, and dp/dy and eliminate p between the result and the original equation to obtain a singular solution. In each case compare this singular solution with the p-discriminant and with the c-discriminant.

(a) $4pxy = 8y^2 + p^3$;   (b) $py = p^2x + 1$;   (c) $p^3 = y^5 + xpy^4$

4. Solve: (a) $a^2yp^2 + y = 2xp$;   (b) $xy^2p^2 - y^3p = x$

5. Solve in three ways, $xp^2 - 2yp - x = 0$.

42. Clairaut's equation.   The equation

$$y = px + f(p), \qquad (23)$$

known as *Clairaut's equation*, is named after Alexis Claude
Clairaut (1713–1765).   He was the first man to differentiate
a differential equation, as we have done in §§40 and 41, in
order to solve it.

Let us apply the method of §40 to equation (23).   Differentiation with respect to x gives

$$\frac{dy}{dx} = p = p + \left(x + \frac{df}{dp} \right)\frac{dp}{dx}, \text{ or } \left(x + \frac{df}{dp} \right)\frac{dp}{dx} = 0. \quad (24)$$

Then

$$\frac{dp}{dx} = 0, \text{ and } p = c.$$

Substituting c for p in equation (23), we have

$$y = cx + f(c) \qquad (25)$$

as the general solution.   Thus, it appears that *to solve Clairaut's equation, it is necessary only to replace* p *by* c.

The particular solution arising from equating $x + \dfrac{df}{dp}$ to

zero and eliminating p between the result and (23) gives a
singular solution.   In general, the systems of lines represented
by the general solution are the tangent lines of the graph of
the singular solution.

Since the equation

$$f(y - px, p) = 0, \qquad (26)$$

when solved for $y - px$, takes the form

$$y - px = \psi(p),$$

it is really Clairaut's equation, and its solution is

$$f(y - cx, c) = 0. \qquad (27)$$

Exercises

1. Find the general solution and the singular solution of each
equation:

(a) $y = px + p^2$;   (b) $y = px + p^3$;   (c) $y = px + a\sqrt{1 + p^2}$

2. Solve $y - px = \sin (y - px) + p^2$. Show that $y - \sqrt{2\pi n}\, x = 2\pi n$, where n is a positive integer, is a solution. Also show that the envelope would be represented by the equations $y - cx = \sin (y - cx) + c^2$, $x \cos (y - cx) = x + 2c$, where c is to be considered as a parameter.

3. Solve $3p^2 e^y - px + 1 = 0$. Let $z = e^y$.

4. Solve $y = 2px + y^2 p^3$. Let $z = y^2$.

5. Solve $y^2 - p^2 y - xp^3 - x^2 p^2 = 0$ *Hint:* Factor.

6. Find in parametric form the equation of the envelope of straight lines represented by the differential equations:

(a) $y = px + p^3 + p^4$;   (b) $y = px + p\sqrt{p^2 + 1}$;
                 (c) $y = px + p^{\frac{1}{2}} + p^{\frac{2}{3}}$

7. To find the equation of the system of tangent lines to a curve $y = \psi(x)$, let $y = px + f(p)$ be the differential equation of the family. $f(p)$ is to be found. For any point (x_1, y_1) on the curve, we have

(1) $y_1 = \psi(x_1)$;   (2) $y_1 = px_1 + f(p)$;   (3) $p = \left(\dfrac{dy}{dx}\right)_1 = \left(\dfrac{d\psi}{dx}\right)_{x=x_1}$

Solve (1) and (3) for x_1 and y_1 in terms of p, substitute the value thus obtained in (2), and solve the result for $f(p)$.

Find the differential equation of the straight lines having as envelope the curve: (a) $y^2 = x$; (b) $x^2 + y^2 = r^2$; (c) $xy + m = 0$; (d) $3y = x^3$; (e) $y = x^n$

43. Miscellaneous exercises and applications.

The differential equations of this chapter are effective in dealing with many geometric and mechanistic problems relating to families of straight lines. Geometric problems will be found in the following list; the example solved below will serve to illustrate problems relating to mechanisms.

The mechanism represented in Fig. 11 is considered to be in a plane. Cam OMN revolves about fixed point O thus causing bar AB to move vertically without rotation between the fixed guides CA and DB. Find the equation of curve MPN if the bar AB moves at a constant rate when cam OMN revolves with constant angular velocity.

Assume AB to remain horizontal. Let ON be a line fixed in the cam making the variable angle θ with horizontal line OD. Also let x measured along ON and y perpendicular to it be the rectangular coordinates of P, the variable point of contact between bar AB and the cam. Since the rate of change of length GP is proportional to the constant angular velocity $d\theta/dt$ of the cam, we have

$$\frac{d(GP)}{dt} = k\frac{d\theta}{dt}, \text{ or } GP = k\theta + A. \tag{28}$$

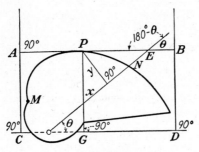

Fig. 11.

Now from Fig. 11 it appears that the slope dy/dx of the curve MPN is $\tan(180° - \theta) = -\tan\theta$, and that $GP = x\sin\theta + y\cos\theta$. Hence

$$p = \frac{dy}{dx} = -\tan\theta, \quad GP = x\sin\theta + y\cos\theta. \tag{29}$$

Substituting GP from (29) in (28), dividing through by $\cos\theta$, and replacing in the result

$$\tan\theta \text{ by } -p, \sec\theta \text{ by } \sqrt{1 + p^2}, \theta \text{ by } -\tan^{-1}p, \tag{30}$$

we get after slight simplification

$$y = px + (A - k\tan^{-1}p)\sqrt{1 + p^2}. \tag{31}$$

Since this is a Clairaut equation, its solution is

$$y = cx + (A - k\tan^{-1}c)\sqrt{1 + c^2}. \tag{32}$$

This equation represents the tangent AB referred to the moving axes and *the singular solution of* (32) *is the required equation of the curve* MPN. This singular solution in parametric form is found by the usual method to be

$$x = \frac{k - Ac + kc \tan^{-1} c}{\sqrt{1 + c^2}},$$

$$y = \frac{ck + A - k \tan^{-1} c}{\sqrt{1 + c^2}}. \tag{33}$$

Observe that (k,A) is the point P of contact between the curve and bar when $c = 0$.

Exercises

1. Find the general solution and the singular solution of the following equations:

(a) $y^2(1 + p^2) = 1$

(b) $p^2(1 - x^2) = x^2$

(c) $p^2x - py + 1 = 0$

(d) $y = px + 3\sqrt{1 + p^2}$

(e) $x^2 - 4y^2 + 2xyp - 3y^2p^2 = 0$

(f) $p^2y^2 \cos^2 \alpha - 2pxy \sin^2 \alpha - x^2 \sin^2 \alpha + y^2 = 0$

(g) $4p^2x = (3x - a)^2$

(h) $p^3 - 4xyp + 8y^2 = 0$

(i) $y = px - p^3$

(j) $4p^2 = 9x$

(k) $8ap^3 = 27y$

(l) $x^3p^2 + x^2yp + a^3 = 0$

(m) $y = px + \sin^{-1} p$

2. Find the curve such that the sum of the intercepts of the tangent on the coordinate axes is constant and equal to k. *Hint:* Since a curve is the envelope of its tangent lines, find the Clairaut equation $y = p(x) + f(p)$ of the tangent lines and then the singular solution of this equation. Evidently the intercepts of $y = px + f(p)$ are $f(p)$ and $-f(p)/p$. Hence $f(p) = pk/(p - 1)$.

3. Find the equation of the curve such that

(a) Each of its tangent lines has intercepts whose difference is constant and equal to k.

(b) Each of its tangent lines together with the coordinate axes encloses a constant area equal to a^2.

(c) The distance from the origin to any tangent line is numerically equal to the square root of the square of the slope increased by 1.

(d) The perpendiculars drawn from $(a,0)$ and $(-a,0)$ to the tangent line have

(1) The difference of their squares constant.

(2) The sum of their squares constant.

(3) Their sum constant.

(4) Their product constant.

(5) Their quotient constant.

4. It can be shown that (33) represents the involute of a circle. Show that when $A = 0$ in (33) the result gives the equations of the involute $x = k(\cos \theta + \theta \sin \theta)$, $y = k(\sin \theta - \theta \cos \theta)$ of a circle if $\theta = \tan^{-1} c$.

5. Find the equation of the curve MPN in Fig. 11 if the cam is so designed that the rate of change of GP with respect to θ is (a) $m \sin \theta$; (b) $m \sin \theta + n \cos \theta$; (c) $(a^2 - b^2)(a^2 \sin^2 \theta + b^2 \cos^2 \theta)^{-\frac{1}{2}} \sin \theta \cos \theta$ and if $x = 0$, $y = b$ when $\theta = 0$.

6. The evolute of a curve is the envelope of its normals. To find the evolute of $y = \psi(x)$, let $y = px + f(p)$ be the differential equation of its family of normals. At any point (x_1, y_1) of the given curve we have

$$(1)\ y_1 = \psi(x_1);\ (2)\ y_1 = px_1 + f(p);\ (3)\ p = -\left(\frac{dx}{dy}\right)_1 = \left(\frac{-1}{d\psi/dx}\right)_{x=x_1}.$$

Solve (1) and (3) for x and y in terms of p, substitute the values thus obtained in (2), and solve the result for $f(p)$. Then find the envelope of the family represented by $y = px + f(p)$.

Find the evolute of the following curves: (a) $y^2 = 4x$; (b) $x^2 = 2y + 2$; (c) $2x^2y = 1$; (d) $2x^2 + y^2 = 2$.

7. The involutes of a curve are the orthogonal trajectories of its tangent lines. Find the equations of the involutes of $8y^3 = 27x^2$.

CHAPTER VI

LINEAR DIFFERENTIAL EQUATIONS WITH CONSTANT COEFFICIENTS

44. Operators. For convenience, as well as information, some ideas relating to operators will be introduced here. Writing D for d/dx, we have

$$Du = \frac{du}{dx}, \; D^2u = \frac{d^2u}{dx^2}, \; \cdots, \; D^ku = \frac{d^ku}{dx^k}, \tag{1}$$

where u represents a function of x. These operators obey the fundamental laws of algebra, for we have from calculus:

$$(D^m + D^n)u = (D^n + D^m)u,$$
$$[(D^m + D^n) + D^r]u = [D^m + (D^n + D^r)]u,$$
$$D^m \cdot D^nu = (D^n \cdot D^m)u = D^{m+n}u,$$
$$D^m(D^n \cdot D^r)u = (D^m \cdot D^n)D^ru = D^{m+n+r}u,$$
$$D^m(D^n + D^r)u = (D^m \cdot D^n + D^m \cdot D^r)u.$$

It will be convenient to deal with negative indices. *We define* $D^{-1}u = (1/D)u = v$ *to be such an expression* v *that* $Dv = u$, that is, an operator with a negative index is equivalent to an integration. We write then

$$v = D^{-1}u, \; Dv = D(D^{-1}u) = u, \; D \cdot D^{-1} = 1. \tag{2}$$

These negative indices obey the laws of algebra except in considerations relating to the constants of integration. In general if $f(y)$ represents a polynomial, $f(D)$ will be an operator and the symbol $f^{-1}(D)$ will represent another operator such that

$$f(D) f^{-1}(D)u(x) = u(x). \tag{3}$$

Thus $y = (D - a)^{-1}u\,(x) = \dfrac{1}{D - a}u(x)$ is defined to be a function y such that
$$(D - a)y = (D - a)\,\{[D - a]^{-1}\,u(x)\} = u(x).$$
In other words $(D - a)^{-1}u(x)$ is the general solution of the differential equation $(D - a)y = u(x)$.

From the definitions and laws just stated it appears that many elementary transformations involving operators of the type $f_1(D)/f_2(D)$ may be carried out in accordance with the fundamental laws of algebra.

Example 1. Perform the operations indicated in
$$(D^2 - 2aD + a^2)(e^{ax} \sin x).$$

Solution.
$$(D^2 - 2aD + a^2)(e^{ax} \sin x) = (D - a)[(D - a)(e^{ax} \sin x)]$$
$$= (D - a)\left[\frac{d}{dx}(e^{ax} \sin x) - ae^{ax} \sin x\right] = (D - a)\,[e^{ax}\cos x$$
$$+ ae^{ax} \sin x - ae^{ax} \sin x] = -e^{ax} \sin x + ae^{ax} \cos x$$
$$- ae^{ax} \cos x = -e^{ax} \sin x.$$

Example 2. Express $y = (D - a)^{-1}x$ without operators.
Solution. Since $y = (D - a)^{-1}x$, we have
$$(D - a)y = (D - a)(D - a)^{-1}x = x.$$

The solution of this differential equation, found by the method of §26, is
$$y = (D - a)^{-1}x = \left(\frac{-1}{a^2}\right)(ax + 1) + ce^{ax}.$$

Exercises

Perform the operations indicated in the following exercises:

1. (a) $f(D)e^{3x}$; (b) $f(D) \sin 3x$; (c) $f(D)x^2$, where
$$f(D) = D^3 - 2D^2 - 4D + 8$$

2. (a) D^2e^{3x}. (b) $(D - a)e^{ax}$. (c) $(D^2 - a^2) \sin (bx)$. (d) $(D^2 - a^2)^2 \cos bx$. (e) $(D^2 + 2aD + a^2)(x^2e^{-ax})$. (f) $(D - 1)^3(x^2e^x)$.

3. (a) $(D + 1)^2 (x^2 e^{-x})$. (b) $(D + 1)^3 e^{3x}$. (c) $(D - a)^3 (xe^{ax})$.

4. (a) $D^{-1}(x)$.   (b) $D^{-2}(6x) = D^{-1}[D^{-1}(6x)]$.   (c) $D^{-3}(x^2) = D^{-1}[D^{-2}(x^2)]$.   (d) $D^{-4}(12x)$.

5. $(D - a)^{-2}(2)$.   *Hint:* Write $(D - a)[(D - a)y] = 2$, let $z = (D - a)y$, etc.

6. (a) $(aD + b)^{-1}e^{mx}$.   (b) $(2D - 1)^{-1} \sin(2x)$.

7. Find $y = (D - 1)^{-1}x^3$ by writing $(D - 1)^{-1}x^3 = \dfrac{-1}{1 - D} x^3 = -(1 + D + D^2 + \dots)x^3$ and performing the indicated operations.

45. Theorems relating to operators.

THEOREM I.   If $\varphi(y)$ represents a polynomial, then

$$\varphi(D)\, (e^{ax}X) = e^{ax}\, \varphi(D + a)X, \tag{4}$$

where X *is any function of* x *possessing all the derivatives indicated in* (4).

Proof.   First we shall use mathematical induction in proving that

$$D^n(e^{ax}X) = e^{ax}(D + a)^n X. \tag{5}$$

When $n = 0$ each member of (5) is equal to $e^{ax}X$; when $n = 1$ each member is equal to $e^{ax}DX + ae^{ax}X$. Hence (5) is true when $n = 0$ or 1. Let k be any positive integer for which (5) holds. Then

$$D^k(e^{ax}X) = e^{ax}\, (D + a)^k X$$

and

$$D^{k+1}\, (e^{ax}X) = D[e^{ax}\, (D + a)^k X] = e^{ax}\, D(D + a)^k X + ae^{ax}\, (D + a)^k X = e^{ax}\, (D + a)^{k+1}X.$$

That is, if (5) holds when $n = k$, it holds when $n = k + 1$. Therefore, by complete induction, (5) is true when $n = 0$ or a positive integer. Consequently (4) holds because each term in the left member equals the corresponding term in the right member.

As illustrations of (4) consider that

$(D^2 + D)(e^{2x}x^3) = e^{2x}[(D + 2)^2 + D + 2]x^3 = e^{2x}\, (D^2 + 5D + 6)x^3 = e^{2x}(6x + 15x^2 + 6x^3)$, and $[(D + 3)^3 + 5(D + 3)^2]$ $(e^{-3x} \sin x) = e^{-3x}\, (D^3 + 5D^2) \sin x = e^{-3x}\, (-\cos x - 5 \sin x)$.

THEOREM II.   If $\varphi(y)$ is a polynomial, then
$$\varphi(D)(e^{ax}) = e^{ax}\varphi(a). \qquad (6)$$

Proof.   Observing that $\varphi(D + a)1 = \varphi(a)$, we get (6) as the special case obtained from (4) by replacing X in it by 1.

As an illustration of (8), consider that
$$(D^3 + 3D^2 + D - 1)\, e^{ax} = e^{ax}(a^3 + 3a^2 + a - 1).$$

The following special cases of (4) will be used later. Replacing $\varphi(D)$ in (4) by $(D - a)^n$, we get
$$(D - a)^n\, (e^{ax}X) = e^{ax}\, (D - a + a)^n X = e^{ax}D^n X. \quad (7)$$

If X in (7) represents a polynomial of the $(n - 1)$th degree, $D^n X = 0$; hence
$$(D - a)^n\, [e^{ax}\, (c_0 + c_1 x + \cdots + c_{n-1}x^{n-1})] = 0. \quad (8)$$
Thus $(D - 2)^4 [e^{2x}(x^3 + x - 1)] = e^{2x}D^4(x^3 + x - 1) = 0.$

Exercises

1. Use (6) to carry out the operations indicated: (a) $(D^3 + 3D^2 - 21)e^{2x}$; (b) $(D + a)^5 e^{ax}$; (c) $(D - a)^5 e^{ax}$; (d) $(D^2 + 7D + 7)e^{-2x}$; (e) $(D + a)^5 (D - a)^5 e^{-ax}$; (f) $(D - 1)(D - 2)(D - 3)e^{-3x}$

2. Use (7) to carry out the operations indicated: (a) $(D - 3)^3$ $(x^2 e^{3x})$; (b) $(D - 2)^3(x^4 e^{2x})$; (c) $(D + 1)^8(\sin x \cdot e^{-x})$; (d) $(D + 2)^4$ $(\cos x \cdot e^{-2x})$; (e) $(D + 1)^5\,(D + 3)^3(x^3 e^{-3x})$

3. Use (8) to prove that (a) $y = e^{3x}(ax^3 + bx^2 + cx + d)$ is a solution of $(D - 3)^4 y = 0$; (b) $y = e^{-x}(ax^2 + bx + c)$ is a solution of $(D + 2)$ $(D + 1)^3 y = 0$

4. Use (4) to prove that (a) $(D^2 + D - 7)(e^{3x}\cos 2x) = e^{3x}$ $[(D + 3)^2 + (D + 3) - 7]\cos 2x = e^{3x}(D^2 + 7D + 5)\cos 2x$; (b) $(D^2 + D - 5)(e^{-x}\sin 2x) = e^{-x}(D^2 - D - 5)\sin 2x$; (c) $[(D + 2)^3 - 10](x^4 e^{-2x}) = e^{-2x}(D^3 - 10)x^4$; (d) $[(D + 1)^{4n} + 1](e^{-x}\cos 2x) = e^{-x}(D^{4n} + 1)\cos 2x$. Carry out the operations indicated in (a), (b), (c), and (d).

5. Find (a) $(D^3 + 1)(x^4 e^{-x})$; (b) $(D^3 - 3D^2 + 3D - 7)(e^x \cos x)$; (c) $(D^2 - 6D + 7)(e^{3x}\tan x)$

6. Prove that (a) $y = (x^3 + ax + b)e^x$ is a solution of $(D^2 - 2D + 1)y = 6xe^x$; (b) $y = (\tfrac{1}{42}x^7 + ax + b)e^x$ is a solution of $(D - 1)^2 y = x^5 e^x$; (c) $y = (x \log x + c_1 x + c_2)e^{2x}$ is a solution of $(D - 2)^2 y = x^{-1}e^{2x}$

7. Show that $\varphi(D^2)(\sin ax) = \varphi(-a^2)\sin ax$ and that $\varphi(D^2)\cos ax = \varphi(-a^2)\cos ax$. Then find $(D^6 + 2D^4 + 1)\sin 2x$ and $(3D^4 - 5D^2)\cos 3x$.

46. Linear differential equation. A linear differential equation contains the dependent variable and all its derivatives to the first degree only. Its general form is

$$L(D)y = (a_0 D^n + a_1 D^{n-1} + \cdots + a_{n-1} D + a_n)y = X, \quad (9)$$

where the a's and X are functions of x. If $X = 0$, the equation is said to be *homogeneous*, since each term is of the first degree in y and its derivatives.

A very important theorem relating to the operator $L(D)$ may be expressed by writing

$$L(D)(y_1 + y_2 + \cdots) = L(D)y_1 + L(D)y_2 + \cdots, \quad (10)$$

where $y_1, y_2, \ldots$ represent functions of x. To prove (10), observe that

$$D^k(y_1 + y_2 + \cdots) = D^k y_1 + D^k y_2 + \cdots, \quad (11)$$

multiply both members of (11) by $a_0, a_1, \ldots, a_n$ in succession, and add the results to obtain (10).

Let $y_1(x)$, $y_2(x)$, ... be solutions of (9) with $X = 0$. For these functions, the right member, and therefore the left member of (10), will be zero. Hence the following theorem is true:

THEOREM. *If* $y_1(x)$, $y_2(x)$, ... *are solutions of a linear homogeneous equation, then their sum* $y_1(x) + y_2(x) + \ldots$ *is also a solution.*

The *principle of superposition* is said to apply to an operator obeying the law (10). To see a reason for this consider a beam projecting horizontally from a wall and being supported at its outer end. Its deflection $y(x)$ is found approximately by means of a *linear differential equation*. For this reason deflection y may be found as the sum of two parts y_1 and y_2, y_1 being due to the weight of the beam and other forces, y_2 to the support at its outer end and other forces. The positions of the beam due to the two sets of forces are *superposed* to obtain the actual position. In the applications of linear differential equations numerous illustrations of the principle of superposition are found.

47. Homogeneous linear differential equation with constant coefficients. We shall first find a method of solving equations of the type

$$(a_0D^n + a_1D^{n-1} + \cdots + a_{n-1}D + a_n)y = 0, \quad (12)$$

where the a's are constants.

A very special case of equation (12) is $Dy + ay = 0$, and its solution is $y = ce^{-ax}$. This suggests that an equation of the form

$$y = ce^{mx} \quad (13)$$

might be a solution of (12). Substituting $y = ce^{mx}$, $dy/dx = cme^{mx}, \ldots, d^ky/dx^k = cm^ke^{mx}$ in (12), we obtain

$$ce^{mx}(a_0m^n + a_1m^{n-1} + \cdots + a_{n-1}m + a_n) = 0.$$

This equation will be satisfied if m is a root of the equation

$$a_0m^n + a_1m^{n-1} + \cdots + a_{n-1}m + a_n = 0. \quad (14)$$

Equation (14) is referred to as the *auxiliary equation*. Therefore, if $r_1, r_2, \ldots, r_n$ are the roots of (14), then the equations

$$y = c_1e^{r_1x}, y = c_2e^{r_2x}, \ldots, y = c_ne^{r_nx} \quad (15)$$

are all solutions of (12). Therefore, in accordance with the theorem of §46,

$$y = c_1e^{r_1x} + c_2e^{r_2x} + \cdots + c_ne^{r_nx} \quad (16)$$

is a solution of (12). Since (16) contains n arbitrary constants, it is the general solution of (12) provided no two of the roots of (14) are equal.

Example. Solve $\dfrac{d^3y}{dx^3} + 2\dfrac{d^2y}{dx^2} - 3\dfrac{dy}{dx} = 0.$ $\quad (a)$

Solution. The auxiliary equation (14) in this case is

$$m^3 + 2m^2 - 3m = 0. \quad (b)$$

The roots of (b) are $1, -3, 0$. Hence the solution of (a), according to (16), is

$$\mathbf{y = c_1e^x + c_2e^{-3x} + c_3.}$$

Exercises

1. $(D^2 - 3D + 2)y = 0$ **5.** $D^3y = Dy$

2. $(D^3 - 3D^2 - D + 3)y = 0$ **6.** $D^2y + 3y = 5Dy$

3. $D^2y = k^2y$ **7.** $(4D^3 - 5D)y = 0$

4. $(D^3 - 7D + 6)y = 0$ **8.** $(D^4 - D^3 - 7D^2 + 3D)y = 0$

48. Auxilary equation contains repeated roots. Let r_1, $r_2, \ldots, r_n$ be the roots of the auxiliary equation and for convenience let us write

$$f(m) = a_0m^n + a_1m^{n-1} + \cdots + a_{n-1}m + a_n \quad (17)$$
$$= a_0(m - r_1)(m - r_2) \cdots (m - r_n).$$

Equation (12) may then be written

$$a_0(D - r_1)(D - r_2) \cdots (D - r_n)y = f(D)y = 0. \quad (18)$$

If $f(m) = 0$ has a double root r, then by §47 the solution of (18) contains the two terms $c_1e^{rx} + c_2e^{rx}$; but since this may be written $(c_1 + c_2)e^{rx} = (\text{constant})e^{rx}$, only one arbitrary constant is involved. The solution according to §47 involves fewer than n independent arbitrary constants and consequently is not the general solution. Suppose that equation (14) contains r as a p-fold root. Equation (18) may then be written

$$a_0(D - r_1)(D - r_2) \cdots (D - r_{n-p})[(D - r)^py] = 0. \ (19)$$

Substituting

$$y = (c_0 + c_1x + c_2x^2 + \cdots + c_{p-1}x^{p-1})e^{rx} \quad (20)$$

in (19), and noting that, in accordance with equation (8), $(D - r)^p[(c_0 + c_1x + \cdots + c_{p-1}x^{p-1})e^{rx}] = 0$, we obtain

$$a_0(D - r_1) (D - r_2) \cdots (D - r_{n-p}) [0] = 0.$$

Evidently this equation is true. Hence (20) is a particular solution of (18) corresponding to the p-fold root r. Since a like expression will apply for any other multiple root, it appears that *if the roots of the auxiliary equation are*

$$r(p\text{-fold}), s(q\text{-fold}), \ldots,$$

the general solution is

$$y = e^{rx}(c_0 + c_1 x + \cdots + c_{p-1} x^{p-1}) +$$
$$e^{sx}(b_0 + b_1 x + \cdots + b_{q-1} x^{q-1}) + \cdots. \quad (21)$$

Example.   Find the general solution of

$$(D^5 - 2D^4 + D^3)y = 0.$$

Solution.   The auxiliary equation is

$$m^5 - 2m^4 + m^3 = 0.$$

and its roots are 0, 0, 0, 1, 1. Hence in accordance with (21) the general solution is

$$\mathbf{y = c_0 + c_1 x + c_2 x^2 + e^x(c_3 + c_4 x).} \quad (a)$$

49. Constants of integration from initial conditions.   *To determine the constants of integration from the general solution of a differential equation, replace the variables in the solution and the derivatives of the solution by given corresponding values, and solve the resulting equations for the required constants.*

Example.   Find the particular solution of

$$(D^3 - 6D^2 + 9D)y = 0$$

which satisfies the initial conditions $y = 0$, $Dy = 2$, $D^2 y = -6$ when $x = 0$.

Solution.   The auxiliary equation is $m^3 - 6m^2 + 9m = 0$, its roots are 0, 3, 3, and the general solution of the given equation is

$$y = c_1 + e^{3x}(c_2 + c_3 x). \quad (a)$$

By differentiation we obtain from (a)

$$Dy = e^{3x}(3c_2 + c_3 + 3c_3 x),$$
$$D^2 y = e^{3x}(9c_2 + 6c_3 + 9c_3 x). \quad (b)$$

Substitution of the initial conditions in (a) and (b) gives

$$0 = c_1 + e^0(c_2 + c_3 \cdot 0) = c_1 + c_2,$$
$$2 = 3c_2 + c_3, \ -6 = 9c_2 + 6c_3. \quad (c)$$

Solving these equations for c_1, c_2, and c_3, we get

$$c_1 = -2, \ c_2 = 2, \ c_3 = -4.$$

The required particular solution, obtained by substituting these values of the c's in (a), is

$$y = -2 + e^{3x}(2 - 4x).$$

Exercises

For each of the following equations, find the general solution and, for each of exercises 7 to 11 the particular solution satisfying the given initial conditions:

1. $(D^3 - 2D^2 + D)y = 0$ **4.** $D^3y = 0$

2. $(D^3 - D^2 - D + 1)y = 0$ **5.** $(D^6 - 8D^4 + 16D^2)y = 0$

3. $(D^3 - 3D^2 + 3D - 1)y = 0$ **6.** $(D^5 - 12D^3 + 16D^2)y = 0$

7. $(D^2 - 2D + 1)y = 0.$ $y = 5, Dy = -9$ when $x = 0$

8. $(D^3 + D^2)y = 0.$ $y = 4, Dy = -2, D^2y = 4$ when $x = 0$

9. $(D^3 - 4D^2 + 4D)y = 0.$ $y = 1, Dy = 2, D^2y = 8$ when $x = 0$

10. $(D^3 - D^2 - D + 1)y = 0.$ $y = 0, Dy = 0, D^2y = 4$ when $x = 0$

11. $(D^4 - D^2)y = 0.$ $y = 0, Dy = 3, D^2y = 0, D^3y = 2$ when $x = 0$

50. Auxiliary equation contains complex roots.

If the coefficients of the auxiliary equation $f(m) = 0$ are real, and if $a + ib(i = \sqrt{-1})$ is a root of it, then $a - ib$ is also a root. The corresponding terms of the general solution are

$$Ae^{(a+ib)x} + Be^{(a-ib)x}, \text{ or } e^{ax}(Ae^{ibx} + Be^{-ibx}), \qquad (22)$$

since $Ae^{(a+ib)x} + Be^{(a-ib)x}$ may be written

$$Ae^{ax}e^{ibx} + Be^{ax}e^{-ibx}.$$

By applying the following equation from complex variable theory

$$e^{i\theta} = \cos \theta + i \sin \theta, (i = \sqrt{-1})$$

to (22), we get

$$e^{ax}(A \cos bx + Ai \sin bx + B \cos bx - Bi \sin bx),$$

or

$$e^{ax}[(A + B) \cos bx + i(A - B) \sin bx]. \qquad (23)$$

Now letting $A = \dfrac{c_1 - ic_2}{2}, B = \dfrac{c_1 + ic_2}{2}$ in (23), we obtain

$$e^{ax}(c_1 \cos bx + c_2 \sin bx). \qquad (24)$$

If we take $c = \sqrt{c_1^2 + c_2^2}$ and $\tan \alpha = c_1/c_2$, then (see Fig. 1)

$$\sin \alpha = \frac{c_1}{\sqrt{c_1^2 + c_2^2}} \text{ and } \cos \alpha = \frac{c_2}{\sqrt{c_1^2 + c_2^2}}.$$

Hence (24) may be written

$$e^{ax}\sqrt{c_1^2 + c_2^2}\left[\frac{c_1}{\sqrt{c_1^2 + c_2^2}} \cos bx + \frac{c_2}{\sqrt{c_1^2 + c_2^2}} \sin bx\right], \quad (25)$$

or

$$ce^{ax} (\sin \alpha \cos bx + \cos \alpha \sin bx), \quad (26)$$

or

$$ce^{ax} \sin (bx + \alpha), \quad (27)$$

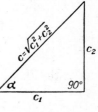

Fig. 1.

where c and α are arbitrary constants. The part of the general solution corresponding to a pair of complex roots $a \pm ib$ is generally written in the form (24) or (27).

In the case of a double pair of complex roots, the corresponding terms of the general solution are

$$e^{ax}[(A_0 + A_1x) \cos bx + (B_0 + B_1x) \sin bx]* \quad (28)$$

or

$$e^{ax}[c_0 \sin (bx + \alpha_0) + c_1x \sin (bx + \alpha_1)], \quad (29)$$

and a similar extension applies for a p-fold multiple pair of complex roots.

Example. Solve $(D^3 - 3D^2 + 9D + 13)y = 0$.

Solution. The roots of the auxiliary equation are $-1, 2 \pm 3i$. Hence the general solution is

$$y = c_1e^{-x} + e^{2x}(c_2 \sin 3x + c_3 \cos 3x),$$

or

$$\mathbf{y = c_1e^{-x} + ce^{2x} \sin (3x + \alpha).}$$

Exercises

Integrate the following equations and determine the constants of integration where initial conditions are given:

* This may be proved by substituting expression (28) or (29) for y in $[(D - a)^2 + b^2]^2y = 0$.

  1. $(D^2 - 2D + 2)y = 0$
  2. $(D^3 + k^2D)y = 0$
  3. $(D^4 + 8D^2 + 16)y = 0$
  4. $(D^4 - a^4)y = 0$
  5. $(D^6 + 6D^4 + 9D^2)y = 0$
  6. $(D^4 - D^2 - 18D - 18)y = 0$
  7. $(D^3 + a^3)y = 0$
  8. $(D^3 - 2D^2 + 2D)y = 0$. $y = 1,\ Dy = 1,\ D^2y = 2$ when $x = 0$
  9. $(D^3 - 2D + 4)y = 0$. $y = -2,\ Dy = 8,\ D^2y = 0$ when $x = 0$
  10. $(D^2 + k^2)y = 0$. $y = 4,\ Dy = 30$ when $x = 0$, and $y = 3$ when $x = \pi/2k$

51. Right-hand member not zero.

To solve the equation

$$(a_0D^n + a_1D^{n-1} + \cdots + a_{n-1}D + a_n)y = X, \qquad (30)$$

where the a's are constants and X is a function of x, we shall write

$$y = y_c + y_p, \qquad (31)$$

where $y = y_c$ is the general solution of (30) with X replaced by zero, and $y = y_p$ is a particular solution of (30). Equation (31) is a solution of (30) involving n independent arbitrary constants and hence is the general solution. y_c is referred to as the *complementary function* and is found as in §§47, 48, and 50. y_p may be found by various methods, one of which, the *method of undetermined coefficients*, is illustrated below. *This method applies when the right-hand member contains only terms from which a finite number of terms can be got by differentiation.* Many of the equations arising in practice may be solved by this method.

Consider the solution of the equation

$$(D^2 + 3D + 2)y = 4x - 20 \cos 2x. \qquad (a)$$

Solving the equation obtained by replacing the right member by zero, we get,

$$y_c = c_1e^{-x} + c_2e^{-2x}. \qquad (b)$$

To get a particular solution of (a) let

$$y_p = Ax + B + C \cos 2x + E \sin 2x, \qquad (c)$$

and try to find numbers for A, B, C, and E such that y_p from

(c) when substituted for y in (a) satisfies it. Substituting y_p from (c) and

$$Dy_p = A - 2C \sin 2x + 2E \cos 2x,$$
$$D^2y_p = -4C \cos 2x - 4E \sin 2x \qquad (d)$$

in (a) for y, Dy, D^2y, we obtain after simplification

$$2Ax + (2B + 3A) + (6E - 2C) \cos 2x -$$
$$(6C + 2E) \sin 2x = 4x + 0 - 20 \cos 2x + 0 \sin 2x. \quad (e)$$

Since (e) is to be an identity, the coefficients of like terms must be equal. Hence

$$2A = 4, 2B + 3A = 0, 6E - 2C = -20, -6C - 2E = 0. \quad (f)$$

Solving (f) for A, B, C, and E, we get

$$A = 2, B = -3, C = 1, E = -3. \qquad (g)$$

Hence, from (c) and (g), $y_p = 2x - 3 + \cos 2x - 3 \sin 2x$ and the general solution is

$$\mathbf{y = y_c + y_p = c_1 e^{-x} + c_2 e^{-2x} + 2x - 3 + \cos 2x - 3 \sin 2x.}$$

The question arises: What terms are assumed in the trial y_p? *To get the trial form of* y_p, *write the variable part of each term in the right-hand member* X *together with the variable parts of any terms that may be derived by differentiating* X *repeatedly, multiply each of these terms by an arbitrary constant, and equate* y_p *to the sum of the terms thus obtained.* Observe in forming y_p in (c) that we chose a term Ax and a term $C \cos 2x$, also a constant term B since $Dx = 1$, a constant, and a term $E \sin 2x$ because $D \cos 2x = -2 \sin 2x$. If any of these terms had been omitted, the corresponding number of equations would have been greater than the number of unknowns and there would have been no solution.

Exercises

Integrate the following equations and determine the constants of integration where initial conditions are given:

1. $(D^2 + 2D - 8)y = 64x$
2. $(D^2 - D - 2)y = 6e^x$
3. $(D^2 + a^2)y = a^2 x$

4. $(D^2 - a^2)y = \sin ax + a^2$

5. $(D^4 - a^4)y = x^3.$ Assume $y_p = Ax^3 + Bx^2 + Cx + E$

6. $(D^2 + 4D + 3)y = 8xe^x - 6$

7. $(D^2 - 4)y = 16x \sin 2x.$ $y = 1, Dy = 4,$ when $x = 0$

8. $(D^3 + 1)y = \sin 2x + xe^x$

9. $(D^3 - 2D^2 + D - 2)y = 4x^2.$ $y = 4, Dy = -2, D^2y = 0,$ when $x = 0$

10. $(D^3 - 4D)y = 6e^{-x} - 3e^x.$ $y = -2, Dy = -3, D^2y = -7,$ when $x = 0$

52. Special case when the right-hand member is not zero.

Terms having the same variable part will be referred to as *like terms*. Thus, $5 \sin 2x$, $A \sin 2x$, and $(3B + C) \sin 2x$ are like terms.

It may happen that a term in the trial solution of $f(D)y = X$, found in accordance with the method of §51, is like a term in the complementary function. Such a term will give zero when substituted in the left member $f(D)y$ because it is a solution of $f(D)y = 0$; hence it cannot function to give a term like itself. For example, consider the equation

$$(D^2 + 4)y = \sin 2x. \qquad (32)$$

Here $y_c = c_1 \sin 2x + c_2 \cos 2x.$ Letting $y_p = A \sin 2x + B \cos 2x$ and substituting in (32), we get the impossible equation $0 \equiv \sin 2x.$ The process for multiple roots suggests that a factor x be introduced. Hence we use

$$y_p = x(A \sin 2x + B \cos 2x). \qquad (33)$$

Substituting this value of y_p in (32), we obtain after slight simplification

$$4A \cos 2x - 4B \sin 2x = \sin 2x.$$

Hence

$$4A = 0, -4B = 1, \text{ or } A = 0, B = -\tfrac{1}{4},$$

and the solution of (32) is

$$\mathbf{y = y_c + y_p = c_1 \sin 2x + c_2 \cos 2x - \tfrac{1}{4}x \cos 2x.} \quad (34)$$

As another example, consider

$$(D^2 - 2D + 1)y = xe^x + 5. \qquad (35)$$

The complementary function is

$$y_c = (c_1 + c_2 x)e^x. \tag{36}$$

Divide the task of finding y_p into two parts: that of finding the particular solution relating to xe^x, and that relating to 5. For the part xe^x we write

$$y_{p_1} = x^2(A + Bx)e^x. \tag{37}$$

The part $(A + Bx)e^x$ was written in accordance with §51 and the factor x^2 was supplied to make y_{p_1} unlike the complementary function. Substituting y_{p_1} from (37) in the left member of (35) and equating the result to xe^x, we obtain after simplification

$$e^x(6Bx + 2A) = xe^x.$$

Equating the coefficients of like terms, we get $B = \frac{1}{6}$, $A = 0$, and $y_{p_1} = \frac{1}{6}x^3 e^x$. The particular solution of (35) relating to 5, found by the regular procedure of §51 is $y_{p_2} = 5$. Hence the solution of (35) is

$$y = y_c + y_{p_1} + y_{p_2} = (c_1 + c_2 x)e^x + \frac{1}{6}x^3 e^x + 5.$$

Observe that, in forming a trial y_p for any term in the right-hand member, it is first formed by the method of §51 and then multiplied by x^n where n is the least integer that will make each term of the trial y_p unlike any term in the complementary function.

Exercises

1. Solve $(D^4 + D^3)y = 48 + 24x$. Write the complementary function and then observe that $y_p = x^3(Ax + B)$.

2. $(D^2 - 2D + 1)y = e^x + 3$ 5. $(D^2 + 1)y = \sin x$

3. $(D^3 + D^2)y = 12x$ 6. $(D^2 + 4D + 3)y = 3x + e^{-x}$

4. $(D^2 + 2D)y = 4x + 2 + 2e^{-x}$ 7. $(D^3 + 4D)y = 8 \cos 2x + 4$

8. $(D^3 - 2D^2 + 5D)y = 10 + 15 \cos 2x$

9. $(D^2 - 2D + 1)y = 6xe^x$

10. $(D^2 - 2D + 2)y = e^x \sin x$

53. Variation of parameters.

The rules stated in §§51 and 52 generally fail to give a solution when the derivatives of the right-hand member of X do not contain a finite number of terms. We shall therefore consider the general method of variation of parameters. The following solutions illustrate this method.

Example 1. Solve

$$(D^2 + 1)y = \tan x. \tag{a}$$

Solution. The solution of $(D^2 + 1)y = 0$ is

$$y = A \sin x + B \cos x. \tag{b}$$

Now let us assume that A and B are such functions of x that (b) is the general solution of (a). Then

$$Dy = A \cos x - B \sin x + \sin xA' + \cos xB', \tag{c}$$

where the primes denote derivatives with respect to x. A and B, being two arbitrary functions, may be subjected to two conditions; hence, let us assume further that

$$\sin xA' + \cos xB' = 0. \tag{d}$$

Then

$$D^2y = -A \sin x - B \cos x + \cos xA' - \sin xB'. \tag{e}$$

Substituting from (e) and (b) in (a), we get

$$\cos xA' - \sin xB' = \tan x. \tag{f}$$

Solving (d) and (f) simultaneously for A' and B', we obtain

$$A' = \sin x, \; B' = \frac{-\sin^2 x}{\cos x} = \cos x - \sec x. \tag{g}$$

The solutions of (g) are

$$A = c_1 - \cos x, \; B = c_2 + \sin x - \log (\sec x + \tan x). \tag{h}$$

Substituting A and B from (h) in (b), we obtain

$$y = \sin x \, (c_1 - \cos x) + \cos x \, [c_2 + \sin x - \log (\sec x + \tan x)],$$

or

$$y = c_1 \sin x + c_2 \cos x - \cos x \log (\sec x + \tan x).$$

Example 2. Solve $(D^3 + D)y = \sec x.$ $\qquad\qquad (a)$

Solution. The solution of $(D^3 + D)y = 0$ is

$$y = A \sin x + B \cos x + C. \tag{b}$$

Assume that (b) is the solution of (a) where A, B, C, are functions of x to be determined. From (b)

$$D(y) = A \cos x - B \sin x + \sin x A' + \cos x B' + C'. \quad (c)$$

Let

$$\sin x A' + \cos x B' + C' = 0. \qquad (d)$$

Then

$$D^2 y = -A \sin x - B \cos x + \cos x A' - \sin x B'. \quad (e)$$

Let

$$\cos x A' - \sin x B' = 0. \qquad (f)$$

Then

$$D^3 y = -A \cos x + B \sin x - \sin x A' - \cos x B'. \quad (g)$$

Substituting y and its derivatives from (b), (c), (e), and (g) in (a) while taking account of (d) and (f), we get after slight simplification

$$-\sin x A' - \cos x B' = \sec x. \qquad (h)$$

The solution of (d), (f), and (h) for A', B', and C' is

$$A' = -\tan x, B' = -1, C' = \sin x \tan x + \cos x = \sec x. \quad (i)$$

Solving (i) for A, B, and C and substituting the results in (b), we get

$$y = (\log \cos x + c_1) \sin x + (c_2 - x) \cos x + \log (\sec x + \tan x) + c_3.$$

The method may be summed up as follows: *To solve a differential equation*

$$(D^n + a_1 D^{n-1} + \cdots + a_n)y = X, \qquad (\alpha)$$

where the a's are constants and X is a function of x, (a) find the complementary function $f(x, c_1, c_2, \ldots, c_n)$; *(b) assuming that the c's in*

$$y = f(x, c_1, c_2, \cdots, c_n) \qquad (\beta)$$

are such functions of x that (β) is the general solution, find Dy, and equate to zero the part of it that would not have appeared if the c's had been considered constant; treat similarly $D^2 y$, $D^3 y$, $\ldots$, $D^{n-1} y$; (c) find $D^n y$ and substitute y *and its derivatives in* (α);* (d) *solve simultaneously the equations got in steps* (b) *and* (c) *for* $\dfrac{dc_1}{dx}, \dfrac{dc_2}{dx}, \ldots, \dfrac{dc_n}{dx}$ *and integrate the results;* (e) *substitute the values of* $c_1, c_2, \ldots, c_n$ *from step* (d) *in equation* (β).

Exercises

Integrate the following equations by the method of variation of parameters:

1. $(D^2 + 1)y = \sec x$

2. $(D^2 + 4)y = 4 \cot 4x$

3. $(D^2 - 4D + 4)y = x^n e^{2x}$

4. $(D^2 + 4D + 4)y = \dfrac{e^{-2x}}{x^2}$

5. $(D^2 + 1)y = \sec x \csc x$

6. $(D^2 - 2D + 2)y = e^x (\tan x + \cot x)$

7. $(D^3 - 3D^2 + 4D - 2)y = e^x \sec x$

54. Methods using symbolic operator.

The symbolic operator, discussed in §§44 and 45, is used in various ways to solve linear equations with constant coefficients. The following examples illustrate several methods.

Example 1. Solve

$$(D^2 - 4D + 4)y = x^5 e^{2x}. \qquad (a)$$

Solution. We may write (a) in the form

$$(D - 2)(D - 2)y = x^5 e^{2x}.$$

Let

$$u = (D - 2)y. \qquad (b)$$

Then

$$(D - 2)u = x^5 e^{2x}.$$

Solving this as a first-order linear equation by the method of §26, we have

$$ue^{-2x} = \int x^5 dx = \frac{x^6}{6} + c_1, \text{ or } u = \left(\frac{x^6}{6} + c_1\right)e^{2x}. \qquad (c)$$

---

* The student should save time by noticing that, because (β) has the same form as the complementary function, step (c) gives the result of equating to X the part of $D^n y$ that would not have appeared if the c's had been considered constant.

Substituting u from (b) for u in (c), we get

$$(D - 2)y = \left(\frac{x^6}{6} + c_1\right)e^{2x}.$$

Hence, by §26,

$$ye^{-2x} = \frac{x^7}{42} + c_1x + c_2,$$

or

$$\mathbf{y} = \left(\mathbf{c_1x} + \mathbf{c_2} + \frac{\mathbf{x^7}}{\mathbf{42}}\right)\mathbf{e^{2x}}.$$

A short cut can often be made by using equation (4). If we define the function φ by the relation $\varphi(D) = \psi(D - a)$, we may replace D by $D + a$ in both members and write

$$\varphi(D) \equiv \psi(D - a), \quad \varphi(D + a) = \psi(D). \tag{38}$$

Substituting these values for $\varphi(D)$ and $\varphi(D + a)$ in (4) and interchanging the members of the equation, we obtain

$$e^{ax}\psi(D)X = \psi(D - a)(e^{ax}X), \tag{39}$$

that is, e^{ax} *may be moved from the left of the operator ψ to the right of it, provided the operator is changed by replacing* D *in it by* D − a.

Example 2. Solve

$$(D - 2)^3(D - 1)y = 6(x^2 + 2x)e^{2x}. \tag{a}$$

Solution. To obtain a particular solution, divide (a) by e^{2x} to obtain

$$e^{-2x}(D - 2)^3(D - 1)y = 6(x^2 + 2x). \tag{b}$$

Use (39) to write (b) in the form

$$(D + 2 - 2)^3(D + 2 - 1)(ye^{-2x}) = D^3(D + 1)(ye^{-2x}) = \\ 6(x^2 + 2x). \quad (c)$$

Substitute $z = ye^{-2x}$ in (c) and solve for z to obtain

$$z = \frac{1}{D^3}\frac{1}{1 + D}(6x^2 + 12x) = \frac{1}{D^3}(1 - D + D^2 + \cdots)$$

$$(6x^2 + 12x).$$

Perform the operations indicated to obtain

$$z = \frac{1}{D^3}[6x^2 + \cancel{12x} - \cancel{12x} - \cancel{12} + \cancel{12}] = \frac{x^5}{10}. \qquad (d)$$

Replacing z by ye^{-2x} in (d) and solving for y, we get

$$y = \tfrac{1}{10}x^5 e^{2x}.$$

This is a particular solution, as may be seen by substituting it in (a) or (c). The general solution is

$$y = c_1 e^x + \left(c_2 + c_3 x + c_4 x^2 + \frac{x^5}{10}\right)e^{2x}.$$

Another way of using the symbolic operator is illustrated below.

Example 3. Solve

$$(D - 1)(D - 2)y = xe^{2x}. \qquad (a)$$

Solution. Solve (a) for y to obtain

$$y = \frac{1}{(D-1)(D-2)}(xe^{2x}). \qquad (b)$$

Express the operator in simplest fractions to get

$$y = \left(\frac{1}{D-2} - \frac{1}{D-1}\right)(xe^{2x}) = \frac{1}{D-2}(xe^{2x}) -$$

$$\frac{1}{D-1}(xe^{2x}). \qquad (c)$$

To see that the step from (b) to (c) is valid, substitute the expression for y from (c) in the left member of (a) and, keeping in mind the principles of §44, obtain

$$(D-1)(D-2)[(D-2)^{-1} - (D-1)^{-1}]xe^{2x}$$
$$= [(D-1)(D-2)(D-2)^{-1} - (D-2)(D-1)(D-1)^{-1}]$$
$$xe^{2x} = xe^{2x}.*$$

Let $z_1 = \left[\dfrac{1}{(D-2)}\right](xe^{2x})$ and $z_2 = \left[\dfrac{-1}{(D-1)}\right](xe^{2x})$ and

---

* Observe that the method just used may be applied to justify replacement of an operator $P_1(D)/P_2(D)$, where P_1 and P_2 represent polynomials, by its algebraically identical expression in simple fractions.

write
$$(D - 2)z_1 = xe^{2x}, \ (D - 1)z_2 = - xe^{2x}. \qquad (d)$$
Solving (d) by the method of §26, we obtain
$$z_1 = \frac{x^2}{2}e^{2x}, \ z_2 = (1 - x)e^{2x}. \qquad (e)$$
Hence a particular solution is
$$y = z_1 + z_2 = \left(1 - x + \frac{x^2}{2}\right)e^{2x},$$
and the general solution is
$$\mathbf{y = c_1 e^x + \left(c_2 - x + \frac{x^2}{2}\right)e^{2x}.}$$

Exercises

In the following exercises the symbol (I) refers to the method of Example 1, the symbol (II) to the method using equation (39) as in Example 2, and the symbol (III) to the method of Example 3.   Find particular solutions of the following equations by each of the methods indicated:

1. $(D - 1)^2 y = x^5 e^x$ (I), (II)

2. $(D + 1)^3 y = \dfrac{16e^{-x}}{(2x + 3)^3}$ (I), (II)

3. $(D + 2)(D + 4)y = 4e^{e^x}$ (I)

4. $(D - 1)^n y = n! \ e^x$ (II)

5. Use (II) combined with the method of §53 to solve exercises 4, 6, and 7 of §53.

6. $(D + 3)(D + 2)y = xe^{-2x}$ (II), (III)

7. $(D - 1)^3 y = e^x \sin x + e^{2x} \cos x$ (II).   *Hint:* Find the particular solution in two parts, one for each term of the right-hand member.

8. $(D^2 - 2D + 2)y = 4e^x \cos x$ (II).   *Hint:* Replace $\cos x$ by $\frac{1}{2}(e^{ix} + e^{-ix})$, and treat separately each term of the right-hand member.

9. $(D - 1)^2(D - 2)^2 y = 2(e^x + e^{2x})$

55. Simultaneous differential equations.   A solution of n simultaneous equations in $n + 1$ unknowns consists of n independent relations involving one or more of these unknowns but not their derivatives; if these n relations are solved for n of the unknown quantities in terms of the remaining one, and if the results are substituted in the given differential equations, identities must result. *The first object in solving such a system is so to combine the given equations and other equations derived from them as to obtain an equation in two unknowns.* This may be integrated to obtain one relation, and the result may be used to obtain other relations. In the process of eliminating variables, we often find that operators can be used to advantage. Using the facts relating to operators in §§44 and 45, we shall find the process of elimination in the case of linear equations with constant coefficients to be very much like an analogous process of elimination used in algebra

Example.   Solve

$$\left.\begin{array}{r} \dfrac{dx}{dt} + \dfrac{dy}{dt} + y - x = e^{2t}, \\[2mm] \dfrac{d^2x}{dt^2} + \dfrac{dy}{dt} = 3e^{2t}. \end{array}\right\} \qquad (a)$$

Solution.   Replacing d/dt by D, we may write the equations (a) in the form

$$\left.\begin{array}{r} (D - 1)x + (D + 1)y = e^{2t}, \\ D^2x + Dy = 3e^{2t}. \end{array}\right\} \qquad (b)$$

Operating on the first of equations (b) with D and on the second with $(D + 1)$, we obtain

$$\left.\begin{array}{l} (D^2 - D)x + D(D + 1)y = De^{2t} = 2e^{2t}, \\ (D^3 + D^2)x + (D + 1)Dy = D(3e^{2t}) + 3e^{2t} = 9e^{2t}. \end{array}\right\} \qquad (c)$$

Subtracting the first of equations (c) from the second, we get

$$(D^3 + D)x = 7e^{2t}. \qquad (d)$$

The solution of this equation is

$$x = c_1 + c_2 \sin t + c_3 \cos t + \tfrac{7}{10}e^{2t}. \qquad (e)$$

Substituting the value of x from (e) in the second equation of (b) and integrating the resulting equation, we obtain

$$y = \tfrac{1}{10}e^{2t} - c_2 \cos t + c_3 \sin t + c_4. \tag{f}$$

There may be too many constants of integration in the solution given by (e) and (f). It can be shown* that the number of constants of integration to be expected in the general solution of a system of simultaneous linear differential equations with constant coefficients is the same as the degree in D of the determinant of the equations. Thus the determinant of (b) is

$$\begin{vmatrix} D - 1 & D + 1 \\ D^2 & D \end{vmatrix},$$

its degree is three, and there should be only three constants of integration in the solution of (a).

The general procedure in finding any relation that may exist between the constants is to substitute the solution in one of the original equations, simplify as much as possible, and equate the coefficients of like terms in the two members of the result. Substituting the value of x from (e) and y from (f) in the first equation of (b), we obtain after simplification

$$c_4 - c_1 = 0, \text{ or } c_4 = c_1.$$

It therefore appears that the solution is

$$\mathbf{x = c_1 + c_2 \sin t + c_3 \cos t + \tfrac{7}{10}e^{2t}},$$
$$\mathbf{y = c_1 + c_3 \sin t - c_2 \cos t + \tfrac{1}{10}e^{2t}}.$$

Remark. Extraneous constants of integration can often be avoided by deriving from the given set of equations an equation of low order to be used in finding the expression for an additional variable after the expressions for several variables have already been found. Thus, after equation (e) was obtained, y could have been found without introducing another constant, by subtracting the second equation of (b) from the first, substituting x from (e) in the result, and solving for y.

* See INCE, E. L., "Ordinary Differential Equations," p. 150.

Exercises

Solve the following systems of differential equations. $D = \dfrac{d}{dt}$.

1. $(D - 7)x + y = 0$, $Dy + 3x - 5y = 0$

2. $D^2x = y$, $D^2y = x + 1$

3. $Dx + Dy + 3x = \sin t$, $Dx + y - x = \cos t$

4. $(D^2 - 3)x - 4y = 0$, $x + (D^2 + 1)y = 0$

5. $(2D^2 - 4)y - Dx = 4t$, $(4D - 3)x + 2Dy = 0$

6. $Dx - 3y = 0$, $Dy + z = x$, $Dz + y = 0$

7. $x + y + z = t$, $Dx + z = 0$, $2x - Dy = 0$

8. $(D^2 - 1)x + 8Dy = 16e^t$, $Dx + 3(D^2 + 1)y = 0$

9. Find the particular solution of the system
$$(D^2 - 3)x - 4y + 3 = 0, \quad (D^2 + 1)y + x + 5 = 0$$
for which $x = y = Dx = Dy = 0$ when $t = 0$.

10. $(D^2 - 1)x + 2(D + 1)y + (D + 1)z = e^t$
$(D + 1)^2x + 2(D + 1)y - (D + 1)z = 0$
$(D - 1)x - 2y - z = 0$

CHAPTER VII

APPLICATIONS OF LINEAR EQUATIONS WITH CONSTANT COEFFICIENTS

56. Harmonic motion. Damping. For convenience of reference we shall recall, at this point, a few facts concerning harmonic motion and damping.

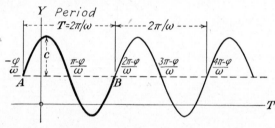

Fig. 1.

If, as a particle moves in a straight line, its motion is defined by

$$y = c \sin (\omega t + \varphi) + a, \tag{1}$$

where a is a constant, y is the distance of the particle from a fixed point on the line, and t is the time, its motion is called *simple harmonic motion*. The number c, representing the greatest value of $y - a$, is called the *amplitude of the motion*. Because of the periodic nature of $\sin (\omega t + \varphi)$, it is clear that the motion consists of an endless repetition of the movement that takes place while the angle $\omega t + \varphi$ changes by 2π radians; hence the motion is called *periodic*. The time T required for the angle $\omega t + \varphi$ to change by 2π radians is called the *period of the motion*. Therefore we must have

$$\omega(t + T) + \varphi - (\omega t + \varphi) = 2\pi$$

or $$\text{Period } T = \frac{2\pi}{\omega}. \qquad (2)$$

The number n of repetitions of the least complete motion, that is, the number of cycles, per unit of time, is called the *frequency*. Hence

$$\text{Frequency } n = \frac{1}{T} = \frac{\omega}{2\pi}. \qquad (3)$$

The angle φ is often referred to as the *angle of epoch*, and $\omega t + \varphi$ as the phase. Figure 1 represents the motion. The heavy part of the curve between A and B represents one period of the motion, the length c is the amplitude, and the distance from A to B represents the period $T = (2\pi - \varphi)/\omega - (-\varphi/\omega) = 2\pi/\omega$.

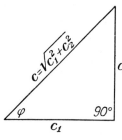

FIG. 2.

An equation having the form $y - a = c_1 \sin \omega t + c_2 \cos \omega t$ may be written in the form (1). For

$$c_1 \sin \omega t + c_2 \cos \omega t = \sqrt{c_1^2 + c_2^2} \left[\frac{c_1 \sin \omega t}{\sqrt{c_1^2 + c_2^2}} + \frac{c_2 \cos \omega t}{\sqrt{c_1^2 + c_2^2}} \right],$$

and this, in view of Fig. 2, may be written

$$\sqrt{c_1^2 + c_2^2} \, (\sin \omega t \cos \varphi + \cos \omega t \sin \varphi) = \sqrt{c_1^2 + c_2^2} \sin (\omega t + \varphi). \quad (4)$$

Hence, it appears from Fig. 2 that

$$y - a = c_1 \sin \omega t + c_2 \cos \omega t = c \sin (\omega t + \varphi), \quad (5)$$

where

$$c = \sqrt{c_1^2 + c_2^2}, \; \varphi = \tan^{-1}\frac{c_2}{c_1} \qquad (6)$$

A very important damped oscillatory motion is represented by

$$y = ce^{-at} \sin (\omega t + \varphi), a > 0.$$

Observe that the factor $\sin (\omega t + \varphi)$ describes an oscillatory kind of motion, and e^{-at} becomes smaller and smaller as t increases so that the oscillations become smaller and smaller in magnitude. Figure 3 represents the motion. Observe that the length of time for each wave is the same, but that the heights of the waves become smaller and smaller with in-

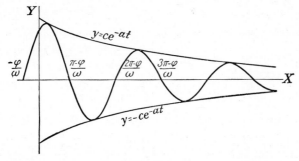

Fig. 3.

creasing t; that is, the motion is damped. *The factor* e^{-at} *is called the damping factor,* a *the damping constant,* $2\pi/\omega$ *the period of oscillation, and* $\omega/2\pi$ *the frequency of* y. For example, if

$$y = 10e^{-0.02t} \sin (120\pi t - \pi/2),$$

the period is $2\pi/(120\pi) = 1/60$, the frequency is 60 cycles, 0.02 is the damping constant, and $e^{-0.02t}$ is the damping factor. To find the time required by the damping factor to decrease one-half its value, we have $e^{-0.02t} = \frac{1}{2}$; hence $\log e^{-0.02t} = \log(1/2)$, or $-0.02t = -\log 2 = -0.6931$, and $t = 34.7$. This shows that the magnitude of the damping factor at the end of a 34.7-sec. interval is one-half its magnitude at the beginning.

Exercises

In the following exercises assume distance in feet and time in seconds.

1. For a straight-line motion represented by $y = 5 \sin (12\pi t + \pi/6)$, find the amplitude, the period, the frequency, and two positive values of t for which $y = 0$.

2. For a straight-line motion represented by $y = 5 \sin 32t + 12 \cos 32t$, find the period, frequency, and amplitude, and show that the maximum value of dy/dt is 416.

3. The equation $\dfrac{d^2y}{dt^2} + 100y = 0$ represents a simple harmonic motion. Find the general solution of the equation and determine the constants of integration if $y = 10$, $dy/dt = 50$, when $t = 0$. Tell the frequency, the period, and the amplitude of the motion represented.

4. The equation $\dfrac{d^2y}{dt^2} + y = 0$ represents a simple harmonic motion. Find its period, frequency, and amplitude if $y = 5$, $dy/dt = 0$, when $t = 0$.

5. For a straight-line motion represented by
$$y = 25e^{0.035t} \sin (377t + 1),$$
find the period and frequency and show that the damping factor decreases from 1 when $t = 0$ to $\frac{1}{2}$ when t is approximately 20 units of time.

6. What must be true of k in the equation $\dfrac{d^2s}{dt^2} + \dfrac{kds}{dt} + 30s = 0$, if the motion represented is vibratory?

7. An oscillatory motion is represented by
$$\frac{d^2y}{dt^2} + \frac{1}{10}\frac{dy}{dt} + 10y = 0.$$
Find the period of oscillation of y, the damping factor, and the time required for the damping factor to decrease 50 per cent.

8. Solve the differential equation
$$\frac{d^2x}{dt^2} + \frac{dx}{dt} + \frac{37}{4}x = 0,$$
and determine the constants of integration by using the conditions $x = 0$, $dx/dt = 6$, when $t = 0$. Find x in terms of the time, the period of oscillation of x, and the magnitude of the damping factor after 3 sec.

9. Solve the differential equation
$$9\frac{d^2x}{dt^2} + 3a\frac{dx}{dt} + 82x = 0,$$
and determine a and the constants of integration if $dx/dt = 6$, $x = 0$, when $t = 0$ and if the damping factor decreases 50 per cent in 2.08 units of time. Also find the period.

10. An oscillatory motion represented by an equation of the form
$$\frac{d^2x}{dt^2} + b\frac{dx}{dt} + cx = 0$$

has a frequency of oscillation $n = 60$ and a damping constant $a = \frac{1}{10}$. Find b and c.

11. Find b and c in the differential equation of problem 10 if the period of oscillation of x is $\frac{1}{10}$ sec. and the damping factor decreases 50 per cent in 30 sec.

57. Vectors and forces. Inasmuch as the statement of the laws of motion refers to vectors, it may be well to remind the student of some fundamental facts relating to them.

A vector AB (see Fig. 4) is the segment AB of a straight line containing an arrowhead pointed toward B to indicate a direction from its initial point A to its terminal point B. The length of the segment indicates the *magnitude* of the vector and the line with the attached arrowhead indicates direction. If, from the ends A and B of the vector, perpendiculars be dropped to the line

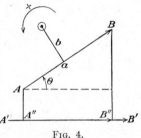

Fig. 4.

of a vector $A'B'$ and meet it in the points A'' and B'', respectively, then the vector $A''B''$ directed from A'' to B'' is called the *component* of vector AB in the direction of $A'B'$ (see Fig. 4).

Consider a vector AB of magnitude a, making an angle θ with the positive direction of vector $A'B'$. Then the absolute value of the quantity $a \cos \theta$ is the magnitude of the component of vector AB in the direction of $A'B'$. If $a \cos \theta$ is positive in sign, the component has the same direction as $A'B'$; if $a \cos \theta$ is negative, the component has the direction opposite to that of $A'B'$. Similarly, if a_i, θ_i $(i = 1, 2, \ldots, n)$ represent, respectively, magnitudes and angles made with vector $A'B'$ for n vectors A_iB_i, the algebraic sum $\Sigma a_i \cos \theta_i$ $(i = 1, 2, \ldots, n)$ will give in magnitude and sense along $A'B'$ the sum of the components of the n vectors in the direction of $A'B'$.

For example, the forces indicated in Fig. 5 have, as the sum of their components along OA, a vector of magnitude $10 \cos 0 + 5 \cos 90° + 7 \cos 240° + 5 \cos (-135°) = 10 - 3.50 - 3.54 = 2.96$ lb. directed along OA, and as sum of components along OB a vector of $10 \cos 90° + 5 \cos 0° + 7 \cos 150° + 5 \cos 135° = 5 - (7 \sqrt{3}/2) - 5/\sqrt{2} = -4.60$ lb. along OB, or 4.60 lb. in the direction opposite to that of OB.

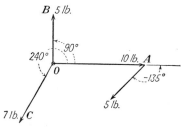

FIG. 5.

Again, consider a force represented by a vector AB lying in a fixed plane, and an axis which is perpendicular to the plane and cuts it in point O (see Fig. 4). The moment or torque of the force about the axis, also referred to as the *torque about* O, is defined to be the magnitude a of the force multiplied by the distance b from O to the line of action AB of the force. Moment measures the tendency to cause turning. Two forces, one tending to turn a body about O in one sense and the other tending to turn it about O in the opposite sense, would have moments about O opposite in sign. For example, forces OB and OC in Fig. 5 have moments about A opposite in sign. In general, *if θ is the angle through which a body attached to the axis is turned from some fixed position of reference, the torque of a force is considered as positive when it tends to turn the body in the sense of increasing angle θ and negative when it tends to turn the body in the opposite sense.*

58. Some fundamental equations of motion. Plane motion of a rigid body is a motion such that each point in the body remains at a constant distance from a fixed plane; for example, a wheel on an automobile has plane motion when the car is moving in a straight line.

When all the particles of the body, rigid or not, have plane motion with respect to the same plane, the sum ΣF_d of the components in any direction of all the external forces acting on it is equal to the product of the component a_d in the same direction of the acceleration of the center of gravity of the body and the mass m of the body; that is,

$$\Sigma F_d = ma_d. \tag{7}$$

Applying this rule for the direction of the X-axis and for the direction of the Y-axis, we obtain

$$\left.\begin{array}{l} \Sigma F_x = ma_x = m\dfrac{d^2x}{dt^2}, \\[2mm] \Sigma F_y = ma_y = m\dfrac{d^2y}{dt^2}. \end{array}\right\} \tag{8}$$

When a rigid body has plane motion, the moment or torque T_g of the external forces acting on it about an axis through the center of gravity of the body and perpendicular to the plane of its motion is equal to the product of the moment of inertia I_g of the body with respect to the same axis and the angular acceleration α of the body; that is,

$$T_g = I_g\alpha = I_g\frac{d^2\theta}{dt^2}, \tag{9}$$

where θ is the angle through which the body is turned from some fixed position of reference. When the motion is pure rotation, we may write

$$T = I\alpha = I\frac{d^2\theta}{dt^2}, \tag{10}$$

where T is the torque of the external forces about the axis of rotation and I is the moment of inertia of the body with respect to the same axis. Note that the axis associated with (10) is not necessarily an axis through the center of gravity.

59. Vibratory motion. Three very important types of motion are referred to as *free* motion, *damped* motion, and *forced* motion. Thus, a weight supported in a vacuum by a spring would tend to move with an oscillatory motion when displaced vertically; if air were admitted, it would tend to slow down or *dampen* the motion; and if the supporting structure

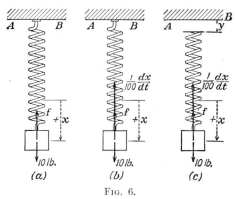

Fig. 6.

were moved up and down, a motion would be *forced* on the weight. These three types of motion or their counterparts occur in a great many physical phenomena. Example 1 below will show how they are associated with the respective terms Bx, $A \, dx/dt$, and $f(x)$ in the equation

$$\frac{d^2x}{dt^2} + A\frac{dx}{dt} + Bx = f(x).$$

Later we shall find the term Bx associated with the oscillatory flow of electricity to and from a condenser, $A\dfrac{dx}{dt}$ with a dampened flow of electricity due to resistance, and $f(x)$ with the forced flow of electricity due to a dynamo or other source of electric energy.

Example 1. The force exerted by a certain spring is proportional to the amount it is stretched, and a force of 10 lb.

stretches it 3 in. A 10-lb. weight hanging at rest on the spring is drawn down 2 in. and released. Describe the motion: (a) if there is no air resistance; (b) if the air resistance in pounds and one-hundredth of the speed in feet per second are equal numerically; (c) if, in addition to the air resistance, the supporting structure is given a motion $y = \cos 5t + \sin 5t$.

Solution. (a) Let x be the number of feet the spring is stretched [see Fig. 6(a)] and let f represent the force exerted by the spring. Then, in accordance with Hooke's law, $f = kx$. Since $f = 10$ lb. when $x = \frac{1}{4}$ ft., it appears that $10 = k\frac{1}{4}$, and $k = 40$. Hence

$$f = 40x. \qquad (a)$$

From the first equation of (8) with downward considered as the positive direction, we get

$$10 - f = 10 - 40x = \frac{10}{32.2} \frac{d^2x}{dt^2}. \qquad (b)$$

The solution of this equation is

$$x = c_1 \sin \sqrt{128.8}\, t + c_2 \cos \sqrt{128.8}\, t + \tfrac{1}{4}, \qquad (c)$$

and

$$v = \frac{dx}{dt} = \sqrt{128.8}\, (c_1 \cos \sqrt{128.8}\, t - c_2 \sin \sqrt{128.8}\, t). \qquad (d)$$

The initial conditions are

$$v = \frac{dx}{dt} = 0,\ x = 3 \text{ in.} + 2 \text{ in.} = \tfrac{5}{12} \text{ ft., when } t = 0. \qquad (e)$$

Substituting these values in (c) and (d), we get

$$\tfrac{5}{12} = c_2 + \tfrac{1}{4},\ 0 = c_1 \sqrt{128.8} = 11.3c_1, \qquad (f)$$

or

$$c_2 = \tfrac{1}{6},\ c_1 = 0.$$

Substituting these values in (c), we get the solution

$$x - \tfrac{1}{4} = \tfrac{1}{6} \cos 11.3t. \qquad (g)$$

This represents a harmonic motion with amplitude **1/6 ft.**, and period $2\pi/11.3 =$ **0.554 sec.**, or frequency $11.3/(2\pi) =$ **1.81** cycles per second.

(b) From Fig. 6 (b), equation (a), and the first equation of (8), we have

$$10 - \frac{1}{100} \frac{dx}{dt} - 40x = \frac{10}{32.2} \frac{d^2x}{dt^2}. \quad (h)$$

The general solution of (h) is

$$x = e^{-0.0161t} (c_1 \sin 11.3t + c_2 \cos 11.3t) + \tfrac{1}{4}. \quad (i)$$

Differentiating this and using the initial conditions (e) to determine the constants of integration, we finally obtain

$$x = e^{-0.0161t} (0.000236 \sin 11.3t + \tfrac{1}{6} \cos 11.3t) + \tfrac{1}{4}. \quad (j)$$

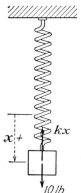

Here the period is the same as before accurate to three figures. The damping factor is $e^{-0.0161t}$. To get an idea of the rate of damping, notice that the damping factor is $\frac{1}{2}$ when $e^{-0.0161t} = \frac{1}{2}$, or when $-0.0161t = -\log 2 = -0.693$, and $t = 43$ sec.; that is, the magnitude of the damping factor at the end of a 43-sec. period is one-half its magnitude at the beginning.

(c) In this case [see Fig. 6(c)] the force f is

$$40(x - y) = 40x - 40 \cos 5t - 40 \sin 5t,$$

and the equation of motion is

kx

$x \downarrow$

$10 lb$

Fig. 7.

$$10 - 40x + 40 \cos 5t + 40 \sin 5t - \frac{1}{100} \frac{dx}{dt} = \frac{10}{32.2} \frac{d^2x}{dt^2}. \quad (k)$$

The solution of (k) subject to the initial conditions

$$x = \frac{17}{12}, \quad v = 0 \text{ when } t = 0,$$

is found by the usual procedure to be

$$\mathbf{x = e^{-0.0161t} (0.18 \cos 11.3t - 0.55 \sin 11.3t) +}$$
$$\mathbf{1.24 (\cos 5t + \sin 5t),}$$

approximately. Observe that the motion of the weight is made up of two motions: a damped oscillatory motion and a harmonic motion. As time increases, the damped harmonic motion dies away while the harmonic motion $1.24(\cos 5t + \sin 5t)$ remains. The flow of electricity in many circuits follows this same plan, being made up of two parts, a *transient part*, which quickly dies out, and a *steady-state part*, which remains indefinitely.

Problems

1. The force exerted by a spring is proportional to the amount the spring is stretched and is 10 lb. when the spring is stretched 2 in. (see Fig. 7). A 10-lb. weight is hung on the spring and is drawn down slowly until the spring is stretched 4 in. and then released. Find the equation, the period, the amplitude, and the frequency of the resulting motion.

2. A 5-lb. weight hanging at rest on the spring of problem 1 is drawn down slightly and released. Assuming the weight to be acted on by gravity, the force exerted by the spring, and a retarding force whose magnitude in pounds is one-fiftieth the magnitude of the velocity of the weight in feet per second, find the period of oscillation, the damping factor, and the time it takes the damping factor to decrease 50 per cent.

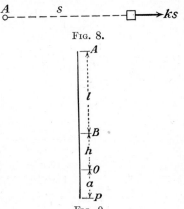

Fig. 8.

Fig. 9.

3. A particle of mass 1 slug moves toward a fixed center of force which repels it with a magnitude in pounds equal to k times the distance of the particle from the center (see Fig. 8). Initially the particle is distant a from the center and is moving toward it with a velocity equal in magnitude to $\sqrt{ka^2}$. Prove that the particle will continually approach but never reach the center.

4. A rubber band of natural length $AB = l$ (see Fig. 9) is suspended vertically from a point A and a weight is attached to it at B. The weight stretches the band to a length $AO = l + h$. The weight is given a displacement $OP = a(a < h)$ and then released. Find the equation of the motion.

5. A spring is stretched 1 in. when a 4-lb. weight is hung on it. If a 12-lb. weight is hanging at rest on the spring when the upper end of the spring is given the motion $y = \sin \sqrt{3g}\, t$, find a differential equation of the motion of the weight, solve this equation, and determine all constants of integration. Find the position of the weight $50\pi/\sqrt{g}$ sec. after the motion starts. *Hint:* At time t (see Fig. 10), y is the distance of the upper end above its initial position, and we let x be the

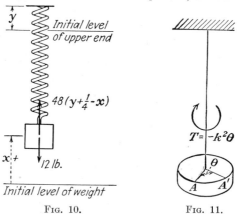

Fig. 10.   Fig. 11.

distance of the weight above its initial position. Hence, at time t, the spring is stretched $y + \frac{1}{4} - x$, and the upward force on the weight is $48(y + \frac{1}{4} - x) - 12$.

6. Solve the preceding problem when $y = \sin \sqrt{3g}\, t$ is replaced by $y = \sin 2\sqrt{g}\, t$. Is there a theoretical upper limit to the distance of the weight from the starting point?

7. A rigid body suspended by a wire (see Fig. 11) has a motion of pure rotation about the line of the wire as an axis. If the only torque acting is a torque in the wire proportional to the angle that the body is turned from the position in which it hangs in equilibrium, find the period of the motion. *Hint:* Let θ be the angle through which the body is turned from equilibrium. Then use (9) to obtain

$$-k^2\theta = I\frac{d^2\theta}{dt^2}.$$

8. A uniform sphere rotates about a supporting wire as an axis. If the number expressing the torque in the wire in pound-feet is equal to the number of radians through which the sphere is turned from the position in which it will hang in equilibrium, and if the sphere makes two complete oscillations per second, find the moment of inertia of the sphere with respect to the line of the wire.

9. If, for the sphere and wire of problem 8, change of motion is caused by a frictional torque proportional to the angular velocity together with the torque in the wire, and if the corresponding damping factor decreases to 25 per cent of its initial value during the first

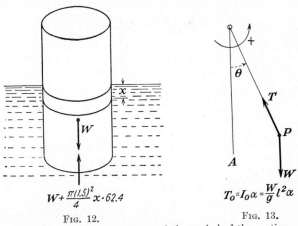

$$W + \frac{\pi(1.5)^2}{4} x \cdot 62.4$$

$$T_0 = I_0 \alpha = \frac{W}{g} l^2 \alpha$$

Fig. 12.   Fig. 13.

2 sec. of motion, find the equation and the period of the motion. Use the value of *I* found in problem 8.

10. A cylindrical spar buoy 18 in. in diameter stands in fresh water with its axis vertical (see Fig. 12). When depressed slightly and released, the period of vibration is found to be 2.7 sec. Find the weight of the cylinder.

11. A rectangular block of wood 2 by 2 by 1 ft. floats in fresh water with its 1-ft. edge vertical. If the block weighs 160 lb., find the time of vibration when it is depressed slightly and released. Find also the time of vibration of the same block in a liquid of specific gravity ρ.

12. Find, approximately, the period of vibration of a simple pendulum *l* ft. long. Assume that the angle θ between the vertical and the cord of the pendulum is always so small that $\sin \theta$ may be replaced by θ without appreciable error. *Hint:* Use Fig. 13 and apply equation (10).

13. A 10-lb. weight having specific gravity 2 is immersed in water and supported by a spring which it stretches 2 in. It is drawn down 1 ft. from its position of equilibrium and let go. The resistance of the liquid to the motion of the weight is proportional to its velocity. If, at the end of two complete vibrations, the value of damping factor is 25 per cent of its initial value, find the equation of the motion and its period.

14. A particle below the earth's surface is attracted toward the center of the earth with a force proportional to the distance of the particle from the center. If a particle were dropped into a smooth straight vacuum passing through the earth's center, how long would it take the particle to reach the center? Assume that the radius of the earth is 3960 statute miles. *Hint:* $\dfrac{W}{32.2} a = ks$, and $a = -32.2$ ft./sec.^{2} when $s = R$.

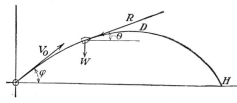

Fig. 14.

15. A body falling from rest in a heavy fluid acquires a velocity which approaches 10 ft./sec. as a limit. Assuming the resistance of the medium to be proportional to the velocity, and the buoyancy of the fluid to be one-half the weight of the body, find the factor of proportionality and the distance traversed during the first 10 sec.

16. A body of weight w lb. moves vertically under the force of gravity and under the action of a force opposite to the direction of motion and equal numerically to $0.4wv/32.2$ where v is the speed in feet per second. Taking y as the distance above the ground, study the motion under the conditions $y = 0$, $v = 100$, when $t = 0$.

60. Plane motions of bodies. In §59 motions in a straight line and simple rotary motions were considered. The equations of §58 will now be applied to the curved-line motion of projectiles and to bodies rotating and translating at the same time. In Fig. 14 the curve ODH is the path, or trajectory, of a projectile fired from a gun at O, φ is the angle of departure, V_0 is the initial velocity, θ is the inclination of the tangent line to the X-axis (taken horizontal), OH is the range, vector W

represents the force of gravity acting on the projectile, and
vector R represents the force due to air resistance assumed to
be acting along the tangent to the trajectory in a direction
opposite to that in which the projectile is moving.

Applying equations (8) of §58, we obtain

$$\frac{W}{g}\frac{d\dot{x}}{dt} = -R\frac{\dot{x}}{v}, \quad \frac{W}{g}\frac{d\dot{y}}{dt} = -W - R\frac{\dot{y}}{v}, \qquad (11)$$

where $\dot{x} = dx/dt$ and $\dot{y} = dy/dt$ represent, respectively, the
horizontal and the vertical components
of the velocity. The force R is a very
complex quantity, so complex in fact
that only approximations to the solutions of equations (11) can be found.
Some rough approximations of special
cases will appear as solutions of problems
in the list of this article.

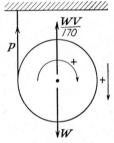

Fig. 15.

The following example will illustrate
a type involving both rotation and
translation.

Example. A homogeneous cylinder, having radius $= r$ ft.,
weight $= W$ lb., $I_g = \dfrac{W}{g}\dfrac{r^2}{2}$ (where $g = 32.2$), has a flexible
cord wrapped around its central plane. One end of the cord
is attached to a fixed plane as shown in Fig. 15. As the body
falls, an air resistance in pounds equal numerically to $W/170$
times its velocity in feet per second retards its motion. If it
starts from rest, find distance y fallen in t sec., limiting velocity, and percentage of limiting velocity acquired in 20 sec.

Solution. If y is the distance fallen from rest and θ the
angle through which the body has turned, we have

$$y = r\theta, \; v = \frac{dy}{dt} = r\frac{d\theta}{dt}, \; a = \frac{d^2y}{dt^2} = r\frac{d^2\theta}{dt^2} = r\alpha. \qquad (a)$$

Here downward is considered as the positive direction and
clockwise as the positive sense of rotation. Applying

equations (8) and (9) to the system represented by Fig. 15, we get

$$-p - \frac{W}{170}v + W = \frac{W}{g}\frac{d^2y}{dt^2},\qquad (b)$$

$$pr = \frac{W}{g}\frac{r^2}{2}\alpha = \frac{Wr}{2g}r\alpha = \frac{Wr}{2g}\frac{d^2y}{dt^2}.\qquad (c)$$

Substituting p from (c) in (b) and simplifying slightly, we obtain

$$\frac{3W}{2g}\frac{d^2y}{dt^2} + \frac{W}{170}\frac{dy}{dt} = W.\qquad (d)$$

The solution of (d) is

$$y = A + Be^{-\frac{g}{255}t} + 170t;\qquad (e)$$

hence

$$v = \frac{dy}{dt} = \frac{-Bg}{255}e^{-\frac{g}{255}t} + 170.\qquad (f)$$

Using the conditions $y = 0$, $v = 0$, when $t = 0$ in (e) and (f), we have

$$0 = A + B, 0 = \frac{-Bg}{255} + 170, \text{ or } \frac{3(170)^2}{2g} = B = -A.\quad (g)$$

Substituting A and B from (g) in (e) and (f) and simplifying, we obtain

$$y = \frac{3(170)^2}{2g}\left(e^{-\frac{gt}{255}} - 1\right) + 170t,\qquad (h)$$

$$v = 170\left(1 - e^{-\frac{g}{255}t}\right).\qquad (i)$$

Substituting $t = \infty$ in (i), we get

$$\lim_{t \to \infty} v = 170 \text{ ft./sec.}$$

Again,

$$\frac{170\left[1 - e^{-\frac{20(32.2)}{255}}\right]}{170}(100\%) = 92\%.$$

Problems

1. Solve equations (11) for x and y in terms of t if $R = 0$. Determine the constants of integration from the initial conditions $\dot{x} = v_0 \cos \varphi$, $\dot{y} = v_0 \sin \varphi$, $x = 0$, $y = 0$, all when $t = 0$.

2. Solve equations (11) for the special case where R is numerically equal to $0.02wv/g$, and v is the speed in feet per second. Assume that $v_0 = 3000$ ft./sec., $\varphi = 30°$, and note that, when $t = 0$, $x = y = 0$, $\dot{x} = 3000 \cos 30°$ ft./sec. and $\dot{y} = 3000 \sin 30°$ ft./sec. Find the greatest height reached by the projectile.

3. When a projectile is fired at a small angle of elevation, the vertical component of its velocity is small, and consequently the vertical component of air resistance is small.

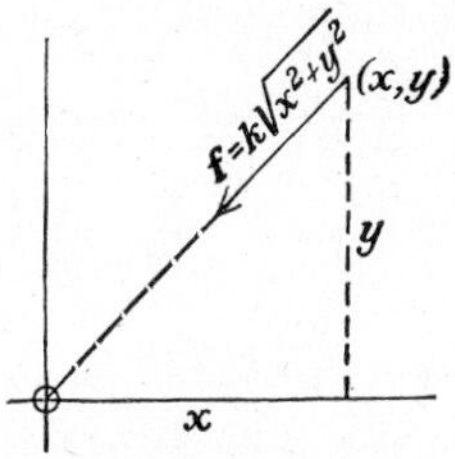

FIG. 16. 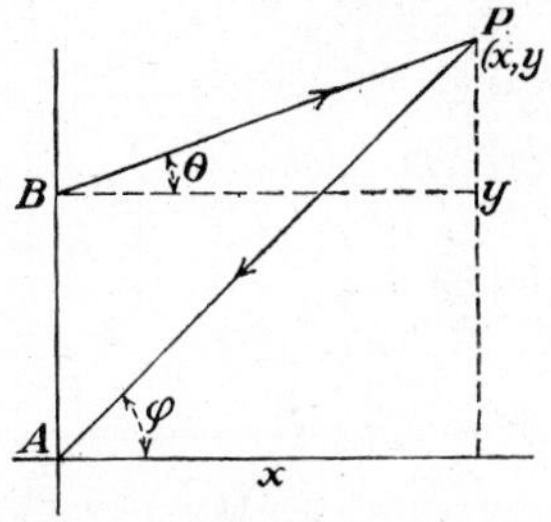   FIG. 17.

A 100-lb. shell is fired with initial velocity $v_0 = 2000$ ft./sec. and with angle of departure $\varphi = 5°$. Assuming in this case that air resistance is horizontal and equal numerically to $\dfrac{100}{25g} \dfrac{dx}{dt}$, derive equations similar to (11); solve these equations for dx/dt, dy/dt, x, and y; and determine the constants of integration.

4. If a projectile is fired at an angle of departure nearly equal to 90°, the horizontal component of air resistance is small.

An anti-aircraft gun fires a projectile of weight W with initial velocity $v_0 = 2000$ ft./sec. and angle of departure $\varphi = 80°$. Assume air resistance to be vertical and equal numerically to $\dfrac{W}{1200} \dfrac{dy}{dt}$. Find the equations of the trajectory, the maximum height attained by the projectile, and the height of the projectile when the vertical component of its velocity is 500 ft./sec.

5. A particle of mass m slugs moves in a plane under the action of a force (see Fig. 16) always directed to a fixed point in the plane and equal in magnitude to k times the distance of the particle from the fixed point. At a certain instant the particle is moving with velocity v_0 at right angles to a line connecting it with the fixed point and is *a* units from it.   Find the equations of motion and tell the nature of the path.   *Hint:* Apply equations (8), to obtain $m\ddot{x} = -kx$, etc.

6. A fixed plane contains a variable point P and two fixed points A and B. P is the position of a particle of unit mass which is acted on by two forces, one equal numerically to the magnitude of BP and exerted in the direction from B toward P, a second equal numerically to the magnitude of $2\,PA$ and exerted in the direction from P toward A. Find the equations of motion if $AB = 2$ ft. and if the particle is initially at A moving 3 ft./sec. in a direction making (*a*) an angle of 90° with AB; (*b*) an angle of 45° with AB.   *Hint:* In Fig. 17, $\Sigma F_x = \overline{BP}\cos\theta -$

$$2AP\cos\varphi = \overline{BP}\frac{x}{\overline{BP}} - \overline{2AP}\frac{x}{\overline{AP}} = x - 2x = -x, \text{ etc.}$$

7. A circular cylinder having radius r, weight W, and I with respect to its axis $\dfrac{W}{g}\dfrac{r^2}{2}$ is rolling on a rough horizontal plane when two horizontal forces perpendicular to its axis are impressed on it: a constant

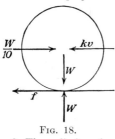

force equal to $\frac{1}{10}\,W$ in the direction of motion and an oppositely directed air resistance proportional to the velocity of its axis.   If no slipping occurs, if the limiting speed is 60 ft./sec., and if the initial speed is zero, describe the motion and find how far the cylinder rolls during the first minute of motion (see Fig. 18).   *Hint:* Apply equations (8) and (9) of §58, eliminate f, and integrate

FIG. 18.   the resulting equations.

8. The cylinder of exercise 7 rolls without slipping and with axis horizontal on a rough plane inclined 30° to the horizontal.   If air resistance is opposite to the direction of motion and is numerically equal to $W/600$ times the magnitude of the velocity of the axis in feet per second, find the limiting speed and the distance traversed during the first minute of motion from rest.

61.* Kirchhoff's current law and electromotive-force law. We may think of electricity as a substance and speak of it quantitatively.   A current of electricity is a rate of flow of this substance; thus, when a current of 1 ampere is flowing

* Good reference books are:
  (*a*) Pierce, G. W., "Electric Oscillations and Electric Waves."
  (*b*) Bedell, F., and A. C. Crehore, "Alternating Currents."

through a conductor, 1 coulomb of electricity per second is passing any point of the conductor, and, if a constant current of I amperes is flowing, $q = It$ coulombs will pass any point in t sec. The following law is known as Kirchhoff's current law.

CURRENT LAW.* *The excess of the current flowing into a given region at a given time over the current flowing out at the same time is the time rate of increase of quantity of electricity within the region at that time.*

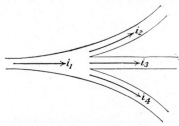

FIG. 19.

If there is no accumulation of electricity within a given region, current flowing into this region equals current flowing out of it; for example, in Fig. 19.

$$i_1 = i_2 + i_3 + i_4. \tag{12}$$

If the region is the positive plate of a condenser, electricity flows into the region, but none, theoretically, flows out. Hence

$$q = \int_c i \, dt, \tag{13}$$

Where q is the charge (quantity of electricity) on the positive plate of the condenser, i is the current, t is the time, and the subscript c on the integral sign indicates that limits are to be taken so as to obtain the total quantity of electricity on the condenser at time t. Differentiating (13) with respect to the time, we obtain

* See reference (a), p. 132.

$$\frac{dq}{dt} = i, \frac{d^2q}{dt^2} = \frac{di}{dt}. \qquad (14)$$

Electromotive force, also called *voltage* and *difference of potential*, causes electricity to move just as physical force causes bodies to move. The *volt* will be used as the unit.

When electricity is flowing through a coil, any change in current sets up a counter electromotive force opposing the change in current. For this reason an electromotive force e_L of magnitude $e_L = L\frac{di}{dt}$ must act to cause the current to flow. L is a constant, called *inductance*. It is analogous to

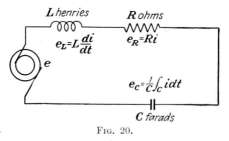

Fig. 20.

the inertia of bodies. The practical unit of inductance is the *henry*.

Conductors offer *resistance* to the flow of electricity through them. Resistance depends upon such things as size and kind of material. If a conductor has a resistance of R *ohms* an electromotive force e_R of magnitude $e_R = Ri$ volts is required to cause a current of i amperes to flow through it. Resistance is analogous to friction.

A condenser consists essentially of two plates separated by a non-conducting substance, or insulator. When a current flows to one plate of a condenser, a charge is deposited there, an equal charge opposite in sign appears at the other plate, and the current away from the condenser is equal to the current flowing to it. The electromotive force e_C across a condenser having a charge of q coulombs and a capacity of C *farads* is given by

$$e_c = \frac{q}{C} = \frac{1}{C} \int_c i \, dt.$$

Figure 20 represents the elements mentioned above, and Kirchhoff's electromotive-force law, which follows, gives an equation connecting them.

ELECTROMOTIVE-FORCE LAW. *When several elements, resistance* R, *inductance* L, *and capacity* C, *all constant, are connected in series, and when an instantaneous current* i *is flowing in them, there is impressed in the direction of* i *at the terminals of this series from a source of power external to the elements a difference of potential* e *such that*

$$e = L\frac{di}{dt} + Ri + \frac{1}{C} \int_c i \, dt, \tag{15}$$

where $\int_c$ i dt *represents the total quantity of electricity on the condenser considered.*

It is worthy of note that *Kirchhoff's laws may be applied to any part or the whole of a circuit but that, in such application, fall of potential must be considered positive in the direction of the current and negative in the opposite direction.* Also L, R, and C do not necessarily apply to concentrated elements in a circuit but are sums of inductances, resistance, or capacities for the part of the circuit considered.

Substitution of q for $\int_c i \, dt$, dq/dt for i, and d^2q/dt^2 for di/dt in (15) gives

$$L\frac{d^2q}{dt^2} + R\frac{dq}{dt} + \frac{q}{C} = e, \tag{16}$$

and differentiation of (15) with respect to the time gives

$$L\frac{d^2i}{dt^2} + R\frac{di}{dt} + \frac{1}{C}i = \frac{de}{dt}. \tag{17}$$

62. Simple circuits containing constant electromotive force. To illustrate the use of equations (16) and (17), consider the charging of a condenser of capacity C through a resistance R and an inductance L by a constant electromotive force E. For this case equation (16) becomes

$$LD^2q + RDq + \frac{1}{C}q = E, \qquad (18)$$

where $D = d/dt$. Assume as initial conditions $q = 0$, $i = 0$, when $t = 0$. The roots of the auxiliary equation $Lm^2 + Rm + 1/C = 0$ are

$$m = \frac{-R}{2L} \pm \sqrt{\frac{R^2}{4L^2} - \frac{1}{LC}}, \text{ or } \frac{-R}{2L} \pm \sqrt{\frac{1}{LC} - \frac{R^2}{4L^2}} j, \qquad (19)$$

where $j = \sqrt{-1}$. First let us assume that the roots are imaginary and let

$$a = \frac{R}{2L}, \ \omega_1 = \sqrt{\frac{1}{LC} - \frac{R^2}{4L^2}}. \qquad (20)$$

Then we have

$$m = -a \pm \omega_1 j, \ \frac{1}{LC} = \omega_1^2 + a^2, \qquad (21)$$

and the solution of (18) is

$$q = \epsilon^{-at}(c_1 \sin \omega_1 t + c_2 \cos \omega_1 t) + CE.^* \qquad (22)$$

From (14) we get

$$i = \frac{dq}{dt} =$$

$$\epsilon^{-at}\left[(-c_1 a - c_2 \omega_1) \sin \omega_1 t + (c_1 \omega_1 - c_2 a) \cos \omega_1 t\right]. \qquad (23)$$

From the initial conditions $q = 0$, $i = 0$ when $t = 0$, we get

$$0 = c_2 + CE, \ 0 = c_1 \omega_1 - c_2 a,$$
$$c_2 = -CE, \ c_1 = -aCE/\omega_1.$$

* Here $\epsilon(= 2.7183$, approximately) is used to represent the base of natural logarithms.

Substituting these values in (22) and (23), and using (21), we obtain after slight simplification

$$q = \frac{-CE}{\omega_1}\epsilon^{-at}(a \sin \omega_1 t + \omega_1 \cos \omega_1 t) + CE,$$ (24)

$$i = \frac{E}{L\omega_1}\epsilon^{-at} \sin \omega_1 t.$$

In (24) the terms having ϵ^{-at} as a factor approach zero; hence the current i approaches zero and the charge q on the condenser approaches CE.

If $R = 0$, then $a = R/(2L)$ is zero, $\epsilon^{-at} = 1$, and no part of the solution approaches zero. In this case the charge q and the current i both oscillate with period $2\pi/\omega_1$. Since a circuit always has some resistance, this situation will never actually arise.

If the roots (19) are not imaginary, both of them are negative. Call them $-\alpha_1$, and $-\alpha_2$. Then the solution is

$$q = c_1\epsilon^{-\alpha_1 t} + c_2\epsilon^{-\alpha_2 t} + CE, \quad i = -c_1\alpha_1\epsilon^{-\alpha_1 t} - c_2\alpha_2\epsilon^{-\alpha_2 t}.$$

In this case there is no oscillatory surging of electricity, current i approaches zero, and charge q approaches CE.

A so-called critical case arises when the roots of (19) are equal, that is, when both are $-a$. Then the solution is

$$q = (c_1 + c_2 t)\epsilon^{-at} + CE, \quad i = (-ac_1 + c_2 - ac_2 t)\epsilon^{-at},$$

there is no oscillatory fluctuation of current or charge, and, since the terms having ϵ^{-at} as a factor approach zero, q approaches CE and i approaches zero.

Exercises

1. Solve equations (16) and (14) to find i and q for a circuit in which $L = 0.1$ henry, $R = 1$ ohm, $C = 250 \times 10^{-6}$ farad, $e = E = 100$ volts, if the initial conditions are $q = 0$, $i = 0$, when $t = 0$. In what time does the damping factor of the current decrease to $\frac{1}{10}$ of its value when $t = 0$ and what is the period of the current? What are the limiting values of q and i?

2. Solve equations (14) and (16) to find i and q in terms of t for a circuit in which $L = 1$ henry, $R = 1$ ohm, $C = 4$ farads, and $e = E = 100$ volts, if $q = 0$, $i = 0$, when $t = 0$. Show that the maximum value of the current is $200\epsilon^{-1}$ (where $\epsilon = 2.718$, nearly) and that the ratio of the current when $t = 10$ sec. to this maximum value is $5\epsilon^{-4} < 0.1$.

3. To find i and q for a circuit during the discharge of a condenser, take $L = 0.1$ henry, $R = 1$ ohm, $C = 250 \times 10^{-6}$ farad, $e = 0$, and the initial conditions $q = 0.05$ coulomb, $i = -0.25$ ampere, when $t = 0$. What is the period of the current and the limiting values of i and q?

4. A circuit consists of an impedance coil of inductance L and negligible resistance connected in series with a condenser of capacity C. Use equations (14) and (16) to find the charge q on the condenser and current i at time t, if t is the number of seconds since i was zero and q was q_0. Describe the fluctuation of i and q. *Hint:* $e = 0$.

5. Solve equations (16) and (14) with e replaced by the constant E and R by zero, for i and q in terms of t. Assume that $i = 0$, $q = 0$ when $t = 0$.

6. A circuit consists of an impedance coil having an inductance L and resistance R connected in series with a condenser having a capacity C. Initially the current is zero, and the charge on the condenser is q_0. Find i and q at any time, if $4L > CR^2$.

7. Taking $L = 2$ henrys, $R = 10$ ohms, $C = 200 \times 10^{-6}$ farad, and $q_0 = 0.05$ coulomb in the solution of exercise 6, find i and q at any time t.

63. Simple circuits containing a sinusoidal electromotive force.

The type of equation to be considered in this article has the form

$$LD^2q + RDq + \left(\frac{1}{C}\right)q = E \sin \omega t. \tag{25}$$

The current i is found from the equation $i = dq/dt$. The electromotive force $e = E \sin \omega t$ is generally supplied by a dynamo.

In what follows it will be convenient to let

$$X = L\omega - \frac{1}{C\omega}, \quad Z = \sqrt{R^2 + X^2}. \tag{26}$$

X is called the *reactance* and Z the *impedance*.

A particular solution y_p of (25) could be found by methods previously used. A simple procedure is to *replace* sin ωt *in*

(25) *by* $\epsilon^{j\omega t}$ (= cos ωt + j sin ωt), j = $\sqrt{-1}$), *find a particular solution of the resulting equation, and take* $1/j$ *times the pure imaginary part of the solution thus formed.* Substituting for q, $Q_p = A\,\epsilon^{j\omega t}$ in $LD^2q + RDq + (1/C)q = E\epsilon^{j\omega t}$, we obtain $A(-L\omega^2 + R\omega j + 1/C)\epsilon^{j\omega t} = E\epsilon^{j\omega t}$. Hence

$$A = \cfrac{E}{\omega\left[-\left(L\omega - \dfrac{1}{C\omega}\right) + Rj\right]} = \frac{E(-X - Rj)}{\omega(-X + Rj)(-X - Rj)} =$$

$$\frac{-E(X + Rj)}{\omega Z^2}.$$

Therefore,

$$Q_p = \frac{-E}{\omega Z^2}(X + Rj)\epsilon^{j\omega t} = \frac{-E}{\omega Z^2}(X + Rj)(\cos \omega t + j \sin \omega t),$$

$$q_p = \frac{1}{j}(\text{Pure Imag. part of } Q_p) = \frac{-E}{\omega Z^2}(X \sin \omega t + R \cos \omega t).$$

Supplying the solution of the auxiliary equation, we obtain the general solution of (25).

$$q = \epsilon^{-at}(c_1 \sin \omega_1 t + c_2 \cos \omega_1 t) - \tag{27}$$
$$\frac{E}{\omega Z^2}(X \sin \omega t + R \cos \omega t).$$

The equation of the current is obtained by differentiating (27) and replacing dq/dt by i.

The part containing the factor ϵ^{-at} generally becomes negligible in a very short time. It is called a *transient*. Transients are important in the theory of radio and of radar. The other part of the solution is permanent and is called the *steady-state solution*. Dropping the transient term from (27), we have for the steady state

$$q = \frac{-E}{\omega Z^2}(X \sin \omega t + R \cos \omega t), \tag{28}$$

and, since $i = dq/dt$, for the *steady-state value of* i

$$i = \frac{dq}{dt} = \frac{E}{Z^2}(R \sin \omega t - X \cos \omega t). \tag{29}$$

64. Resonance. Equation (29) may be written in the form

$$i = \frac{E}{Z} \sin\left(\omega t - \tan^{-1}\frac{X}{R}\right), \qquad (30)$$

where the quadrant of $\tan^{-1}(X/R)$ is that of point (X,R) when plotted in rectangular coordinates. Observe that the amplitude of i

$$\frac{E}{Z} = \frac{E}{\sqrt{R^2 + X^2}} = \frac{E}{\sqrt{R^2 + [L\omega - 1/(C\omega)]^2}} \qquad (31)$$

will be a minimum for given values of L, R, E, and ω when C is chosen so that $X = 0$, that is, so that

$$L\omega - \frac{1}{C\omega} = 0, \text{ or } \omega = \frac{1}{\sqrt{LC}}. \qquad (32)$$

With this condition is associated the name *current resonance*. A person tuning a radio in to a station takes advantage of current resonance.

Exercises

1. Reproduce the solution of (25) to obtain (27) without using the text.

2. Obtain the steady-state equation for i by differentiating (27) while omitting the term having ϵ^{-at} as a factor.

3. A sinusoidal electromotive force of frequency $200/\pi$ and maximum value 110 volts is connected in series in a circuit with an inductance of 0.1 henry, a resistance of 10 ohms, and a condenser of capacity 250×10^{-6} farad. Find the steady-state solution of i and q in terms of t and the maximum values of the steady-state charge on the condenser and the current.

4. If $e = E \sin \omega t$ in the circuit of Fig. 20, derive the steady-state solution for i and for q: (a) when $R = 0$ and there is no condenser; (b) when $L = 0$ and there is no condenser; (c) when $L = 0$ and $R = 0$; (d) when $L = 0$; (e) when there is no condenser; (f) when $R = 0$.

5. Find the expression of i in terms of t for the circuit of Fig. 20 provided $e = 20 \sin 500t$, $R = 2$ ohms, $L = 0.2$ henry, $C = 20 \times 10^{-6}$ farad, and if i and q are zero when $t = 0$. Find the value of the damping factor of the transient at time $t = 1$ sec.

6. Use (32) to find C at current resonance when the frequency is 10^5 cycles per second and $L = 6 \times 10^{-6}$ henry. If $R = 100$ ohms, find the ratio of the maximum current E/Z from (30) at current resonance to the current in the same circuit with no condenser.

65. Application of Kirchhoff's laws to networks. The e.m.f. (electromotive-force) law and the current law stated in §61 may be applied when elements involving inductance, resistance, and capacity are connected in a more or less com-

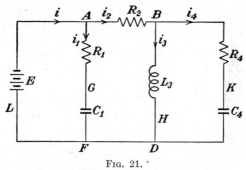

FIG. 21.

plicated network. Equations can be obtained by applying the e.m.f. law to complete circuits or the current law at points where two or more conductors meet.

For example in Fig. 21, apply the current law at A and at B to obtain

$$i = i_1 + i_2, \ i_2 = i_3 + i_4.$$

Apply the e.m.f. law to circuit $LAGF$ to obtain

$$R_1 i_1 + \frac{1}{C_1} \int_{c_1} i_1 \, dt = E.$$

Also apply the e.m.f. law to the circuits $LABHDF$ and $BKDH$ to obtain

$$R_2 i_2 + L_3 \frac{di_3}{dt} = E, R_4 i_4 + \frac{1}{C_4} \int_{c_4} i_4 \, dt - L_3 \frac{di_3}{dt} = 0.$$

Observe in this last circuit that there was no externally applied e.m.f. and that a negative sign was given to $L_3 \, di_3/dt$ because in following the circuit in the direction B to K to D

to H, the element of inductance L_3 was traversed opposite to the direction of the assumed current i_3. Using the equations just derived with $i_1 = dq_1/dt$, $i_4 = dq_4/dt$, we could solve the derived equations to find the current in each branch of the network and the charge of electricity on each condenser at time t.

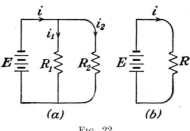

(a)   (b)

Fig. 22.

As another application, apply Kirchhoff's laws to the circuits of Fig. 22 (a).   We have
$$R_1 i_1 = E, \; R_2 i_2 = E, \; i = i_1 + i_2. \tag{33}$$
Substituting i_1 and i_2 from the first two equations of (33) in the third and transforming slightly, we have
$$i = E\left(\frac{1}{R_1} + \frac{1}{R_2}\right), \text{ or } \frac{i}{1/R_1 + 1/R_2} = E. \tag{34}$$
Comparing this last equation with $Ri = E$ from Fig. 22 (b), it appears that two resistances R_1 and R_2 in parallel are together equivalent to a resistance $R = 1 / \left(\dfrac{1}{R_1} + \dfrac{1}{R_2}\right)$.

In general, to find the currents in the branches of a network and the charges on the condensers, proceed as follows: (1) *Draw a figure representing the elements involved indicating inductance by* ⟋⟋⟋⟋⟋⟋, *resistance by* ⟋⟍⟋⟍⟋⟍, *and a condenser by* ⊣⊢; (2) *draw arrowheads to indicate the assumed directions of currents through the various branches;* (3) *apply the current law at points where conductors intersect and the e.m.f. law to complete circuits to find as many independent equations as are necessary to determine the unknown quantities involved; (4) solve these equations for the unknowns.* The following example will illustrate the procedure:

Example. An impedance coil which has a resistance of 14 ohms and an inductance of 0.05 henry and a branch having

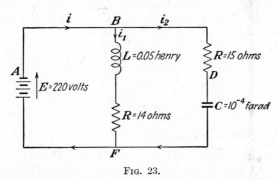

FIG. 23.

a non-inductive resistance of 15 ohms and a condenser of capacity 10^{-4} farad in series are connected in parallel across the terminals of a 220-volt source of e.m.f. Find expressions in terms of the time for the charge on the condenser, the current in the impedance coil, the current in the non-inductive resistance, and the total current.

Solution. Figure 23 represents the circuit with indicated elements and currents. The current law applied at point B gives

$$i = i_1 + i_2. \qquad (a)$$

The e.m.f. law applied to circuit $ABFA$ gives

$$0.05\frac{di_1}{dt} + 14i_1 = 220, \qquad (b)$$

and, applied to circuit $ABDFA$, it gives

$$15i_2 + 10^4\int i_2\, dt = 220. \qquad (c)$$

Finally we have from equation (13),

$$q = \int_c i_2 \, dt, \; i_2 = \frac{dq}{dt}. \tag{d}$$

Elimination of i_2 from (c) by using (d) gives

$$15\frac{dq}{dt} + 10^4 q = 220. \tag{e}$$

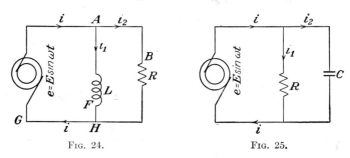

Fig. 24.   Fig. 25.

The solution of equation (e) is

$$q = c_1 e^{-\frac{10000}{15}t} + 0.022 = c_1 e^{-\frac{2000}{3}t} + 0.022.$$

When $t = 0$, $q = 0$, therefore

$$0 = c_1 + 0.022, \text{ or } c_1 = -0.022.$$

Hence

$$q = 0.022\left(1 - e^{-\frac{2000}{3}t}\right).$$

Therefore

$$i_2 = \frac{dq}{dt} = \frac{44}{3}e^{-\frac{2000}{3}t}.$$

The solution of (b) is

$$i_1 = C_2 e^{-\frac{14}{0.05}t} + \frac{220}{14}.$$

When $t = 0$, $i_1 = 0$.   Therefore

$$C_2 = \frac{-220}{14} = -15.71, \text{ and } i_1 = 15.71(1 - e^{-280t}).$$

Finally

$$\mathbf{i} = \mathbf{i_1} + \mathbf{i_2} = \mathbf{15.71}(\mathbf{1} - \mathbf{e}^{-280t}) + \frac{\mathbf{44}}{\mathbf{3}}\mathbf{e}^{-\frac{2000}{3}t}.$$

As the values of e^{-280t} and $e^{-\frac{2000}{3}t}$ are practically zero after a fraction of a second, it appears that the condenser very soon is practically charged and that the inductance in BF opposes the current for only a small fraction of a second. Hence we have practically $q = 0.022$ coulomb and $i = 15.71$ amperes in a very short time.

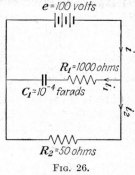

Fig. 26.

Problems

1. For the system represented in Fig. 24 obtain by the current law at point A

$$i = i_1 + i_2,$$

and from the e.m.f. law applied to circuits $AFHG$ and $ABHG$

$$L\frac{di_1}{dt} = E \sin \omega t, \quad Ri_2 = E \sin \omega t.$$

Solve these equations for i_1, i_2, and i in terms of t and determine a constant of integration by using the condition $i = 0$ when $t = 0$.

2. From Fig. 25 derive by Kirchhoff's laws

$$i = i_1 + i_2, \quad Ri_1 = E \sin \omega t, \quad \frac{1}{C}\int_c i_2 \, dt = \frac{q}{C} = E \sin \omega t.$$

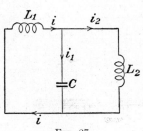

Fig. 27.

Find q, i_1, i_2, and i in terms of t.

3. For the system indicated in Fig. 26 derive three equations by applying Kirchhoff's laws. Assume that the charge on the condenser is zero when $t = 0$, deduce that $i_2 = 2$ amperes always, and that $i_1 = (\frac{1}{10})e^{-10t}$ and therefore rapidly approaches zero.

4. Replace the 100-volt e.m.f. in Fig. 26 by a sinusoidal e.m.f. represented by $100 \sin 400t$ and then find q, i_1, and i_2 at time t. Assume that the charge on the condenser is zero when $t = 0$.

5. If initially the charge on the condenser of Fig. 27 is q_0 and $i_1 = 0$, show that $q = q_0 \cos\sqrt{(L_1 + L_2)/(CL_1L_2)}\ t$.   *Hint: e = 0.*

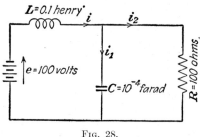

FIG. 28.

6. If, in the system represented by Fig. 28, there is initially no charge on the condenser and no current flowing, find i in terms of the time and describe its fluctuation.

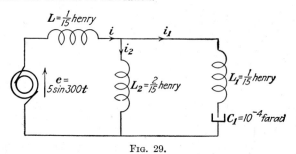

FIG. 29.

7. Find i in terms of the time t in the system represented by Fig. 29 if all initial currents and the initial charge on the condenser are zero.

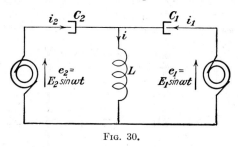

FIG. 30.

8. Find i in terms of the time t in the system represented in Fig. 30, if the initial currents and the initial charges on the condensers are zero and $\omega \neq 1/\sqrt{L(C_1 + C_2)}$.

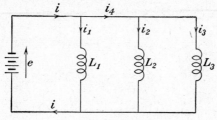

Fig. 31.

9. Show that the current i indicated in Fig. 31 is the same as it would be if the three inductances were replaced by a single inductance of magnitude $1/\left(\dfrac{1}{L_1} + \dfrac{1}{L_2} + \dfrac{1}{L_3}\right)$ in series with the e.m.f. Also show

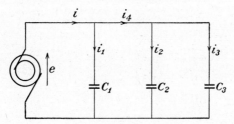

Fig. 32.

that, in the same sense, the three condensers in parallel in Fig. 32 are equivalent to a single one of capacity $C_1 + C_2 + C_3$.

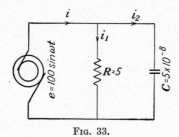

Fig. 33.

10. A hot-wire galvanometer having a resistance of 5 ohms is shunted with a condenser of capacity $C = 5 \times 10^{-8}$ farad as indicated in Fig. 33. If effective current is $(1/\sqrt{2})$ (*maximum current*), find the ratio of the effective current i_1 through the galvanometer to the total effective current i when (*a*) $\omega = 2 \times 10^4$; (*b*) $\omega = 2 \times 10^5$; (*c*) $\omega = 2 \times 10^6$; (*d*) $\omega = 2 \times 10^7$.

11. The following equations are important in the theory of the transformer:

$$(L_1D + R_1)i_1 + MDi_2 = E \sin \omega t,$$
$$MDi_1 + (L_2D + R_2)i_2 = 0,$$

where $D = d/dt$. Show that

$$(L_1L_2 - M^2)D^2i_1 + (L_1R_2 + L_2R_1)Di_1 + R_1R_2i_1 = R_2E \sin \omega t +$$

$$E\omega L_2 \cos \omega t, \quad i_2 = -\frac{1}{MR_2}[L_2E \sin \omega t + (M^2D - L_1L_2D - L_2R_1)i_1].$$

CHAPTER VIII

MISCELLANEOUS DIFFERENTIAL EQUATIONS OF ORDER HIGHER THAN THE FIRST

66. Reduction of order by substitution. In Chapter VI we found general methods for solving linear equations with constant coefficients. This was unusual, for we cannot solve most equations of order higher than the first in finite form. Certain types, however, are readily solvable. One method of attack is to *make such a substitution as to reduce the order and then try to solve the result.* For example, consider the equation

$$\frac{d^n y}{dx^n} = f(x). \tag{1}$$

To solve this, substitute p for $\frac{d^{n-1}y}{dx^{n-1}}$ and obtain

$$\frac{d^n y}{dx^n} = \frac{d}{dx}\left(\frac{d^{n-1}y}{dx^{n-1}}\right) = \frac{dp}{dx} = f(x). \tag{2}$$

Therefore

$$p = \int f(x)dx + c_1, \text{ or } \frac{d^{n-1}y}{dx^{n-1}} = \int f(x)dx + c_1. \tag{3}$$

Clearly we can treat equation (3) in a similar manner and obtain

$$\frac{d^{n-2}y}{dx^{n-2}} = \int\left[\int f(x)dx\right]dx + c_1 x + c_2, \tag{4}$$

and it appears that we may continue this process until we find y in terms of x by n successive integrations.

Various types of differential equations with appropriate substitutions will be considered in the following articles.

67. Dependent variable absent. If an equation contains derivatives of the dependent variable y but does not contain y directly, then the substitution

$$p = \frac{dy}{dx}, \frac{dp}{dx} = \frac{d^2y}{dx^2}, \ldots, \frac{d^{n-1}p}{dx^{n-1}} = \frac{d^ny}{dx^n} \tag{5}$$

will reduce the order of the equation by unity; if the result can be solved for p in terms of x,

$$p = \frac{dy}{dx} = f(x), \tag{6}$$

a single integration will give y in terms of x. In fact, if d^ky/dx^k is the derivative of lowest order in an equation which does not contain y directly, then the substitution

$$p = \frac{d^ky}{dx^k}, \frac{dp}{dx} = \frac{d^{k+1}y}{dx^{k+1}}, \ldots, \frac{d^{n-k}p}{dx^{n-k}} = \frac{d^ny}{dx^n} \tag{7}$$

will reduce the order by k; if the result can be solved for p in terms of x,

$$p = \frac{d^ky}{dx^k} = f_1(x), \tag{8}$$

y may be found in terms of x by k successive integrations, as indicated in §66.

Example. Solve

$$(1 + x^2)\frac{d^2y}{dx^2} + x\frac{dy}{dx} + ax = 0. \tag{a}$$

Solution. In equation (a) substitute

$$p = \frac{dy}{dx}, \frac{dp}{dx} = \frac{d^2y}{dx^2} \tag{b}$$

and obtain

$$(1 + x^2)\frac{dp}{dx} + px + ax = 0. \tag{c}$$

Separating the variables in equation (c) and integrating, we have

$$p + a = c_1(1 + x^2)^{-\frac{1}{2}}.$$

Replacing p by dy/dx and integrating, we obtain

$$\mathbf{y = -ax + c_1 \sinh^{-1} x + c_2.}$$

Exercises

Solve the following differential equations and determine the constants of integration where sufficient conditions are given:

1. $x^3 \dfrac{d^3y}{dx^3} = 1$

2. $x \dfrac{d^2y}{dx^2} + \dfrac{dy}{dx} = 16x^3$

3. $(x + 1)\dfrac{d^2y}{dx^2} - (x + 2)\dfrac{dy}{dx} = 0$

4. $\dfrac{d^2y}{dx^2} + \cos x \left(\dfrac{dy}{dx}\right)^2 = 0;\ y = 0,\ \dfrac{dy}{dx} = \dfrac{5}{8},$ when $x = \dfrac{\pi}{2}$

5. $x\dfrac{d^3y}{dx^3} - 2\dfrac{d^2y}{dx^2} = 12x^3;\ y = 0,\ \dfrac{dy}{dx} = 1,\ \dfrac{d^2y}{dx^2} = 0,$ when $x = 1$

6. $a\dfrac{d^3y}{dx^3} = \dfrac{d^2y}{dx^2};\ y = 1,\ \dfrac{dy}{dx} = 0,\ \dfrac{d^2y}{dx^2} = \dfrac{1}{a^2},$ when $x = 0$

7. $a\dfrac{d^3y}{dx^3} = \sqrt{1 + \left(\dfrac{d^2y}{dx^2}\right)^2};\ y = 0,\ \dfrac{dy}{dx} = -a,\ \dfrac{d^2y}{dx^2} = 0,$ when $x = 0$

8. $\left(x^2 + 2\dfrac{dy}{dx}\right)\dfrac{d^2y}{dx^2} + 2x\dfrac{dy}{dx} = 0;$ if $y = 1,\ \dfrac{dy}{dx} = 0$ when $x = 0$

68. Independent variable absent. If p is substituted for dy/dx, we have

$$\left.\begin{aligned} \frac{dy}{dx} &= p, \quad \frac{d^2y}{dx^2} = \frac{dp}{dy}\frac{dy}{dx} = \frac{p\,dp}{dy}, \\ \frac{d^3y}{dx^3} &= \frac{d}{dy}\left(p\frac{dp}{dy}\right)\frac{dy}{dx} = p^2\frac{d^2p}{dy^2} + p\left(\frac{dp}{dy}\right)^2, \text{ etc.} \end{aligned}\right\} \quad (9)$$

Therefore, if a differential equation does not contain x directly, the substitution (9) will give a new differential equation in p and y of order one less than that of the original equation. If this new equation can be solved for p in terms of y to get

$$p = \frac{dy}{dx} = f(y), \tag{10}$$

then x may be found in terms of y from

$$x = \int \frac{dy}{f(y)} + c. \tag{11}$$

Example. Solve

$$y\frac{d^2y}{dx^2} + \left(\frac{dy}{dx}\right)^2 = \frac{dy}{dx}. \tag{a}$$

Solution. Substitution of

$$p = \frac{dy}{dx}, \frac{p\,dp}{dy} = \frac{d^2y}{dx^2} \tag{b}$$

in (a) gives

$$yp\frac{dp}{dy} + p^2 = p, \text{ or } p\left(y\frac{dp}{dy} + p - 1\right) = 0. \tag{c}$$

From (c),

$$y\frac{dp}{dy} + p - 1 = 0, p = 0. \tag{d}$$

Hence,

$$\frac{dp}{p-1} + \frac{dy}{y} = 0. \tag{e}$$

The solution of (e) is

$$p = 1 + \frac{c_1}{y}. \tag{f}$$

Replacing p by dy/dx and separating the variables, we obtain

$$\frac{y\,dy}{y + c_1} = dx. \tag{g}$$

The solution of (g) is

$$\mathbf{x = y - c_1 \log (y + c_1) + c_2.}$$

From the second equation of (d) or by inspection, it appears that $y = c$ satisfies equation (a).

Exercises

Solve the following differential equations and determine constants of integration when initial conditions are given:

1. $y\dfrac{d^2y}{dx^2} + \left(\dfrac{dy}{dx}\right)^2 = 0$

2. $y^2\dfrac{d^2y}{dx^2} + \left(\dfrac{dy}{dx}\right)^3 = 0$

3. $\dfrac{d^2y}{dx^2} + y\dfrac{dy}{dx} = 0$; $y = -1, \dfrac{dy}{dx} = \dfrac{3}{2}$, when $x = 0$

4. $y\dfrac{d^2y}{dx^2} + 4y^2 - \dfrac{1}{2}\left(\dfrac{dy}{dx}\right)^2 = 0$; $y = 1, \dfrac{dy}{dx} = \sqrt{8}$, when $x = 0$

5. $y\dfrac{d^2y}{dx^2} + 2\left(\dfrac{dy}{dx}\right)^2 + a^2\dfrac{dy}{dx} = 0$; $y = 3a, \dfrac{dy}{dx} = -a^2$, when $x = -\dfrac{6}{a}$

6. $2(2a - y)\dfrac{d^2y}{dx^2} = 1 + \left(\dfrac{dy}{dx}\right)^2$; $y = 0, \dfrac{dy}{dx} = 0$, when $x = 0$

7. $2\dfrac{d^2y}{dx^2} = e^y$; $y = 0, \dfrac{dy}{dx} = 0$, when $x = 0$

69. Homogeneous linear equation.

The equation

$$x^n\frac{d^ny}{dx^n} + A_1x^{n-1}\frac{d^{n-1}y}{dx^{n-1}} + \cdots + A_{n-1}x\frac{dy}{dx} + A_ny = X, \quad (12)$$

where the A's are constant and X represents a function of x, is often referred to as the homogeneous linear equation. The substitution

$$z = \log x \qquad (13)$$

reduces this to the linear equation with constant coefficients. Using the notation

$$\frac{d^ky}{dz^k} = D^ky, \qquad (14)$$

we have

$$\frac{dy}{dx} = \frac{dy}{dz}\frac{dz}{dx} = \frac{1}{x}\frac{dy}{dz} = \frac{1}{x}Dy,$$

$$\frac{d^2y}{dx^2} = \frac{d(dy/dx)}{dz}\frac{dz}{dx} = \frac{1}{x^2}\frac{d^2y}{dz^2} - \frac{1}{x^2}\frac{dy}{dz} = \frac{1}{x^2}D(D - 1)y,$$

$$\frac{d^3y}{dx^3} = \frac{1}{x^3}D^2(D - 1)y - \frac{2}{x^3}D(D - 1)y = \qquad (15)$$

$$\frac{1}{x^3}D(D - 1)(D - 2)y,$$

$$\cdot \quad \cdot \quad \cdot \quad \cdot \quad \cdot \quad \cdot \quad \cdot$$

$$\frac{d^ny}{dx^n} = \frac{1}{x^n}D(D - 1) \cdots (D - n + 1)y.$$

Substitution of the values of $d^k y/dx^k$ from (15) in (12) evidently gives a linear equation with constant coefficients. Solving this equation by the methods of Chapter VI, and replacing z by $\log x$ in the result, we obtain the solution of (12).

Example. Solve $x^3\frac{d^3y}{dx^3} + 6x^2\frac{d^2y}{dx^2} + 8x\frac{dy}{dx} - 8y = x^2.$ $\quad (a)$

Solution. Using (13), (14), and (15), we have

$$\frac{x^3}{x^3}D(D - 1)(D - 2)y + 6\frac{x^2}{x^2}D(D - 1)y +$$

$$8\frac{x}{x}Dy - 8y = e^{2z}, \quad (b)$$

or

$$(D^3 + 3D^2 + 4D - 8)y = e^{2z}. \qquad (c)$$

The solution of equation (c) is

$$y = c_1 e^z + e^{-2z}(c_1 \sin 2z + c_2 \cos 2z) + \tfrac{1}{20}e^{2z}. \qquad (d)$$

Replacing z in (d) by $\log x$ from (13), we have

$$\mathbf{y = c_1 x + \frac{1}{x^2}[c_1 \sin (2 \log x) + c_2 \cos (2 \log x)] + \tfrac{1}{20}x^2.}$$

Exercises

1. $x^3\frac{d^3y}{dx^3} + 3x^2\frac{d^2y}{dx^2} - 6x\frac{dy}{dx} - 6y = 0$

2. $x^2\dfrac{d^2y}{dx^2} + x\dfrac{dy}{dx} - 9y = x^n \ (n \neq \pm 3)$

3. $(x - 1)^3\dfrac{d^3y}{dx^3} + 2(x - 1)^2\dfrac{d^2y}{dx^2} - 4(x - 1)\dfrac{dy}{dx} + 4y = 4\log (x - 1);$

let $z = \log (x - 1)$

4. $x\dfrac{d^3y}{dx^3} + 2\dfrac{d^2y}{dx^2} = 0$

70. Second-order linear equation. The general linear equation of the second order has the form

$$\frac{d^2y}{dx^2} + f_1(x)\frac{dy}{dx} + f_2(x)y = f_3(x). \tag{16}$$

To get an idea of how this may be solved, let us try the substitution

$$y = v(x) \cdot \varphi(x). \tag{17}$$

Substituting y from (17) in (16) and rearranging the terms, we find

$$\varphi\frac{d^2v}{dx^2} + \left(2\frac{d\varphi}{dx} + f_1\varphi\right)\frac{dv}{dx} + \left(\frac{d^2\varphi}{dx^2} + f_1\frac{d\varphi}{dx} + f_2\varphi\right)v = f_3. \tag{18}$$

If now $\varphi(x)$ is chosen so that the coefficient of v in (18) is zero, that is,

$$\frac{d^2\varphi}{dx^2} + f_1\frac{d\varphi}{dx} + f_2\varphi = 0, \tag{19}$$

equation (18) does not contain v. Hence the method of §67 may be applied to solve it. In other words, *if* $y = \varphi(x)$ *is any particular solution of the equation obtained by setting the left-hand member of* (16) *equal to zero, then the substitution* (17) *applied to* (16) *reduces it to an equation that can be solved by methods already considered.*

Example. Solve

$$(1 + x)\frac{d^2y}{dx^2} + (4x + 5)\frac{dy}{dx} + (4x + 6)y = e^{-2x}. \tag{a}$$

Solution. First we try to find a particular solution of

$$(1 + x)\frac{d^2y}{dx^2} + (4x + 5)\frac{dy}{dx} + (4x + 6)y = 0. \qquad (b)$$

Often particular solutions are obtained by trial. The usual plan is to substitute simple expressions such as $y = e^{ax}$, $y = x^a$, $y = x + a$, $y =$ polynomial in x in the equation to be solved, and then try to determine the arbitrary constants so that the equation will be satisfied. Substituting $y = e^{ax}$ in (b), we find, after slight simplification,

$$[(a^2 + 5a + 6) + x(a^2 + 4a + 4)]e^{ax} = 0. \qquad (c)$$

This will be true, if

$$a^2 + 5a + 6 = 0 \text{ and } a^2 + 4a + 4 = 0.$$

Both of these equations have a root -2. Hence $y = e^{-2x}$ is a particular solution. Therefore, in accordance with (17), we substitute

$$y = ve^{-2x} \qquad (d)$$

in (a) to obtain, after considerable simplification,

$$(1 + x)\frac{d^2v}{dx^2} + \frac{dv}{dx} = 1. \qquad (e)$$

The solution of this equation, found by the method of §67, is

$$v = x + c_1 \log (x + 1) + c_2. \qquad (f)$$

Substitution of this value of v in (d) gives the required solution of (a):

$$\mathbf{y = e^{-2x}[x + c_1 \log (x + 1) + c_2].}$$

Exercises

1. $(x^2 - 1)\dfrac{d^2y}{dx^2} + x\dfrac{dy}{dx} - y = 0$; let $y = vx$

2. $x^2\dfrac{d^2y}{dx^2} + x^2\dfrac{dy}{dx} + (x - 2)y = 0$. *Hint:* Try $v = x^n$

3. $(x^2 + 1)\dfrac{d^2y}{dx^2} - 2x\dfrac{dy}{dx} + 2y = 6(1 + x^2)^2$; let $y = vx$

4. $x\dfrac{d^2y}{dx^2} - (x + 3)\dfrac{dy}{dx} + 3y = 4x^4e^x$

5. $\sin^2 x\dfrac{d^2y}{dx^2} - \sin x \cos x\dfrac{dy}{dx} + y + \sin^3 x = 0$

71. Exact equation. An exact equation is one that can be obtained by equating to zero the derivative of a function of $x, y, dy/dx, d^2y/dx^2, \cdots$. That the equation

$$x^2D^3y + (x^2 + 2x) D^2y - 2Dy - 2y - 10 = 0 \quad (20)$$

is exact will now be proved.
Since

$$\frac{d}{dx} (x^2D^2y) = x^2D^3y + 2xD^2y,$$

or

$$x^2D^3y = \frac{d}{dx} (x^2D^2y) - 2xD^2y, \quad (21)$$

replace x^2D^3y in (20) by its value from (21) to get

$$\frac{d}{dx} (x^2D^2y) + x^2D^2y - 2Dy - 2y - 10 = 0. \quad (22)$$

Using the same process, replace in (22) x^2D^2y by $\frac{d}{dx} (x^2Dy)$ $- 2xDy$ to obtain

$$\frac{d}{dx} (x^2D^2y) + \frac{d}{dx} (x^2Dy) - (2x + 2)Dy -$$
$$2y - 10 = 0. \quad (23)$$

Finally replace in (23) $(2x + 2)Dy$ by $\frac{d}{dx}[(2x + 2)y] - 2y$ and multiply through by dx to obtain

$$d(x^2D^2y) + d(x^2Dy) - d[(2x + 2)y] +$$
$$2y - 2y - 10dx = 0. \quad (24)$$

Now integrate (24) term by term to obtain

$$x^2D^2y + x^2Dy - (2x + 2)y - 10x = c. \quad (25)$$

Equation (20) is exact because it is the derivative of the left member of (25) equated to zero.

Next consider any linear equation of the third order

$$P_0D^3y + P_1D^2y + P_2Dy + P_3y = \varphi(x), \quad (26)$$

Where the P_i represent functions of x. Treat this as we did equation (20) to get

$$\frac{d}{dx}[P_0D^2y] + \frac{d}{dx}[(P_1 - P_0')Dy] + \frac{d}{dx}[(P_2 - P_1' + P_0'')y] +$$

$$(P_3 - P_2' + P_1'' - P_0''')y = \varphi(x), \quad (27)$$

where the primes indicate derivatives with respect to x. The process used to integrate (24) will apply to integrate (27) or will fail, according as the coefficient of y in (27) is or is not zero. *Hence the condition that* (26) *be exact is*

$$P_3 - P_2' + P_1'' - P_0''' = 0. \quad (28)$$

Suppose that (26) is not exact but becomes exact when multiplied by $\mu(x)$. Then applying (28) to (26) multiplied through by $\mu(x)$, we get as *the condition that* $\mu(x)$ *be an integrating factor of* (26)

$$P_3\mu - (P_2\mu)' + (P_1\mu)'' - (P_0\mu)''' = 0. \quad (29)$$

Equation (29) *is called the* **adjoint** *of* (26). Any solution $\mu(x)$ of (29) is an integrating factor of (26).

The theory just considered for an equation of the third order is readily extended to a linear differential equation of the nth order.

Exercises

1. Write the condition, similar to (28), that

$$P_0D^2y + P_1Dy + P_2y = \varphi(x)$$

be exact, and write its adjoint.

2. Write the condition that

$$P_0D^ny + P_1D^{n-1}y + P_2D^{n-2}y + \cdots + P_{n-1}Dy + P_ny = \varphi(x)$$

be exact and write its adjoint.

3. Show that $x^2D^3y + (2x^2 + 2x)D^2y + (4x - 3x^2)Dy - 6xy = 10$ is exact by applying (28). From this equation derive

$$D^2y + 2Dy - 3y = (10/x) + c/x^2.$$

4. The condition that $P_0D^2y + P_1Dy + P_2y = \varphi(x)$ be exact is $P_2 - P_1' + P_0'' = 0$. Show that $x^3D^2y + 4x^2Dy + 2xy = 20x$ is exact, from it derive $xDy + y = 10 + cx^{-2}$, and integrate this result to obtain $x^2y = 10x^2 - c + c_1x$.

5. Write the adjoint of $x^2D^2y + 2xDy - 2y = 4x^2$. Show that the solution of the adjoint is $\mu = c_1x + c_2/x^2$. Using the condition for exactness show that both x and $1/x^2$ are integrating factors of the given equation. Derive two first-order differential equations by using the two integrating factors separately, and eliminate Dy from these to obtain the solution of the original equation.

6. Find the adjoint of $x^3D^3y + x^2D^2y - 14xDy - 10y = 30x^4$ and show that its general solution is $\mu = c_1x^{-6} + c_2x + c_3$. Using the corresponding integrating factors 1, x, and x^{-6}, derive three second-order differential equations from the given one. The general solution of the given equation could be found by eliminating D^2y and Dy from these three second-order equations.

72. Miscellaneous Exercises

1. $(x + 1)\dfrac{d^3y}{dx^3} = (x + 2)\dfrac{d^2y}{dx^2}$

2. $x\dfrac{d^2y}{dx^2} + \dfrac{dy}{dx} + x = 0$

3. $y\dfrac{d^2y}{dx^2} + \left(\dfrac{dy}{dx}\right)^2 = 1$

4. $x^3\dfrac{d^2y}{dx^2} + \left(\dfrac{dy}{dx}\right)^3 = 0$

5. $y\dfrac{d^2y}{dx^2} - \left(\dfrac{dy}{dx}\right)^2 = y^2 \log y$: let $y = e^z$.

6. $(x + 1)^2\dfrac{d^2y}{dx^2} + (x + 1)(x - 2)\dfrac{dy}{dx} + (2 - x)y = 0$. *Hint:* $y = x + 1$ is a particular solution.

7. $(1 - x)\left(\dfrac{d^2y}{dx^2} - \dfrac{dy}{dx}\right) + \dfrac{dy}{dx} = 0$

8. $x^2\dfrac{d^2y}{dx^2} - x\dfrac{dy}{dx} - 9y = 12x^3$

9. $x^2\dfrac{d^2y}{dx^2} + 2y = x\dfrac{dy}{dx} + x \log x$

10. Show that $(x^2 + x - 3)D^3y + (6x + 3)D^2y + 6Dy = 0$ is exact and find its first integral. Find the solution of the given differential equation.

11. Show that $(x^3 + x)D^3y + (7x^2 + 1)D^2y + 10xDy + 2y = 0$ is exact and find its first integral. Show that $1/x$ is an integrating factor of the first integral and use this information to derive another integral. Solve the original differential equation.

12. $x^2\dfrac{d^3y}{dx^3} + 2x\dfrac{d^2y}{dx^2} = x + \dfrac{1}{x^3}$

13. $\dfrac{d^2y}{dx^2} = \dfrac{1}{a\sqrt{y}}$

14. $x^2\dfrac{d^2y}{dx^2} + 4x\dfrac{dy}{dx} + 2y = x$

Hint: Solve left member equated to zero by §69, and then use variation of parameters.

15. $xy\dfrac{d^2y}{dx^2} + y\dfrac{dy}{dx} - x\left(\dfrac{dy}{dx}\right)^2 = 0$; let $x = e^\theta$, $y = ze^\theta$

16. $x^3\dfrac{d^2y}{dx^2} - 2x^2\dfrac{dy}{dx} - \left(\dfrac{dy}{dx}\right)^3 = 0$

17. $(x + 1)\dfrac{d^2y}{dx^2} - \dfrac{dy}{dx} = (x + 1)\sqrt{\dfrac{dy}{dx}}$

CHAPTER IX

APPLICATIONS

73. Radius of curvature. Some problems relating to the radius of curvature are rather interesting. As an illustration, consider the following:

Example. Find the equation of the curve whose radius of curvature is double the normal and oppositely directed.

Solution. Equating the expression for the radius of curvature and twice the expression for the normal, we obtain

$$\left[1 + \left(\frac{dy}{dx}\right)^2\right]^{\frac{3}{2}} \div \frac{d^2y}{dx^2} = \pm\, 2y\sqrt{1 + \left(\frac{dy}{dx}\right)^2}. \qquad (a)$$

Assuming that the radius of curvature R is positive and is directed from the curve toward the center of curvature, and that the normal N is directed from the curve toward the X-axis, we see that y and d^2y/dx^2 will have the same sign when R and N are directed oppositely. Hence the plus sign in (a) must be used. Substitution of p for dy/dx and $p\,dp/dy$ for d^2y/dx^2 in (a) gives

$$\frac{(1 + p^2)^{\frac{3}{2}}}{p\,dp/dy} = 2y(1 + p^2)^{\frac{1}{2}}. \qquad (b)$$

Separating the variables and integrating (b), we obtain

$$\log\,(1 + p^2) = \log\frac{y}{c}, \text{ or } \frac{dy}{dx} = \pm\sqrt{\frac{y}{c} - 1}. \qquad (c)$$

Integrating (c) and simplifying, we obtain

$$(x - c_1)^2 = 4cy - 4c^2. \qquad (d)$$

This represents a system of parabolas with their axes parallel to the Y-axis.

74. Cables. The catenary. Figure 1 represents a loaded cable. Let us assume that it is perfectly flexible, inextensible, homogeneous, and hanging from two points under the action of gravity on a load distributed along it in a continuous way. Let H be the tension in the cable at its lowest

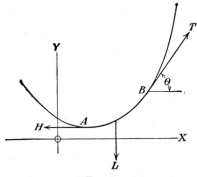

FIG. 1.

point A, T the tension at any point B of the cable, and L the resultant force of gravity exerted between A and B. Since the forces T, H, and L are in equilibrium,

$$T \cos \theta = H, \tag{1}$$
$$T \sin \theta = L, \tag{2}$$

where θ is the angle between the direction of force T and the horizontal. Evidently the tension H at A is horizontal and the tension T at B is directed along the tangent to the curve of the cable; hence, if we take the X-axis horizontal and the Y-axis vertical, we have $\tan \theta = dy/dx$. Then division of (2) by (1), member by member, gives

$$\tan \theta = \frac{dy}{dx} = \frac{L}{H}. \tag{3}$$

Differentiating both sides, we obtain

$$\frac{d^2y}{dx^2} = \frac{1}{H}\frac{dL}{dx} \tag{4}$$

as the differential equation of the curve of the cable.

The curve in which a uniform chain hangs under its own weight is called the *catenary*. In this case, we have

$$L = ws, \tag{5}$$

where s represents the arc length AB in Fig. 1 and w represents weight per unit length of the chain. Substitution of L from (5) in (4) gives

$$\frac{d^2y}{dx^2} = \frac{w}{H}\frac{ds}{dx} = \frac{w}{H}\sqrt{1 + \left(\frac{dy}{dx}\right)^2}. \tag{6}$$

Substituting in (6) p for dy/dx and dp/dx for d^2y/dx^2, we obtain

$$\frac{dp}{dx} = \frac{w}{H}\sqrt{1 + p^2}. \tag{7}$$

Integrating (7), we obtain

$$\sinh^{-1} p = \frac{w}{H}x + c_1, \text{ or } p = \sinh\left(\frac{w}{H}x + c_1\right). \tag{8}$$

Replacing p by dy/dx in (8) and integrating, we find

$$y = \frac{H}{w}\cosh\left(\frac{w}{H}x + c_1\right) + c_2. \tag{9}$$

If the origin is taken at the lowest point, $y = 0$ and $dy/dx = 0$, when $x = 0$. Substitution of these values in (8) and (9) gives

$$c_1 = 0, \; c_2 = -\frac{H}{w}.$$

Substituting these values in (9), we obtain

$$y = \frac{H}{w}\left(\cosh\frac{w}{H}x - 1\right). \tag{10}$$

75. Equation of elastic curve. Deflection. Consider a horizontal beam acted upon by vertical loads, and assume that the forces due to these loads lie in a vertical plane containing the centroidal axis (central longitudinal axis) of the beam and that they are such that no part of the beam is stressed beyond its elastic limit. These stresses cause the beam to bend, as indicated in Fig. 2, and the curve of its

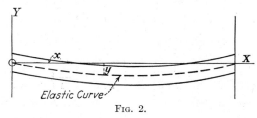

Fig. 2.

centroidal axis is called the *elastic curve* of the stressed beam. An important problem in the consideration of strength of materials is to find the equation of this elastic curve. If a beam is loaded as just indicated, is made of uniform material satisfying Hooke's law, and fulfills certain other conditions relating to shape and to properties of materials, it can be shown that its elastic curve satisfies approximately the differential equation

$$EI\frac{d^2y}{dx^2} = M, \tag{11}$$

where the X-axis is horizontal along the beam, the Y-axis is vertical, E is the modulus of elasticity of the material of the beam, I is the moment of inertia of the cross section of the beam perpendicular to its axis with respect to a horizontal line in the cross section passing through its centroid, and M is the *bending moment* at the cross section. Since the material of the beam is uniform, E *is constant* and, if the beam has a uniform cross section, I *is constant*.

The bending moment M *at any cross section may be found by taking the algebraic sum of the moments of the external forces on the part of the beam on one side of the cross section about a horizontal line in this cross section.* In finding the bending moment *consider upward forces as giving positive moments and downward forces negative moments* about the horizontal line in

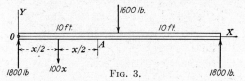

Fig. 3.

the cross section. Consider for example the beam of Fig. 3 loaded as indicated in addition to a uniform running load of 100 lb./ft. To find the bending moment at point A, consider the forces to the left of A: 1800 lb. at O with arm x ft.,

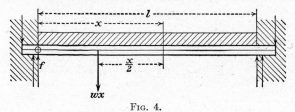

Fig. 4.

and $100x$ lb. of running load downward and thought of as concentrated at the center of OA. Taking moments about A, we have

$$M = 1800x - 100x \cdot \frac{x}{2} = 1800x - 50x^2.$$

Example. A uniform beam (see Fig. 4) l ft. long is fixed at both ends and carries a uniformly distributed load of w lb. per foot of length. Find the equation of its elastic curve and its maximum deflection.

Solution. Since the beam is fixed at the ends, the elastic curve is horizontal at both ends. Hence, taking the origin at the left end, we have

$$y = 0, \frac{dy}{dx} = 0, \text{ when } x = 0,$$
$$\left.\begin{array}{l}\\ \\\end{array}\right\} \quad (a)$$
$$y = 0, \frac{dy}{dx} = 0, \text{ when } x = l.$$

The forces acting on the beam to the left of the cross section x ft. from the left end are: (1) wx lb. due to the running load; (2) a supporting force at the left end; (3) a couple exerted by the masonry. Writing f for the supporting force and A for the moment of the couple, we have for the bending moment x ft. from the left end (see Fig. 4),

$$M = A + fx - wx \cdot \frac{x}{2}. \qquad (b)$$

Substitution of M from (b) in (11) gives

$$EI\frac{d^2y}{dx^2} = A + fx - w\frac{x^2}{2}. \qquad (c)$$

Integrating (c), we obtain

$$EI\frac{dy}{dx} = Ax + f\frac{x^2}{2} - \frac{wx^3}{6} + c_1, \qquad (d)$$

$$EIy = \frac{Ax^2}{2} + f\frac{x^3}{6} - w\frac{x^4}{24} + c_1x + c_2. \qquad (e)$$

Substituting the conditions (a) in (d) and (e), we get

$$c_1 = 0, \ c_2 = 0, \ Al + f\frac{l^2}{2} - w\frac{l^3}{6} = 0, \ \frac{Al^2}{2} + \frac{fl^3}{6} - \frac{wl^4}{24} = 0,$$

or

$$c_1 = 0, \ c_2 = 0, \ f = \frac{wl}{2}, \ A = \frac{-wl^2}{12}. \qquad (f)$$

Substituting in (e) the values of c_1, c_2, f, and A from (f) and simplifying, we have the equation of the elastic curve,

$$y = \frac{-w}{24EI}(x^2l^2 - 2lx^3 + x^4). \qquad (g)$$

Here $-y$ represents the deflection of the beam x ft. from
the left end, and, since the maximum deflection $(d_{\max})$ will
evidently be at the center of the beam where $x = l/2$, we
have from (g),

$$d_{\max} = (-y)_{x=l/2} = \frac{w}{24EI}\left(\frac{l^4}{4} - 2\frac{l^4}{8} + \frac{l^4}{16}\right) = \frac{wl^4}{384EI}.$$

76. Components of acceleration in polar coordinates.
Polar coordinates lend themselves to the solution of certain

problems more readily than rectangular coordinates. Accordingly
we shall find an expression for the
component a_ρ of the acceleration
in the direction of the radius vector and an expression for the
component a_θ at right angles to
the radius vector. The component a_ρ is the projection of the

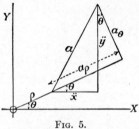

Fig. 5.

acceleration vector a on the radius vector, or, what amounts
to the same thing, the sum of the projections of the components of a on the radius vector. Hence denoting derivatives with respect to t by dots thus,

$$\frac{dx}{dt} = \dot{x}, \frac{d^2x}{dt^2} = \ddot{x}, \frac{d\rho}{dt} = \dot{\rho}, \frac{d\theta}{dt} = \dot{\theta}, \text{ etc.,} \tag{12}$$

we see from Fig. 5 that

$$a_\rho = \ddot{x}\cos\theta + \ddot{y}\sin\theta \tag{13}$$

and

$$a_\theta = -\ddot{x}\sin\theta + \ddot{y}\cos\theta. \tag{14}$$

Repeated differentiation of each of the equations

$$x = \rho\cos\theta, \ y = \rho\sin\theta \tag{15}$$

with respect to the time gives

$$\dot{x} = \dot{\rho}\cos\theta - \rho\dot{\theta}\sin\theta, \ \dot{y} = \dot{\rho}\sin\theta + \rho\dot{\theta}\cos\theta, \tag{16}$$

$$\ddot{x} = \ddot{\rho}\cos\theta - 2\dot{\rho}\dot{\theta}\sin\theta - \rho\dot{\theta}^2\cos\theta - \rho\ddot{\theta}\sin\theta, \tag{17}$$

$$\ddot{y} = \ddot{\rho}\sin\theta + 2\dot{\rho}\dot{\theta}\cos\theta - \rho\dot{\theta}^2\sin\theta + \rho\ddot{\theta}\cos\theta. \tag{18}$$

Substituting the values of $\ddot{x}$ and $\ddot{y}$ from (17) and (18) in (13) and (14) and simplifying, we have

$$a_\rho = \ddot{\rho} - \rho\dot{\theta}^2, \tag{19}$$

$$a_\theta = \rho\ddot{\theta} + 2\dot{\rho}\dot{\theta} = \frac{1}{\rho}\frac{d}{dt}(\rho^2\dot{\theta}). \tag{20}$$

Similarly, it is easy to show that the component v_ρ of the velocity along the radius vector and the component v_θ at right angles to it are

$$v_\rho = \dot{\rho}, \; v_\theta = \rho\dot{\theta}. \tag{21}$$

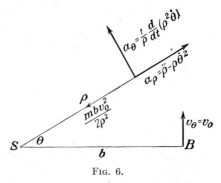

Fig. 6.

Example. A particle of mass m, whose variable distance from a fixed point S is ρ, moves under the action of a single force whose direction is always toward S and whose magnitude is $mbv_0^2/2\rho^2$. If it moves through fixed point B distant b units from S with velocity v_0 at right angles to SB, find the equation of its path.

Note: This problem is a simplified version of the problem of expressing in mathematical form the motion of a comet about the sun.

Solution. Taking the line SB (see Fig. 6) as initial line and S as pole, we have the initial conditions

$$\rho_0 = b, \; \dot{\rho}_0 = 0, \; b\dot{\theta}_0 = v_0, \text{ when } \theta = 0. \tag{a}$$

Equation (7) in §58 applied in the direction SP of the radius vector gives

$$ma_\rho = m(\ddot{\rho} - \rho\dot{\theta}^2) = \frac{-mbv_0^2}{2\rho^2}, \qquad (b)$$

and applied in the direction perpendicular to the radius vector gives

$$ma_\theta = \frac{m}{\rho}\frac{d}{dt}(\rho^2\dot{\theta}) = 0. \qquad (c)$$

From (c) and (a)

$$\rho^2\dot{\theta} = c_1 = bv_0. \qquad (d)$$

Replacing in (b) $\ddot{\rho}$ by $\dot{\rho}\, d\dot{\rho}/d\rho$ and, from (d), $\dot{\theta}$ by bv_0/ρ^2, and simplifying, we obtain

$$m\left(\frac{\dot{\rho}\, d\dot{\rho}}{d\rho} - \frac{b^2v_0^2}{\rho^3}\right) = \frac{-mbv_0^2}{2\rho^2}. \qquad (e)$$

Integrating (e), we find

$$\frac{\dot{\rho}^2}{2} = \frac{bv_0^2}{2\rho} - \frac{b^2v_0^2}{2\rho^2} + c_2. \qquad (f)$$

Since from (a) $\dot{\rho} = 0$ when $\rho = b$, it appears that $c_2 = 0$. Hence from (f)

$$\dot{\rho} = \frac{d\rho}{dt} = \frac{v_0}{\rho}\sqrt{b\rho - b^2}. \qquad (g)$$

Replacing $\dot{\theta}$ in (d) by $d\theta/dt$, solving for dt, substituting the result for dt in (g), and separating the variables, we have

$$\frac{b\, d\rho}{\rho\sqrt{b\rho - b^2}} = d\theta. \qquad (h)$$

Integrating (h), we obtain

$$2\cos^{-1}\sqrt{\frac{b}{\rho}} = \theta + c_3. \qquad (i)$$

Substituting zero for θ and b for ρ, we find $c_3 = 0$. Solving (i) for ρ, we get

$$\rho = \frac{2b}{1 + \cos\theta}.$$

This is the equation of a parabola referred to the focus as pole and the axis as initial line.

77. Problems

1. Determine the curves for which the radius of curvature
(a) Is equal to the normal and in the same direction.
(b) Is equal to the normal and in the opposite direction.
(c) Varies as the cube of the normal.
(d) Projected on the X-axis equals the abscissa.
(e) Projected on the X-axis is the negative of the abscissa.
(f) Projected on the X-axis is twice the abscissa.
(g) Is proportional to the slope of the tangent.

2. Find the equation of all plane curves which have a constant radius of curvature.

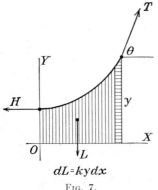

$dL = kydx$

Fig. 7.

3. Integrate completely the differential equation of the curve in which the projection of the radius of curvature upon the X-axis is constant.

4. Find the differential equation of the curve whose radius of curvature is equal to n times the normal. Integrate this equation: (a) when $n = 1$; (b) when $n = 3$. Is this differential equation integrable in terms of ordinary functions for all integral values of n?

5. Find the curve in which the cable (see §74) of a suspension bridge hangs, if it carries a uniform horizontal load of w lb./ft. run; neglect the weight of the cable. *Hint:* In equation (3) $L = wx$.

6. Set up the differential equation for the cable of problem 5, if its weight per running foot is assumed constant and taken into account.

7. Slender uniform rods all of the same diameter are suspended from a string to which each is knotted; two consecutive rods just touch, and they hang so that their ends are in a straight horizontal line. Neglecting the diameter of the rods, find the equation of the curve of the string. *Hint:* dL in equation (4) $= ky \, dx$ (see Fig. 7).

8. What would be the equation of the curve of the string in problem 7, if all the rods were of the same length instead of having their ends in a straight line?

9. Set up the differential equation for the string of problem 7, if its weight per running foot is assumed constant and taken into account.

10. Find the shape of the arch of a stone-arch bridge, if the resultant stress at any point of the arch due to the weight of the masonry above is directed along the tangent to the arch at the point. Assume that the masonry is uniform in density and that the surface of the road is horizontal (see Fig. 8).

11. If an arch carries, in addition to the load of problem 10, a layer of material spread uniformly over the horizontal road surface, the density of the layer being k times that of the masonry, what should be the shape of the arch?

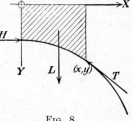

12. An arch is the bottom of a canal carrying a water load. Find the equation of its curve assuming that the stress at each point due to the weight of the water is directed along the tangent. Neglect the weight of the arch and note that the water pressure at each

Fig. 8.

point is directed along the normal to the arch through the point.

13. Solve problem 12 if the water is covered with a uniform layer of fluid having specific gravity k.

14. A beam (see Fig. 9) l ft. long is simply supported at its ends and carries a uniform load of w lb./ft. run. Show that the bending moment

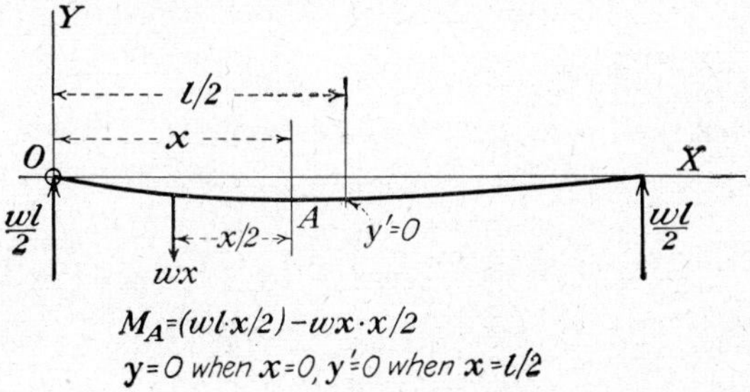

$$M_A = (wl \cdot x/2) - wx \cdot x/2$$
$$y = 0 \text{ when } x = 0, \ y' = 0 \text{ when } x = l/2$$

Fig. 9.

at a point x ft. from the left end is $\dfrac{wl}{2}x - \dfrac{wx^2}{2}$, and use this in equation (11) of §75 to find the deflection y at this point. Also find the maximum deflection.

15. A beam l ft. long and simply supported carries a load of P lb. at its center. Find its deflection x ft. from the left end and its maximum deflection.

16. A beam l ft. long is fixed at both ends and carries a load P at its center. Find its maximum deflection.

17. A beam fixed at one end and unsupported at the other (see Fig. 10) is called a *cantilever beam*. Find the deflection x ft. from the free end of a cantilever beam l ft. long, if it carries a load: (*a*) P lb. at the free end; (*b*) w lb./ft. run; (*c*) w lb./ft. run and P lb. at its free end.

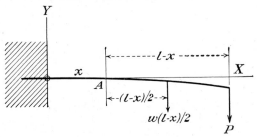

$$M_A = -P(l-x) - w(l-x)^2/2$$
$$y = 0, \, y' = 0 \text{ when } x = 0$$

Fig. 10.

18. A beam l ft. long, fixed at one end and simply supported at the other (see Fig. 11), carries a uniform load of w lb./ft. run. Find the distance from the fixed end to point where maximum deflection occurs.

19. A cantilever beam l ft. long carries a load of material whose width and density are uniform and whose depth is directly proportional to its distance from the free end. Find the maximum deflection of the beam.

20. The differential equation for the potential v at any point between two concentric spheres a distance r from the common center due to an electric charge on the inner sphere is

$$\frac{d^2v}{dr^2} + \frac{2}{r}\frac{dv}{dr} = 0.$$

Solve for v in terms of r given $v = v_1$, when $r = r_1$, and $v = v_0$, when $r = r_0$.

21. A particle of weight w lb. moves in a straight line from a distance a toward a center of force which attracts with a magnitude in pounds equal numerically to $w/(2gr^2)$, r denoting the distance of the particle from the center. If the particle had an initial velocity toward the point of $1/\sqrt{a}$, how long will it take to traverse half the distance to the center?

22. A particle moves in a straight line from rest at a distance a toward a center of attraction, the attraction varying inversely as the cube of the distance. How long will it take the particle to reach the center?

23. The areal velocity of a moving particle P with respect to a fixed point A is the rate at which the line AP generates area. If A is the pole and (ρ,θ), θ in radians, the polar coordinates of P, then the areal velocity is $\frac{1}{2}\rho^2\, d\theta/dt$. Prove that a particle moving in a plane through a point A

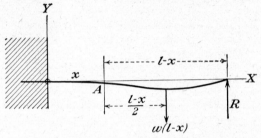

$$y=0,\ y'=0 \text{ when } x=0,\ y=0 \text{ when } x=l$$

Fig. 11.

under the action of a force always directed toward point A has a constant areal velocity with respect to A. *Hint:* First show that a_θ in equation (20) of §76 is zero.

24. A particle of mass m at point P situated b units from a fixed point A is moving at right angles to AP with velocity v_0. Taking AP as initial line and A as pole, find the equation of the path of the particle if it is acted on by a force always directed toward point A and equal in magnitude to $nmb^2v_0^2/\rho^3$, where n is real and positive. Discuss the curve: (a) when $n = 1$ and (b) when $n = 2$.

25. If, in problem 24, the magnitude of the force is $nmbv_0^2/\rho^2$, find the equation of the path of the particle.

26. Prove that a particle moving with constant speed under the action of a force always directed toward a fixed point A in its plane of motion must move in a circle with A as center or move in a straight line.

27. A particle moves in a plane under the action of a force always directed toward a fixed point A in its plane; its velocity is $k\rho^n$, where ρ is its distance from A and the values of k^*, and n are constants. Find

* The dimensions of k are $L^{1-n}t^{-1}$.

the equation of its path. Tell the nature of its path when (a) $n = 0$, (b) $n = -2$, (c) $n = 1$, (d) $n = -3$.

28. Prove that the force in problem 27 is $k^2 nm\rho^{2n-1}$, where m is the mass of the particle.

29. An airplane flying 105 mi./hr. at a height of 2000 ft. lets fall a dummy weighing 180 lb. If v_x and v_y are, respectively, the horizontal component and the vertical component of the velocity, in feet per second, and if air resistance in pounds has a vertical component equal numerically to $0.006v_y^2$ and a horizontal component of $0.006v_x^2$, find (a) the equations of the path; (b) the time of descent; (c) the horizontal distance traveled while coming down.

30. Find the equation of the elastic curve of a beam fixed at both ends and carrying a concentrated load P, distant a ft. from the left end and b ft. from the right end.

31. A uniform cable $2l$ units long has its ends attached at two points, A and B, and hangs under its own weight. A horizontal line through B meets a vertical line through A at point C. If $AC = 2b$ units and $BC = 2c$ units, find the coordinates of the mid-point of line AB referred to a set of rectangular axes with origin at the lowest point of the cable and X-axis horizontal.

CHAPTER X

DIFFERENTIAL EQUATIONS IN MORE THAN TWO VARIABLES. EXISTENCE THEOREMS

78. Foreword. Most of our work so far has related to the solution of differential equations in two unknowns. In §28 some simple simultaneous equations were considered, and in §55 a method of solving simultaneous linear equations was studied. A more general problem may be stated as follows: given a system of n independent differential equations in $n + 1$ unknowns, to find the most general set of n independent non-differential relations among the variables that satisfy the given differential equations. This chapter will consider methods of solving some elementary cases of general differential equations, suggest general methods of attack, and state existence theorems relating to solutions.

79. Differential equations of the first order and first degree. Consider the equations

$$P_1 \, dx + Q_1 \, dy + R_1 \, dz = 0,$$
$$P_2 \, dx + Q_2 \, dy + R_2 \, dz = 0, \tag{1}$$

in which the P's, Q's, and R's represent functions of x, y, and z. *The main line of attack consists in (a) combining the given equations and others derived from them so as to obtain an equation in two unknowns, or an equation which is the result of equating to zero the total derivative of some expression involving the variables; (b) integrating the equations thus obtained and combining the results with the given differential equations to obtain other relations among the variables.*

Dividing equations (1) by dz and solving the results for dx/dz and dy/dz, we obtain

$$\frac{dx}{dz} = \frac{P}{R}, \frac{dy}{dz} = \frac{Q}{R}, \text{ or } \frac{dx}{P} = \frac{dy}{Q} = \frac{dz}{R}, \qquad (2)$$

where

$$P:Q:R = \begin{vmatrix} Q_1 R_1 \\ Q_2 R_2 \end{vmatrix} : \begin{vmatrix} R_1 P_1 \\ R_2 P_2 \end{vmatrix} : \begin{vmatrix} P_1 Q_1 \\ P_2 Q_2 \end{vmatrix}. \qquad (3)$$

From (2) we may write

$$\frac{l \, dx}{lP} = \frac{m \, dy}{mQ} = \frac{n \, dz}{nR}, \qquad (4)$$

and then apply the theorem that in a continued proportion the sum of the antecedents is to the sum of the consequents as any antecedent is to its consequent, to obtain

$$\frac{dx}{P} = \frac{dy}{Q} = \frac{dz}{R} = \frac{l \, dx + m \, dy + n \, dz}{lP + mQ + nR}, \qquad (5)$$

where l, m, and n are functions of x, y, and z at our disposal. (a) *It may happen that, by suitably choosing* l, m, *and* n, *we can find an equation in only two variables or an equation readily integrable.* In either case an integration gives us a required relation. (b) *Again we may be able to choose* l, m, *and* n *so that* lP + mQ + nR = 0 *and so that* l dx + m dy + n dz = du, *where* u *is some function of* x, y, *and* z. In this case, since $lP + mQ + nR = 0$ and the last fraction in (5) is finite, it follows that $l \, dx + m \, dy + n \, dz = 0$; that is, $du = 0$, and $u = c$ (*constant*) is a required relation. The following examples will illustrate these methods of procedure.

Example 1. Solve

$$\frac{dx}{xz} = \frac{dy}{yz} = \frac{2dz}{x + y}. \qquad (a)$$

Solution. Integration of the equation of the first two ratios gives

$$\mathbf{y = c_1 x.} \qquad (b)$$

Writing equations (5) for (*a*) with $l = 1$, $m = 1$, $n = 0$, we obtain

$$\frac{2\,dz}{x + y} = \frac{dx + dy}{z(x + y)}. \tag{c}$$

Multiplying through by $z(x + y)$, and integrating, we have

$$\mathbf{x + y = z^2 + c_2}. \tag{d}$$

Equations (*b*) and (*d*) constitute the solution.

It is instructive to note that, after finding equation (*b*), we could have substituted $c_1 x$ from (*b*) for y in $dx/xz = 2dz/(x + y)$ and have integrated the resulting equation in x and z to obtain

$$x + c_1 x = z^2 + c, \text{ or } x + y = z^2 + c.$$

Also we could have noticed that

$$P + Q - 2zR = xz + yz - xz - yz = 0,$$

and therefore that

$$l\,dx + m\,dy + n\,dz = dx + dy - 2z\,dz = 0.$$

Hence

$$x + y - z^2 = c.$$

Example 2.   Solve

$$\frac{dx}{y - xz} = \frac{dy}{x + yz} = \frac{dz}{x^2 + y^2}. \tag{a}$$

Solution.   Here, taking *l*, *m*, and *n* equal to y, x, and -1, respectively, we have

$$lP + mQ + nR = y^2 - xyz + x^2 + xyz - x^2 - y^2 = 0. \tag{b}$$

Therefore,

$$l\,dx + m\,dy + n\,dz = y\,dx + x\,dy - dz = 0. \tag{c}$$

Integration of (*c*) gives

$$\mathbf{xy - z = c_1}. \tag{d}$$

Clearing of fractions the equation of the first two ratios in (*a*) and replacing z in the result by its value $xy - c_1$ from (*d*), we obtain the exact differential equation,

$$[x + y(xy - c_1)]dx + [-y + x(xy - c_1)]dy = 0. \tag{e}$$

Integrating (e) by the method of §24, we find
$$x^2 + (xy - c_1)^2 - y^2 = c_2, \text{ or } \mathbf{x^2 + z^2 - y^2 = c_2}. \quad (f)$$
Equations (d) and (f) constitute the solution.

Again it is instructive to observe that by taking $l = x$, $m = -y$, and $n = z$, we obtain
$$lP + mQ + nR = xy - x^2z - xy - y^2z + x^2z + y^2z = 0.$$
Therefore
$$l \, dx + m \, dy + n \, dz = x \, dx - y \, dy + z \, dz = 0.$$
Hence,
$$x^2 - y^2 + z^2 = c$$

Exercises

1. $\dfrac{dx}{y} = \dfrac{dy}{x} = \dfrac{dz}{z}$

2. $\dfrac{dx}{ayz} = \dfrac{dy}{bzx} = \dfrac{dz}{cxy}$

3. $y \, dx + (y - 2x)dy + yz \, dz = 0,$
   $(x - y)dy - yz \, dz = 0$

4. $\quad z \, dx + (y - x)dy + z \, dz = 0,$
   $\quad 2z \, dx - (2x + y)dy - z \, dz = 0$

5. $\quad (x + z)dx + (x - z)dy - (x + z)dz = 0,$
   $x(x + z)dx + y(z - x)dy - z(x + z)dz = 0$

6. $\dfrac{dx}{dz} = \dfrac{z - 2x}{z}, \dfrac{dy}{dz} - x - y + 1 = \dfrac{2x}{z}$

7. $\dfrac{dx}{y} = \dfrac{dy}{x} = \dfrac{2 \, dz}{1 - z^2}$

8. $\dfrac{dx}{x^2 - y^2 - z^2} = \dfrac{dy}{2xy} = \dfrac{dz}{2xz}$

9. $\dfrac{dx}{x(y - z)} = \dfrac{dy}{y(z - x)} = \dfrac{dz}{z(x - y)}$

10. $\dfrac{dx}{x^2 - y^2 - yz} = \dfrac{dy}{x^2 - y^2 - xz} = \dfrac{dz}{z(x - y)}$

11. $\dfrac{dx}{ny - mz} = \dfrac{dy}{lz - nx} = \dfrac{dz}{mx - ly}$

12. $\dfrac{dx}{-1 - xz^2} = \dfrac{dy}{1 + yz^2} = \dfrac{dz}{z^2(y - x)}$

13. $\dfrac{dx}{y} = \dfrac{dy}{x} = \dfrac{dz}{w} = \dfrac{dw}{z}$

14. $\dfrac{dx}{w - z} = \dfrac{dy}{w - z} = \dfrac{dz}{x + y - 2w} = \dfrac{dw}{2z - x - y}$

15. The solution of equations of the type indicated in equation (1) can often be obtained by eliminating one variable (say z), solving the result for y in terms of x, and then using this solution to find a relation involving z. For example, to solve

$$dx = \frac{dy}{-5x + 12y - 5z} = \frac{dz}{x + 2y + z}, \tag{a}$$

write

$$\frac{dy}{dx} = -5x + 12y - 5z, \quad \frac{dz}{dx} = x + 2y + z. \tag{b}$$

Differentiate the first of (b) to obtain

$$\frac{d^2y}{dx^2} = -5 + 12\frac{dy}{dx} - 5\frac{dz}{dx}, \tag{c}$$

in (c) replace dz/dx by its value from the second equation of (b), in the result replace z by its value from the first of (b), and simplify to obtain

$$\frac{d^2y}{dx^2} - 13\frac{dy}{dx} + 22y = -5. \tag{d}$$

Solve (d) for y and substitute the result in the second of (b) to obtain, after slight simplification,

$$y = c_1 e^{2x} + c_2 e^{11x} - \tfrac{5}{22}, \tag{e}$$
$$5z = 10c_1 e^{2x} + c_2 e^{11x} - 5x - \tfrac{30}{11}.$$

Equations (e) constitute the solution of (a).

Using the method just illustrated, solve the following systems of equations:

(I) $\quad dx = \dfrac{dy}{10x - y + 5z} = \dfrac{dz}{2x - y + z}$

(II) $\quad dx = \dfrac{dy}{2e^x + y + z} = \dfrac{dz}{4e^x + y + z}$

(III) $\quad dx = \dfrac{dy}{6x^2 - y + 3z} = \dfrac{dz}{2x^2 + y + z}$

(IV) $\quad dx = \dfrac{dy}{a \sin 2x + y + 2z} = \dfrac{dz}{-a \cos 2x - y - z}$

80. Replacement of differential equations by a system of the first order and the first degree.

The solution of each set of equations in §79 consisted of as many non-differential relations as there were differential equations in the set. Also, the number of constants of integration was the same as the number of given equations. In general it can be proved that *the general solution of a set of* n *first-order and first-degree differential equations in* n + 1 *variables consists of* n *non-differential relations among these variables and* n *constants of integration.*

In this article, we shall indicate how the problem of finding the solution of n differential equations in $n + 1$ unknowns can be reduced to that of solving a set of differential equations of the first order and the first degree.

To get an idea of the method of procedure consider the special system

$$\begin{aligned}\frac{d^3y}{dt^3} &= f\left[x,y,t,\frac{dx}{dt},\frac{dy}{dt},\frac{d^2y}{dt^2}\right], \\ \frac{d^2x}{dt^2} &= F\left[x,y,t,\frac{dx}{dt},\frac{dy}{dt},\frac{d^2y}{dt^2}\right].\end{aligned} \right\} \tag{6}$$

Making the substitution $dx/dt = x_1$, $dy/dt = y_1$, $dy_1/dt = y_2$ in (6), we obtain the system of the first order and the first degree:

$$\begin{aligned}\frac{dx}{dt} &= x_1, \frac{dy}{dt} = y_1, \frac{dy_1}{dt} = y_2, \\ \frac{dy_2}{dt} &= f(x,y,t,x_1,y_1,y_2), \frac{dx_1}{dt} = F(x,y,t,x_1,y_1,y_2).\end{aligned} \right\} \tag{7}$$

Solving equations (7) and eliminating x_1, y_1, and y_2 from the resulting five equations, we obtain two equations in x, y, t, and the five constants of integration. These two equations constitute the general solution of equation (6).

Now consider a set of n independent differential equations in n dependent variables and an independent variable. Substitute for each derivative of a dependent variable up to the next to the highest-ordered one a new variable, and solve the resulting system of the first order for the derivatives contained in it. This set of equations, together with the substitution set, constitutes a system of differential equations of the first order and first degree which is equivalent to the original system.

Exercises

1. Replace, in accordance with the principle stated above, each of the following sets of differential equations by an equivalent set of the first order and the first degree:

(a) $x^2\dfrac{d^3y}{dx^3} - xy\dfrac{d^2y}{dx^2} + y^2\dfrac{dy}{dx} + y = x$

(b) $\dfrac{d^3y}{dt^3} = 3y + \dfrac{d^2y}{dt^2} + \dfrac{d^2x}{dt^2},\ \dfrac{d^3y}{dt^3} = 3x - \dfrac{d^2y}{dt^2}$

(c) $\dfrac{d^ny}{dt^n} = x + \dfrac{d^kx}{dt^k},\ \dfrac{d^kx}{dt^k} = y + \dfrac{d^{n-1}y}{dt^{n-1}}$

2. Solve $\dfrac{ds}{x+y} = \dfrac{dy}{s} = \dfrac{dx}{1}$, and write from your result the solution of $\dfrac{d^2y}{dx^2} - y = x$

3. Solve by the method of this article and check:
$$\frac{d^2y}{dx^2} + \frac{dy}{dx} - 2y = -4x$$

4. Write a system of equations of the first order and first degree, equivalent to a linear nth-order differential equation in two variables. How many constants of integration would appear in the solution of this system?

81. Total differential equations.
The number of variables in a system of differential equations may exceed the number of equations by more than one. We shall consider here only the special case of one first-order, first-degree differential equation in three variables. Under certain conditions such an equation is integrable; for example, the solution of

$$2x\,dx + 2y\,dy + 2z\,dz = 0$$

evidently is

$$x^2 + y^2 + z^2 = c,$$

and, in general, the solution of

$$\frac{\partial f(x,y,z)}{\partial x}dx + \frac{\partial f(x,y,z)}{\partial y}dy + \frac{\partial f(x,y,z)}{\partial z}dz = 0 \qquad (8)$$

is

$$f(x,y,z) = c. \qquad (9)$$

The object of this article is to arrive at the condition of integrability of an equation

$$P\, dx + Q\, dy + R\, dz = 0, \tag{10}$$

where P, Q, and R are continuous functions of x, y, and z, possessing continuous first partial derivatives with respect to x, y, and z.

If (10) is integrable, there exists a function $\mu(x,y,z)$ such that the expression

$$\mu P\, dx + \mu Q\, dy + \mu R\, dz \tag{11}$$

is exactly the derivative of some function, say $f(x,y,z)$. Hence, comparing the left-hand member of (8) with (11), we have

$$\frac{\partial f}{\partial x} = \mu P, \quad \frac{\partial f}{\partial y} = \mu Q, \quad \frac{\partial f}{\partial z} = \mu R. \tag{12}$$

Now $\dfrac{\partial^2 f}{\partial x\, \partial y} = \dfrac{\partial^2 f}{\partial y\, \partial x}$ provided all first- and second-order partial derivatives of $f(x,y,z)$ are continuous functions of x, y, and z. Under these conditions we have, from (12),

$$\mu\frac{\partial P}{\partial y} + P\frac{\partial \mu}{\partial y} = \mu\frac{\partial Q}{\partial x} + Q\frac{\partial \mu}{\partial x}. \tag{13}$$

Similarly

$$\mu\frac{\partial Q}{\partial z} + Q\frac{\partial \mu}{\partial z} = \mu\frac{\partial R}{\partial y} + R\frac{\partial \mu}{\partial y} \tag{14}$$

$$\mu\frac{\partial R}{\partial x} + R\frac{\partial \mu}{\partial x} = \mu\frac{\partial P}{\partial z} + P\frac{\partial \mu}{\partial z}. \tag{15}$$

Multiplying equation (13) by R, (14) by P, and (15) by Q, adding the results, and rearranging, we have

$$P\left(\frac{\partial Q}{\partial z} - \frac{\partial R}{\partial y}\right) + Q\left(\frac{\partial R}{\partial x} - \frac{\partial P}{\partial z}\right) + R\left(\frac{\partial P}{\partial y} - \frac{\partial Q}{\partial x}\right) = 0. \tag{16}$$

This equation states a necessary condition that (10) be integrable; we shall prove that it is also a sufficient one.

Since the equation $P\, dx + Q\, dy = 0$ is always integrable if z is considered constant, there will be no loss in generality in assuming that $P\,dx + Q\,dy$ is an exact differential with respect to x and y. The solution of

$$P\,dx + Q\,dy = 0, \qquad (17)$$

considering z as constant, may now, in accordance with §24, be written in the form

$$f(x,y,z) - \varphi(z) = \int^x P\,dx + \int^y \left(Q - \frac{\partial}{\partial y}\int^x P\,dx\right)dy$$
$$- \varphi(z) = 0, \quad (18)$$

where φ represents an arbitrary function of z. Since $P\,dx + Q\,dy$ has been assumed to be an exact differential, we may write

$$\frac{\partial P}{\partial y} = \frac{\partial Q}{\partial x}, \; P = \frac{\partial f}{\partial x}, \; Q = \frac{\partial f}{\partial y}. \qquad (19)$$

Taking account of (19), we may write $P\,dx + Q\,dy + R\,dz = 0$ in the form

$$\frac{\partial f}{\partial x}dx + \frac{\partial f}{\partial y}dy + \frac{\partial f}{\partial z}dz + \left(R - \frac{\partial f}{\partial z}\right)dz = 0, \qquad (20)$$

or

$$df + \left(R - \frac{\partial f}{\partial z}\right)dz = 0. \qquad (21)$$

Equation (21) can be integrated, if there exists a relation independent of x and y between $R - \dfrac{\partial f}{\partial z}$ and f; that is, if f and $R - \dfrac{\partial f}{\partial z}$ considered as functions of x and y (z constant) are dependent. Since the condition* that two functions of x and y, f_1 and f_2, be dependent is

$$\frac{\partial f_1}{\partial x}\frac{\partial f_2}{\partial y} - \frac{\partial f_1}{\partial y}\frac{\partial f_2}{\partial x} = 0, \qquad (22)$$

the condition that $f_1 = f$ and $f_2 = R - \dfrac{\partial f}{\partial z}$ be dependent is

* See Sokolnikoff, I. S., "Advanced Calculus," p. 422.

$$\frac{\partial f}{\partial x}\left(\frac{\partial R}{\partial y} - \frac{\partial^2 f}{\partial z\,\partial y}\right) - \frac{\partial f}{\partial y}\left(\frac{\partial R}{\partial x} - \frac{\partial^2 f}{\partial z\,\partial x}\right) = 0. \qquad (23)$$

From (19),

$$\frac{\partial f}{\partial x} = P, \frac{\partial f}{\partial y} = Q, \frac{\partial^2 f}{\partial z\,\partial y} = \frac{\partial}{\partial z}\left(\frac{\partial f}{\partial y}\right) = \frac{\partial Q}{\partial z}, \frac{\partial^2 f}{\partial z\,\partial x} = \frac{\partial}{\partial z}\left(\frac{\partial f}{\partial x}\right) = \frac{\partial P}{\partial z}.$$

Substituting these results in (23), we have

$$P\left(\frac{\partial R}{\partial y} - \frac{\partial Q}{\partial z}\right) - Q\left(\frac{\partial R}{\partial x} - \frac{\partial P}{\partial z}\right) = 0. \qquad (24)$$

Since, from (19), $\dfrac{\partial P}{\partial y} - \dfrac{\partial Q}{\partial x} = 0$, it appears that (24) is the same as (16) with the signs changed. Hence, if (16) holds, (21) can be expressed in terms of the two variables f and z and solved. Since (21) and (10) are the same equation, this solution with f replaced by its value in terms of x and y will be the integral of (10).

The proof just given suggests the following rule.

RULE. *To integrate a total differential equation*

$$P\,dx + Q\,dy + R\,dz = 0 \qquad (10)$$

which satisfies the condition (16), *first integrate the equation*

$$P\,dx + Q\,dy = 0$$

treating z as constant, to obtain

$$f(x,y,z) + \varphi(z) = 0, \qquad (18)$$

$\varphi(z)$ *being an arbitrary function. Then differentiate this equation and determine the function φ by comparing the result of the differentiation with* (10).

If (10) is not exact, we may assume any second relation

$$\varphi(x,y,z) = 0 \qquad (25)$$

and solve it simultaneously with (10) to get a particular solution.

Example 1. Solve

$$yz^2\,dx - xz^2\,dy - (2xyz + x^2)dz = 0. \qquad (a)$$

Solution.   Substitution from (*a*) in (16) shows that (*a*) is integrable.   The solution of

$$yz^2 \, dx - xz^2 \, dy = 0, \tag{b}$$

got by considering *z* as constant, is

$$\frac{y}{x} + \varphi(z) = 0. \tag{c}$$

Differentiating (*c*) and multiplying the result by $-x^2z^2$, we obtain

$$yz^2 \, dx - xz^2 \, dy - z^2x^2\frac{d\varphi}{dz}dz = 0. \tag{d}$$

Comparing (*d*) with (*a*), we find

$$z^2\frac{d\varphi}{dz} = 2z\frac{y}{x} + 1. \tag{e}$$

Replacing y/x in the right-hand member of (*e*) by its value $-\varphi(z)$ from (*c*), we obtain

$$z^2\frac{d\varphi}{dz} = -2z\varphi + 1. \tag{f}$$

The solution of this equation by §26 is

$$\varphi = \frac{1}{z} + \frac{c}{z^2}. \tag{g}$$

Substituting φ from (*g*) in (*c*) we find

$$\frac{y}{x} + \frac{1}{z} + \frac{c}{z^2} = 0, \text{ or } z^2y = x(c_1 - z).$$

Example 2.   Prove that

$$dx + dy + y \, dz = 0 \tag{a}$$

is not integrable and then solve it simultaneously with

$$x - y + z = d. \tag{b}$$

Solution.   The equation (16) is not satisfied by (*a*). The derivative of (*b*) is

$$dx - dy + dz = 0. \tag{c}$$

Solving (a) and (c) simultaneously for dx/dz and dy/dz, we find

$$\frac{dx}{y+1} = \frac{dy}{y-1} = \frac{dz}{-2}. \tag{d}$$

The solution of (d) is

$$x = y + 2\log(y-1) + c_1, \ \mathbf{y} = \mathbf{1} + \mathbf{ce}^{-z/2}. \tag{e}$$

Equation (b) and either of the equations (e), considered simultaneously, constitute a solution.

Exercises

Apply the condition of integrability and find the integrals of the following differential equations:

1. $x\,dy - y\,dx + 2x^2z\,dz = 0$

2. $(y - z)dx + dy - dz = 0$

3. $(a - z)(y\,dx + x\,dy) + xy\,dz = 0$

4. $2x\,dx + 2y\,dy + (x^2 + y^2 + e^{-z})dz = 0$

5. $2zxy^2\,dx + (2x^2yz + 1)dy + x^2y^2\,dz = 0$

6. $y^2z\,dx + 2xyz\,dy + (z^2 - xy^2)dz = 0$

7. $z\,dx + (x + a)^2\,dy - (x + a)dz = 0$

8. $dz = (3x^2 + y^2)dx + (2xy + 3y^2)dy$

9. $dz = \dfrac{2x - z}{x + y}dx + \dfrac{2y - z}{x + y}dy$

10. $(ay - bz)dx + (cz - ax)dy + (bx - cy)dz = 0$

11. $yz\,dx - (xz + x^2)dy - (xy + x^2)dz = 0$

12. Find the condition that $dz = M\,dx + N\,dy$ be integrable: (a) if M and N represent functions of x, y, and z; (b) if M and N are functions of x and y only.

13. Solve simultaneously

$$z\,dx + x\,dy + y\,dz = 0$$
$$ax + 2by - (a + 2b)z = c$$

14. Remembering that a homogeneous function $f(x,y,z)$ of the nth degree satisfies the equation

$$x\frac{\partial f}{\partial x} + y\frac{\partial f}{\partial y} + z\frac{\partial f}{\partial z} = nf, \tag{a}$$

and that the conditions for exactness of

$$P(x,y,z)\,dx + Q(x,y,z)\,dy + R(x,y,z)\,dz = 0 \tag{b}$$

are

$$\frac{\partial P}{\partial y} = \frac{\partial Q}{\partial x}, \frac{\partial Q}{\partial z} = \frac{\partial R}{\partial y}, \frac{\partial R}{\partial x} = \frac{\partial P}{\partial z} \tag{c}$$

show that $xP + yQ + zR = c$ is a solution of (b) provided that $P, Q,$ and R are homogeneous of the nth degree, $n \neq -1$, and that (b) is exact.

82. Geometrical interpretation.

Consider an integrable differential equation

$$P(x,y,z)dx + Q(x,y,z)dy + R(x,y,z)dz = 0, \qquad (26)$$

its solution

$$f(x,y,z) = c, \qquad (27)$$

and the related equations

$$\frac{dx}{P} = \frac{dy}{Q} = \frac{dz}{R}. \qquad (28)$$

The solution of (28) consists of two relations each representing a surface. If s represents arc length along the curve of intersection of these surfaces the direction cosines of the tangent line are given by dx/ds, dy/ds, dz/ds, and we have

$$\frac{dx}{ds} : \frac{dy}{ds} : \frac{dz}{ds} = dx : dy : dz = P : Q : R. \qquad (29)$$

In other words, *the direction cosines of the tangent line at a point* N *of a curve representing a solution of* (28) *are defined by the ratios* P : Q : R *evaluated at point* N.

Since (27) is the solution of (26), any point (x,y,z) on a surface of the family represented by (27) and values for dx, dy, dz proportional to the direction cosines of any line tangent to this surface at (x,y,z) will satisfy (26). Now analytic geometry teaches that, when $aa' + bb' + cc' = 0$, the two lines having direction cosines proportional to a, b, c and a', b', c', respectively, are perpendicular to each other. Hence (26) is the condition that the directions defined by the respective ratios

$$P : Q : R, \text{ and } dx : dy : dz$$

are orthogonal ones. Remembering that $P : Q : R$ defines the direction of a solution of (28), and $dx : dy : dz$ defines a direction of a tangent line to surface (27), we conclude that the curves defined by (28) cut orthogonally the surfaces represented by the solution of (26).

When a non-integrable total differential equation is solved simultaneously with an equation representing a surface, the solution represents a system of curves in the surface satisfying the differential equation.

Exercises

1. Find the equation of the surfaces orthogonal to the curves represented by

$$\frac{dx}{2x + y} = \frac{dy}{x + z} = \frac{dz}{y}$$

2. Treating r as a parameter, find the equations of a system of curves orthogonal to

(a) $x^2 + y^2 + (z - c)^2 = r^2$

(b) $\dfrac{x^2}{a^2} + \dfrac{y^2}{b^2} + \dfrac{z^2}{c^2} = r$

3. Given a singly infinite family of surfaces defined by $f(x, y, z) = c$, does there always exist a system consisting of an infinite number of curves orthogonal to these surfaces?

4. Find the equation of the surfaces orthogonal to the system of curves defined by the simultaneous equations:

$$z\,dx + x\,dz = 0$$
$$yz\,dx + z^2\,dy + y(x + z)dz = 0$$

5. Find the equation of the surfaces orthogonal to the curves defined by $x^2 + y^2 + z^2 = a^2$, $z = b$.

6. What relation must exist between P and Q if there is an infinite number of surfaces orthogonal to the curves defined by the simultaneous equations $dz = P\,dx + Q\,dy$, $dz = -Q\,dx + P\,dy$, where P is a function of y and Q is a function of x.

83. Existence theorems. The theorems stated below will give an idea of the conditions under which solutions of differential equations exist and of the nature of the solutions; also they will help in understanding the next chapter. As the proofs are rather complicated they are omitted.

Theorem I. *For a differential equation*

$$\frac{dy}{dx} = f(x,y) \tag{30}$$

there exists a unique continuous function y = φ(x) *defined for all values of* x *in a certain region including* x_0, *satisfying the given differential equation, and taking on the value* y_0 *when* x = x_0, *provided that* f(x,y) *is a continuous single-valued function of* x *and* y *in the region* $|\,x - x_0\,| \leqq a$, $|\,y - y_0\,| \leqq$ b, *and that for all values of* x *satisfying* $|\,x - x_0\,| \leqq a$ *and all values* y_1 *and* y_2, $y_1 \neq y_2$, *lying in the region* $|\,y - y_0\,| \leqq$ b, *there exists a number* K *such that* $|\,f(x,y_1) - f(x,y_2)\,| < K(y_1 - y_2)$.

The inequality involving K, called the *Lipschitz condition*, could be replaced by the stronger, and therefore less satisfactory condition that $\partial f/\partial y$ be single-valued and continuous in the region $|\,x - x_0\,| \leqq a$, $|\,y - y_0\,| \leqq$ b.

From the geometric standpoint this theorem indicates that one and only one curve having an equation satisfying the given differential equation passes through each point in the plane at which the specified conditions are fulfilled. It might appear that at points where a regular solution and a singular solution meet there would be two solutions. At such points however one or more of the conditions specified in theorem I would not be satisfied.

Theorem II. *For a system of differential equations*

$$\frac{dy_i}{dx} = f_i(x, y_1, y_2, \ldots, y_n), \ i = 1, 2, \ldots, n \tag{31}$$

there exists a unique set of continuous solutions $y_1(x)$, $y_2(x)$, $\ldots$, $y_n(x)$ *of the given equations which take on the values* $y_1^0, y_2^0, \ldots, y_n^0$ *when* x = x_0 *provided that the functions* f_i *are continuous and single-valued in the regions defined by*

$$|\,x - x_0\,| \leqq a, |\,y_1 - y_1^0\,| \leqq b_1, \ldots, |\,y_n - y_n^0\,| \leqq b_n, \tag{32}$$

where the values of a *and the* b's *are all different from zero, and
that there exist numbers* $K_1, K_2, \ldots, K_n$ *such that*

$$| f_i(x, Y_1, Y_2, \ldots, Y_n) - f_i(x, y_1, y_2, \ldots, y_n) | <$$
$$K_1 | Y_1 - y_1 | + K_2 | Y_2 - y_2 | +$$
$$\cdots + K_n | Y_n - y_n |, \; i = 1, 2, \ldots, n$$

provided

$$| x - x_0 | \leqq a, | Y_i - y_i^0 | \leqq b_i, | y_i - y_i^0 | \leqq b_i, i = 1, 2, \ldots, n,$$

and at least one of the differences $Y_i - y_i$ *is not zero.*

The inequality involving the K's is also often referred to as the *Lipschitz condition.* It could be replaced by the stronger, and therefore less satisfactory, conditions that $f, \dfrac{\partial f}{\partial y_1}, \dfrac{\partial f}{\partial y_2},$

$\ldots, \dfrac{\partial f}{\partial y_n}$ be continuous and single-valued in the region defined by (32).

Observe that theorem II used in connection with the method of §80 may be applied to a set of differential equations of higher order than the first.

Observe also that theorems I and II state sufficient conditions for the existence of solutions but not necessary conditions. There may be a solution when theorem I or theorem II is not satisfied. For example $dy/dx = 2 - y/x$ is satisfied by $y = x$ for which $y = 0$ when $x = 0$, but the conditions of theorem I are not satisfied for this special case when $x_0 = 0$.

To discuss the existence of a solution of any system of n equations in $n + 1$ unknowns, we would first find in accordance with §80 a related set having the form (31) and then apply theorem II. Thus the equation

$$\frac{d^3 y}{dx^3} = f\left(x, y, \frac{dy}{dx}, \frac{d^2 y}{dx^2} \right) \tag{33}$$

is related to the set of equations

$$\frac{dy}{dx} = y_1, \; \frac{dy_1}{dx} = y_2, \; \frac{dy_2}{dx} = f(x, y, y_1, y_2). \tag{34}$$

Applying theorem II to the set (34), we conclude that there exists a unique solution $y = \psi(x)$ of (33) which satisfies the initial conditions

$$y = y_0, \frac{dy}{dx} = y_{10}, \frac{d^2y}{dx^2} = y_{20}, \text{ when } x = x_0,$$

provided that $f(x, y, y_1, y_2)$ satisfies the conditions of theorem II. Here y_0, y_{10}, and y_{20} may be thought of as three constants of integration.

In dealing with a system of m consistent and independent equations in $n + 1$ variables, it is possible to replace $n - m$ variables by arbitrary functions of the remaining $m + 1$ unknowns and then apply theorem II to the result. A single total differential equation in three variables is a case in point. As in the case of total differential equations, a number of equations connecting the variables may often be found by solving exact equations or integrable equations derived from the given set.

Exercises

1. Does theorem II show that the graph of the solution of

$$\frac{dy}{dx} = 2, \frac{dz}{dx} = x + y + z$$

consists of a unique curve through every point of space? Solve the equations and find the solution for which $y = 5$, $z = -10$, when $x = 0$.

2. Is a unique solution of $x \, dy/dx - y = 0$ satisfying the conditions $y = 2$ when $x = 0$ to be expected? Why?

3. Show that the solution of $x^2\frac{d^2y}{dx^2} - 2x\frac{dy}{dx} + 2y = 2x^3$ could be obtained from the solution of $\frac{dy}{dx} = z$, $\frac{dz}{dx} = \frac{2xz - 2y}{x^2} + 2x$. In accordance with theorem II would you expect a unique solution of the pair of equations for which $y = 0$, $z = 1$ when $x = 0$?

Show that the general solution of the pair of equations is $y = c_1x^2 + c_2x + x^3$, $z = 2c_1x + c_2 + 3x^2$ and that an infinite number of solutions $y = c_1x^2 + x + x^3$, $z = 2c_1x + 1 + 3x^2$ satisfy the conditions $y = 0$, $z = 1$ when $x = 0$.

Is there a unique solution of the pair of differential equations for which $y = 4$, $z = 7$ when $x = 1$?

4. Use theorem II and §80 to find the values of a at which irregularities are to be expected in the solution of $x(x - 1)\dfrac{d^2y}{dx^2} + (4x - 2)\dfrac{dy}{dx} + 2y = 0$ subject to the condition $y = 0$, $dy/dx = 1$, when $x = a$. Does the general solution $y = (c_1/x) + c_2/(x - 1)$ bear out your answer?

5. Irregularities in the solution of $x(x - 1)\dfrac{d^2y}{dx^2} - 2x\dfrac{dy}{dx} + 2y = 0$ are to be expected when $x = 0$ or $x = 1$ is involved in the initial conditions. Show that the general solution $y = c(x^2 - 1 - 2x \log x) + c_2 x$ bears out this expectation.

6. The general solution of $y = x\dfrac{dy}{dx} + 1 \Big/ \left(\dfrac{dy}{dx}\right)$ is $y = cx + 1/c$ and the singular solution is $y^2 = 4x$. Investigate the solution in the light of theorem I at point (x_0, y_0) of $y^2 = 4x$ where $y_0 > 0$ and only positive values of $\sqrt{y^2 - 4x}$ are considered.

Hint: First consider the point $(1, 2)$. Show that $f(x, y) = dy/dx = (y + \sqrt{y^2 - 4x})/2x$ is imaginary in a part of every region $|x - 1| \leq a$, $|y - 2| \leq b$ if $a > 0$ and $b > 0$. Next show that $\partial f/\partial y$ does not exist at $(1, 2)$. Finally show that the Lipschitz condition

$$\left| \frac{2}{2} - \frac{y - \sqrt{y^2 - 4}}{2} \right| < K(y - 2)$$

cannot be satisfied by any value K as y approaches 2 through numbers greater than 2. Generalize for any point $(x_0, 2\sqrt{x_0})$.

CHAPTER XI

SOLUTION BY SERIES AND BY METHODS INVOLVING SUCCESSIVE APPROXIMATIONS

84. Introduction. The preceding chapters have been concerned mainly with solving special types of differential equations. This chapter is concerned with general methods. The two methods to be considered, integration in series and methods using successive approximations, may be applied to solve differential equations that satisfy the conditions stated in §83. The method called *integration in series* is comparatively short and generally gives the complete solution. There are many methods of numerical integration; they generally involve much computation and give only a particular solution.

85. Integration in series. When an equation cannot be solved by any of the methods already discussed we may try to find a convergent series which will express the value of the dependent variable in terms of the independent variable to any required degree of accuracy. We shall solve a problem to illustrate a method of finding such a series.

Example. Solve for y in terms of a series arranged in powers of $x - 1$

$$\frac{d^2y}{dx^2} - (x - 1)\, y = 0. \tag{a}$$

Solution. Assume that a solution has the form

$$y = c_0 + c_1(x - 1) + c_2(x - 1)^2 + \cdots +$$
$$c_n(x - 1)^n + \cdots, \tag{b}$$

where the c's are constants to be determined, and substitute this value of y in the given equation to get

$$2c_2 + 3 \cdot 2c_3(x - 1) + 4 \cdot 3c_4(x - 1)^2 + \cdots +$$
$$n(n - 1)c_n(x - 1)^{n-2} + \cdots \quad (c)$$
$$- c_0(x - 1) - c_1(x - 1)^2 - \cdots -$$
$$c_{n-3}(x - 1)^{n-2} - \cdots = 0.$$

Since equation (b) is a solution, equation (c) is an identity, and the coefficients of like terms must be equal. Hence

$$2c_2 = 0, 3 \cdot 2c_3 - c_0 = 0, 4 \cdot 3c_4 - c_1 = 0, \cdots,$$
$$n(n - 1)c_n - c_{n-3} = 0. \quad (d)$$

Solving equations (d) for $c_2, c_3, \cdots$ in terms of c_0 and c_1, we find

$$c_2 = 0, c_3 = \frac{c_0}{2 \cdot 3}, c_4 = \frac{c_1}{3 \cdot 4}, c_5 = 0, c_6 = \frac{c_3}{5 \cdot 6} = \frac{c_0}{2 \cdot 3 \cdot 5 \cdot 6},$$

$$c_7 = \frac{c_4}{6 \cdot 7} = \frac{c_1}{3 \cdot 4 \cdot 6 \cdot 7}, \cdots, c_n = \frac{c_{n-3}}{n(n - 1)}. \quad (e)$$

We may write the first six terms of the solution by substituting the values from (e) in (b) to obtain

$$y = c_0 + c_1(x - 1) + \frac{c_0}{2 \cdot 3}(x - 1)^3 + \frac{c_1}{3 \cdot 4}(x - 1)^4 +$$

$$\frac{c_0}{2 \cdot 3 \cdot 5 \cdot 6}(x - 1)^6 + \frac{c_1}{3 \cdot 4 \cdot 5 \cdot 7}(x - 1)^7 + \cdots. \quad (f)$$

This is the important part of the solution for values of x near 1.

However, a law for writing any number of terms is desired. By rearranging the values for the c's found in (e) and by using the last equation of (e) successively for different values of n, we find

$c_0 = c_0$	$c_1 = c_1$	$c_2 = 0$
$c_3 = \dfrac{c_0}{2 \cdot 3}$	$c_4 = \dfrac{c_1}{3 \cdot 4}$	$c_5 = 0$
$c_6 = \dfrac{1 \cdot 4c_0}{6!}$	$c_7 = \dfrac{2 \cdot 5c_1}{7!}$	$c_8 = 0 \qquad (g)$

$$c_{3n} = \frac{1 \cdot 4 \cdot 7 \cdots (3n - 2)c_0}{(3n)!}; \; c_{3n+1} = \frac{2 \cdot 5 \cdot 8 \cdots (3n - 1)c_1}{(3n + 1)!};$$

$$c_{3n+2} = 0.$$

Substituting the values of the c's from (g) in (b),

$$y = c_0 \left[1 + \frac{(x - 1)^3}{3!} + \frac{1 \cdot 4}{6!}(x - 1)^6 + \cdots + \right.$$

$$\left. \frac{1 \cdot 4 \cdot 7 \cdots (3n - 2)}{(3n)!}(x - 1)^{3n} + \cdots \right] +$$

$$c_1 \left[(x - 1) + \frac{2(x - 1)^4}{4!} + \frac{2 \cdot 5}{7!}(x - 1)^7 + \cdots + \right. \qquad (h)$$

$$\left. \frac{2 \cdot 5 \cdot 8 \cdots (3n - 1)}{(3n + 1)!}(x - 1)^{3n+1} + \cdots \right].*$$

Equation (h) is the required solution. Since it is absolutely convergent for all values of x and since it contains two independent arbitrary constants, it is the general solution of the given differential equation.

In accordance with §80, the solution of (a) is equivalent to that of

$$\frac{dy}{dx} = y_1, \frac{dy_1}{dx} = (x - 1)y.$$

Since the functions y_1 and $(x - 1)y$ satisfy the conditions of theorem II in §83, however large the numbers a, b_1, and b_2 may be, it appears that equation (a) has a unique solution satisfying the conditions $y = y_0$, $dy/dx = y_{10}$ when $x = x_0$. The solution (h) is in accord with this conclusion. In this particular case $y = y_0 = c_0$, $\frac{dy}{dx} = y_{10} = c_1$ when $x = 1$.

In using the method just illustrated, we may employ a series involving powers of x or of $x - a$, where a is any real number, and *the solutions thus found will be valid for the interval of absolute convergence of the series obtained.*

* It is permissible to regroup the terms of series (e) since it is absolutely convergent for all values of x.

The solution (e) could have been obtained more directly. Writing for (b) only the coefficient of $(x - 1)^{n-2}$ and equating it to zero, we get, after slight simplification,

$$c_n = \frac{c_{n-3}}{n(n - 1)}. \qquad (i)$$

From (i) the coefficients in series (f) are obtained by taking c_0 and c_1 arbitrary, $c_2 = 0$, and substituting for n in (i), 3, 4, 5, $\ldots$, successively. However it will often be instructive to write the first few terms in addition to a general term. Thus, in the solution just outlined, inspection of the initial terms in (b) indicates why c_0 and c_1 may be chosen arbitrarily and why it is necessary to take c_2 equal to zero.

Exercises

In the following exercises find y expressed in a power series in $x - a$ where a is given in parentheses after each equation.

1. $\dfrac{dy}{dx} - y = 0,\ (a = 0)$

2. $\dfrac{dy}{dx} - 2xy = 0,\ (a = 0)$

3. $\dfrac{d^2y}{dx^2} = xy,\ (a = 0)$

4. $(x^2 + 1)\dfrac{d^2y}{dx^2} + 6x\dfrac{dy}{dx} + 6y = 0,\ (a = 0)$

5. $(x^2 - 2x)\dfrac{d^2y}{dx^2} + 6(x - 1)\dfrac{dy}{dx} + 6y = 0,\ (a = 1)$

6. $(x^2 + 2x)\dfrac{d^2y}{dx^2} + 8(x + 1)\dfrac{dy}{dx} + 12y = 0,\ (a = -1)$

7. $(x^2 - 1)\dfrac{d^2y}{dx^2} - 6y = 0,\ (a = 0)$

8. Find a particular solution of $x^2\dfrac{dy}{dx} - y = 5x^{-3} + 3x^{-2}$ by series. If $y = c_3x^{-3} + c_4x^{-4} + \cdots + c_nx^{-n} + \cdots$ show that $c_3 = -1$, that $c_4 = -1$, $c_5 = \frac{1}{5}$, etc.

9. $\dfrac{dy}{dx} = 1 + y^2,\ (a = 0)$. Take the constant of integration zero and thus obtain the expansion of $\tan x$.

10. The theory of the oscillator in quantum mechanics uses those solutions of the equation

$$-\frac{d^2u}{dx^2} + x^2u = (2n + 1)u, \; n \text{ constant,} \tag{a}$$

that remain finite as x increases without limit. Find these solutions.

First show that $u = e^{-\frac{1}{2}x^2}$ satisfies (a) when $n = 0$. Then let

$$u = ve^{-\frac{1}{2}x^2}$$

in (a) and deduce the equation

$$\frac{d^2v}{dx^2} - 2x\frac{dv}{dx} + 2nv = 0. \tag{b}$$

Next solve (b) to obtain the solutions v_1 and v_2 as infinite series. Now show that the solutions of (a)

$$u = v_1e^{-\frac{1}{2}x^2}, \quad u = v_2e^{-\frac{1}{2}x^2} \tag{c}$$

satisfy the required condition when and only when n is zero or a positive integer. Write the solutions (c) when $n = 0$, $n = 2$, and $n = 3$.

86. Integration in a series more general in type.

The series to be used in this paragraph has the form

$$y = x^m(c_0 + c_1x + c_2x^2 + \cdots), \tag{1}$$

where m may be any number. If m is negative and $c_0 \neq 0$, y increases without limit as x approaches 0. Also m may be non-integral. Thus, by means of (1), solutions may be obtained that could not be represented by a series having the form (1) with $m = 0$. An example will show how the series is used.

Example. Solve

$$(x^4 + 2x^2)\frac{d^2y}{dx^2} + 3x\frac{dy}{dx} - 6x^2y = 0. \tag{a}$$

Solution. Substituting

$$y = x^m(c_0 + c_1x + c_2x^2 + \cdots) \tag{b}$$

in (a), collecting like terms, and simplifying, we obtain

$$c_0m(2m + 1)x^m + c_1(m + 1)(2m + 3)x^{m+1} +$$
$$[c_2(m + 2)(2m + 5) + c_0(m + 2)(m - 3)]x^{m+2} + \cdots +$$
$$[c_n(m + n)(2m + 2n + 1) + c_{n-2}(m + n)(m + n - 5)]$$
$$x^{m+n} + \cdots = 0. \tag{c}$$

The number m, being at our disposal, will be chosen so as to make the first term vanish.   Therefore let

$$m(2m + 1) = 0, \text{ that is, } m = 0 \text{ or } -\tfrac{1}{2}. \qquad (d)$$

Let $c_1 = 0$, to dispose of the second term.   Finally, equating to zero the coefficient of x^{m+n} and solving for c_n, we have

$$c_n = \frac{-(m + n - 5)}{2m + 2n + 1} c_{n-2}, \ (n = 2, 3, \cdots, \infty). \qquad (e)$$

Since $c_1 = 0$, it appears from (e) that any c having an odd subscript vanishes.   Solving equations (e) for $c_2, c_4, \ldots$, in terms of c_0 and m, we find

$$\left.\begin{array}{l} c_2 = \dfrac{-(m - 3)}{2m + 5} c_0, \ c_4 = \dfrac{(m - 3)(m - 1)c_0}{(2m + 5)(2m + 9)}, \cdots \\[2ex] c_{2k} = (-1)^k \dfrac{(m-3)(m-1)(m+1) \cdots (m+2k-5)}{(2m+5)(2m+9) \cdots (2m+4k+1)} c_0. \end{array}\right\} \ (f)$$

Placing $m = 0$ from (d) in (f) and substituting the results in (b), we obtain

$$y_1 = c_0 \left[1 - \frac{(-3)}{5} x^2 + \frac{(-3)(-1)}{5 \cdot 9} x^4 - \right.$$
$$\left. \frac{(-3)(-1)(1)}{5 \cdot 9 \cdot 13} x^6 + \cdots \right]. \quad (g)$$

Similarly placing $m = -\tfrac{1}{2}$ from (d) in the same way, we obtain

$$y_2 = c_0 \left[x^{-\frac{1}{2}} - \frac{(-\frac{7}{2})}{4} x^{\frac{3}{2}} + \frac{(-\frac{7}{2})(-\frac{3}{2})}{4 \cdot 8} x^{\frac{7}{2}} + \cdots \right]. \quad (h)$$

Hence, in accordance with the theorem of §46, the general solution is

$$\mathbf{y} = A\mathbf{y}_1 + B\mathbf{y}_2.$$

The equation obtained by equating to zero the coefficient of the lowest power of x in the expression got by substituting y from (1) in the differential equation to be solved is called the *indicial equation*.   When the degree in m of the indicial equation is less than the order of the equation to be solved, a solution may be found by using a series of descending powers of x, having the form

$$y = x^m(c_0 + c_1 x^{-1} + c_2 x^{-2} + \cdots). \tag{2}$$

The procedure in this case is the same as when equation (1) is used. Exercises 9, 10, and 11 below involve this type of expansion.

Exercises

1. $2xD^2y + Dy - 2y = 0$

2. $(x^3 - x)D^2y + (8x^2 - 2)Dy + 12xy = 0$

3. $xD^2y + 3Dy - x^2y = 0$

4. $x^2D^2y + (x + 2x^2)Dy - 4y = 0$

5. Show that the regular procedure gives as the solution of $x^2D^2y - x^2Dy + (x - 2)y = 0$

$$y = c_0 x^2 (1 + \frac{1}{4}x + \frac{1}{4 \cdot 5}x^2 + \cdots) + c_1 x^{-1}\left(1 + x + \frac{1}{2!}x^2 + \frac{1}{3!}x^3 + \cdots\right).$$

Then show that this can be written

$$y = c_1(x^{-1} + 1 + \frac{1}{2}x) + cx^2(1 + \frac{1}{4}x + \frac{1}{4 \cdot 5}x^2 + \cdots).$$

where $c = c_0 + 6c_1$.

6. $(x^3 - x)D^2y + (4x^2 - 2)Dy + 2xy = 0$

7. $(x - x^2)D^2y - (x + 1)Dy + y = 0$

8. $x^4D^2y + xDy + y = 0$. *Hint:* Let $y = x^m(c_0 + c_1 x^{-1} + c_2 x^{-2} + \cdots)$

9. Show that the solution of $(x^4 - x^2)D^2y + 2xDy - (2 + 2x^2)y = 0$ is

$$y = Ax^2 + Bx(1 - x^2 - \frac{1}{3}x^4 - \frac{1}{5}x^6 - \frac{1}{7}x^8 - \cdots).$$

Show that

$$y = cx^{-1}(1 + \frac{3}{5}x^{-2} + \frac{3}{7}x^{-4} + \frac{3}{9}x^{-6} + \cdots)$$

is also a solution which converges when $|x| > 1$. Note that the series in the first solution converges when $|x| < 1$ and that y does not exist for either solution when $x = 1$. It is interesting to observe that the conditions of theorem II in §83 for the system

$$\frac{dy}{dx} = y_1, \quad \frac{dy_1}{dx} = \frac{(2 + 2x^2)y - 2xy_1}{x^4 - x^2}$$

are not satisfied for a region in which x may be zero or 1.

10. To solve $x^4D^2y + xDy - 2y = 0$, let $y = x^m(c_0 + c_1 x + c_2 x^2 + \cdots)$ to obtain the solution $y = cx^2(1 - x^2 + 3x^4 - 3 \cdot 5x^6 + \cdots)$ and show that this series diverges for all values of x except zero. Solve the differential equation by using $y = x^n(c_0 + c_1 x^{-1} + c_2 x^{-2} + \cdots)$, and

show that the series thus obtained converges for all values of x except zero.

11. Show that a solution of
$$(x^4 - x^2)D^2y - (2x^3 - 3x)Dy + (2x^2 - 3)y = 0$$
is
$$y = c_0x + c_1x^3\left(1 + \frac{1}{4}x^2 + \frac{1}{4}\cdot\frac{3}{6}x^4 + \frac{1\cdot3\cdot5}{4\cdot6\cdot8}x^6 + \cdots\right).$$

Also derive the solution
$$y = cx^2[1 + \frac{(-1)}{2}x^{-2} + \frac{(-1)(1)}{2\cdot4}x^{-4} + \frac{(-1)(1)(3)}{2\cdot4\cdot6}x^{-6} + \cdots].$$

12. $x^3D^3y + 6x^2D^2y + 6xDy + a^3x^3y = 0$

87. Particular solutions.

Series of type (1) in §86 may be used to solve equations having the form
$$P_0(x)D^2y + P_1(x)Dy + P_2(x)y = a_0x^{l_0} + a_1x^{l_1} + \cdots. \quad (3)$$
The usual method consists in finding the solution of the equation got from (3) by replacing the right member by zero, finding a particular solution for each term in the right-hand member, and setting y equal to the sum of the solutions derived. In finding a particular solution, a series of type (1) in §86 is used and c_0 and m are so chosen that the term of lowest degree in x is the term in x for which the particular solution is sought. The other terms of the solution are found in the usual way. Consider, for example,
$$(x^4 + 2x^2)D^2y + 3xDy - 6x^2y = 6x^{-\frac{3}{2}}. \quad (a)$$
This equation has the same left-hand member as equation (a) in §86. Hence (g) and (h) of §86 give two parts of the required solution. A particular solution of (a) is to be found. Substituting
$$y = x^m(c_0 + c_1x + \cdots + c_nx^n + \cdots) \quad (b)$$
in (a) and equating the term of lowest degree in x to $6x^{-\frac{3}{2}}$, we get
$$c_0[(2m)(m - 1) + 3m]x^m = 6x^{-\frac{3}{2}}. \quad (c)$$
Hence $m = -\frac{3}{2}$, $c_0[(2)(-\frac{3}{2})(-\frac{5}{2}) + 3(-\frac{3}{2})] = 6$, or $c_0 = 2$, and the initial term is $2x^{-\frac{3}{2}}$. Equating to zero the coeffi-

cient of x^{n+m} in the result of substituting y from (b) in (a), and solving for c_n, we get

$$c_n = \frac{-(n + m - 5)}{2n + 2m + 1} c_{n-2},$$

or since $m = -\frac{3}{2}$,

$$c_n = \frac{-(2n - 13)}{4(n - 1)} c_{n-2}. \qquad (d)$$

Now using the initial term $2x^{-\frac{3}{2}}$ and (d) with $n = 2, 4, 6,$ . . . in succession, we get

$$y_p = 2x^{-\frac{3}{2}}\left(1 + \frac{9}{4}x^2 + \frac{9 \cdot 5}{4^2 \cdot 3}x^4 + \frac{9 \cdot 5 \cdot 1}{4^3 \cdot 3 \cdot 5}x^6 + \cdots\right) \quad (e)$$

The general solution of (a) is $y = y_1 + y_2 + y_p$ where y_1 and y_2 are the solutions (g) and (h) from §86.

If there had been more than one term in the right-hand member of (a), a particular solution for each term would have been found, and their sum would have been the required particular solution.

Exercises

Find a particular solution of each equation:

1. $D^2y - y = 12x^{-\frac{1}{2}}$
2. $xD^2y - y = 3x^{-\frac{1}{2}}$
3. $D^2y - x^2y = 30\sqrt{x}$
4. $x^5D^2y + x^4Dy + y = 9x\sqrt{x}$

Hint: Use a series of the form $y = x^m(c_0 + c_1x^{-1} + c_2x^{-2} + \cdots)$.

88. Important special cases. When two or more roots of the indicial equation are equal or differ by an integer, it often happens that two or more roots give rise to the same solution. This article deals with differential equations of this type.

Consider a differential equation

$$P_0(x)D^ny + P_1(x)D^{n-1}y + \cdots + P_n(x) = 0 \qquad (4)$$

which gives rise to only two different powers of x when y is replaced by x^m. In it substitute

$$y = x^m(c_0 + c_1 x + \cdots + c_n x^n + \cdots),$$

equate the coefficient of a general power of x to zero to obtain a relation having the form

$$c_n = \varphi(n,m)c_{n-s} \qquad (5)$$

and use this solution with (4) to get

$$y_m = c_0 x^m [1 + \varphi(s,m)x^s + \varphi(2s,m)\,\varphi(s,m)x^{2s} + \cdots]. \qquad (6)$$

When this expression for y_m is substituted for y in (4), all terms except the first drop out and we have

$$P_0(x)D^n y_m + P_1(x)D^{n-1}y_m + \cdots + P_n y_m = I(m)x^{m-k}, \qquad (7)$$

where $I(m)$ is the left member of the indicial equation and k is some integer. In general each root m of $I(m) = 0$, when substituted in (6), gives a solution of (4). However if $I(m) = 0$ has a multiple root, there will be fewer than n distinct solutions, the same solution will often derive from two roots differing by an integer, and in many cases infinite terms due to a factor zero in the denominator will appear. Methods of finding the general solutions in these special cases will now be considered.

First suppose that $m = b$, a root of $I(m) = 0$, gives rise to an infinite term in (6). Then replace c_0 by $c(m - b)$ in (6) and (7). Note that the right member of (7) then becomes $(c/c_0)\,(m - b)\,I(m)x^{m-k}$, an expression having $(m - b)^2$ as a factor since $I(m)$ has a factor $m - b$; therefore its partial derivative with respect to m will be zero when $m = b$. Hence differentiating the changed equation (7) partially with respect to m and replacing m by b in the result, we get

$$\left[P_0(x)D^n\!\left(\frac{\partial y_m}{\partial m}\right) + P_1(x)D^{n-1}\!\left(\frac{\partial y_m}{\partial m}\right) + \cdots + P_n(x)\frac{\partial y_m}{\partial m} \right]_{m=b} = 0.* \qquad (8)$$

* It is permissible to replace $\dfrac{\partial}{\partial m}D^n y_m$ by $D^n\dfrac{\partial y_m}{\partial m}$ because each term of y_m is a rational fraction in x and m.

From this it appears that

$$y = \left\{\frac{\partial}{\partial m}\left[\frac{c}{c_0}(m-b)y_m\right]\right\}_{m=b} \tag{9}$$

is a solution of (4). Also it appears from the same type of argument as that used in deriving (9) that any double root r of $I(m) = 0$ gives rise to the solution of (4)

$$y = \left[\frac{\partial y_m}{\partial m}\right]_{m=r}.* \tag{10}$$

To illustrate the use of (9) and (10) consider the differential equation

$$x^2D^4y + 6xD^3y + 6D^2y - y = 0. \tag{a}$$

Substituting

$$y = x^m(c_0 + c_1x + \cdots + c_nx^n + \cdots) \tag{b}$$

in (a), collecting like terms, and simplifying, we obtain

$$c_0(m-1)m^2(m+1)x^m + c_1m(m+1)^2(m+2)x^{m+1} +$$
$$\cdots + [c_n(m+n-1)(m+n)^2(m+n+1) - c_{n-2}]x^{m+n}$$
$$+ \cdots = 0. \tag{c}$$

The first term will vanish, if

$$(m-1)m^2(m+1) = 0, \text{ or } m = 1, 0, 0, -1. \tag{d}$$

Let $c_1 = 0$ to dispose of the second term. Then equate to zero the coefficient of x^{m+n} and solve for c_n to obtain

$$c_n = \frac{c_{n-2}}{(m+n-1)(m+n)^2(m+n+1)},$$
$$(n = 2, 3, \ldots, \infty). \tag{e}$$

Since $c_1 = 0$, it appears from (e) that any c having an odd subscript vanishes. Solving equations (e) for c_2, c_4, ... in terms of c_0 and m and substituting the results in (b), we find

---

* Also the solution (9) with $m = b$ replaced by $m = r$ will serve equally well as may be shown by an argument like the one just given.

$$y = c_0 x^m \left[1 + \frac{x^2}{(m+1)(m+2)^2(m+3)} + \frac{x^4}{(m+1)(m+2)^2(m+3)^2(m+4)^2(m+5)} + \cdots \right]. \quad (f)$$

Substituting $m = 1$ and $m = 0$ in (f), we get

$$y_1 = c_0 x \left(1 + \frac{x^2}{2 \cdot 3^2 \cdot 4} + \frac{x^4}{2 \cdot 3^2 \cdot 4^2 \cdot 5^2 \cdot 6} + \cdots \right), \quad (g)$$

$$y_2 = c_0 \left(1 + \frac{x^2}{1 \cdot 2^2 \cdot 3} + \frac{x^4}{1 \cdot 2^2 \cdot 3^2 \cdot 4^2 \cdot 5} + \cdots \right). \quad (h)$$

The factor $m + 1$ equals zero when $m = -1$. Hence in (f) replace c_0 by $c(m + 1)$ to obtain

$$y_m = c x^m \left[m + 1 + \frac{x^2}{(m+2)^2(m+3)} + \frac{x^4}{(m+2)^2(m+3)^2(m+4)^2(m+5)} + \cdots \right] \quad (i)$$

and take the partial derivative with respect to m to get

$$\frac{\partial y_m}{\partial m} = c x^m \log x \left[m + 1 + \frac{x^2}{(m+2)^2(m+3)} + \cdots \right]$$

$$+ c x^m \left[1 + \frac{x^2 \left(\dfrac{-2}{m+2} - \dfrac{1}{m+3} \right)}{(m+2)^2(m+3)} + \right.$$

$$\left. \frac{x^4 \left(\dfrac{-2}{m+2} - \dfrac{2}{m+3} - \dfrac{2}{m+4} - \dfrac{1}{m+5} \right)}{(m+2)^2(m+3)^2(m+4)^2(m+5)} + \cdots \right]^*. \quad (j)$$

* Observe that by logarithmic differentiation

$$\frac{d}{dm} f(m) = f(m) \left[\frac{a_1}{a_1 m + b_1} + \frac{a_2}{a_2 m + b_2} + \cdots - \frac{c_1}{c_1 m + d_1} - \frac{c_2}{c_2 m + d_2} - \cdots \right]$$

where

$$f(m) = [(a_1 m + b_1)(a_2 m + b_2) \cdots] / [(c_1 m + d_1)(c_2 m + d_2) + \cdots].$$

In accordance with (9), a solution y_3 of (a) is obtained by replacing m by -1 in (j). This gives

$$y_3 = cx^{-1} \log x \left[\frac{x^2}{2} + \frac{x^4}{2^2 \cdot 3^2 \cdot 4} + \cdots \right]$$

$$+ cx^{-1} \left[1 + \frac{x^2(-2 - \frac{1}{2})}{1^2 \cdot 2} + \frac{x^4(-2 - \frac{2}{3} - \frac{3}{3} - \frac{1}{4})}{1^2 \cdot 2^2 \cdot 3^2 \cdot 4} + \cdots \right].$$

Also in accordance with (10) we get a fourth solution y_4 by replacing m in (j) by 0, the double root of the indicial equation. This gives

$$y_4 = c \log x \left[1 + \frac{x^2}{2^2 \cdot 3} + \frac{x^4}{2^2 \cdot 3^2 \cdot 4^2 \cdot 5} + \cdots \right]$$

$$+ c \left[1 + \frac{x^2(-\frac{2}{2} - \frac{1}{3})}{2^2 \cdot 3} + \frac{x^4(-\frac{2}{2} - \frac{2}{3} - \frac{2}{4} - \frac{1}{5})}{2^2 \cdot 3^2 \cdot 4^2 \cdot 5} + \cdots \right].$$

The complete solution of (a) is

$$\mathbf{y = Ay_1 + By_2 + Cy_3 + Ey_4.}$$

Exercises

1. Using the regular procedure for $xD^2y + Dy - xy = 0$, obtain

$$y_m = c_0 x^m \left[1 + \frac{x^2}{(m+2)^2} + \frac{x^4}{(m+2)^2(m+4)^2} + \cdots \right]. \quad (A)$$

Show that the roots of the indicial equation are 0, 0. Hence substitute $m = 0$ in (A) to get one solution, and use (10) with $r = 0$ to get the second solution.

2. Using the regular procedure for $xD^2y - y = 0$, obtain

$$y_m = c_0 x^m \left[1 + \frac{x}{m(m+1)} + \frac{x^2}{m(m+1)^2(m+2)} + \cdots \right]. \quad (B)$$

Show that the roots of the indicial equation are 1 and 0. Get one solution by using (B) with $m = 1$. To get the second solution replace c_0 in (B) by cm and then apply (9) with $b = 0$.

3. Solve $xD^2y + Dy + y = 0$

4. Solve $xD^3y + D^2y - y = 0$

5. $xD^2y + Dy - a^3x^2y = 0$

6. $xD^2y + 3Dy + a^2xy = 0$

7. $(x - x^2)D^2y - xDy + y = 0$

8. $x^3D^2y - y = 0$
9. $(x^3 + x^2)D^3y + (4x^2 + 4x)D^2y + (2 - 2x)Dy - 4y = 0$

89. The Legendre equation.

The Legendre equation and the Bessel equation are famous. They are of considerable importance because of their applications, and the literature relating to them and their solutions is extensive. This article gives a brief treatment of the Legendre equation and the next relates to the Bessel equation.

The Legendre equation having the form

$$(1 - x^2)D^2y - 2xDy + k(k + 1)y = 0 \qquad (11)$$

is named after the famous French mathematician Adrien Marie Legendre. The solution of (11) is generally obtained in a series having the form

$$y = c_0x^m + c_1x^{m-1} + c_2x^{m-2} + \cdots + c_nx^{m-n} + \cdots. \qquad (12)$$

To get the indicial equation, set $y = x^m$ in (11) and equate to zero the coefficient of x^m to get

$$-m^2 - m + k(k + 1) = 0; \text{ or } m = k, -k - 1. \qquad (13)$$

Next substitute y from (12) in (11), equate to zero the coefficient of x^{m-n} and solve for c_n to get

$$c_n = \frac{(m - n + 2)(m - n + 1)}{(m - n - k)(m - n + k + 1)}c_{n-2}. \qquad (14)$$

Using (14) first with $m = k$, and then with $m = -k - 1$, obtain in the usual way

$$y_k = x^k\left[1 - \frac{k(k - 1)}{2(2k - 1)}x^{-2} + \frac{k(k - 1)(k - 2)(k - 3)}{2 \cdot 4 \cdot (2k - 1)(2k - 3)}x^{-4}\right.$$
$$\left. - \cdots\right], \qquad (15)$$

$$y_{-k-1} = x^{-k-1}\left[1 + \frac{(k + 1)(k + 2)}{2(2k + 3)}x^{-2} + \right.$$
$$\left. \frac{(k + 1)(k + 2)(k + 3)(k + 4)}{2 \cdot 4(2k + 3)(2k + 5)}x^{-4} + \cdots\right]. \qquad (16)$$

The general solution is

$$y = c_1 y_k + c_2 y_{-k-1}, \tag{17}$$

and this series converges for all values of x satisfying $|x| > |1$.

If k is zero or a positive integer, the series (15) for y_k will terminate. The polynomials P_k called *Legendre polynomials*, obtained by taking the product of y_k from (15) and $(2k)!/[2^k(k!)^2]$ and replacing k by an integer, are defined by

$$P_k(x) = \frac{(2k)!}{2^k(k!)^2} y_k. \tag{18}$$

From (18) we easily obtain

$$P_0(x) = 1, \; P_1(x) = x, \; P_2(x) = \frac{3x^2 - 1}{2},$$

$$P_3(x) = \frac{5x^3 - 3x}{2}, P_4(x) = \frac{5 \cdot 7}{2 \cdot 4}x^4 - 2\frac{3 \cdot 5}{2 \cdot 4}x^2 + \frac{1 \cdot 3}{2 \cdot 4}, \text{ etc. } \tag{19}$$

A few interesting facts concerning Legendre polynomials will be considered.

The following formula, known as *Rodrigues' formula* is useful:

$$P_k(x) = \frac{1}{k!2^k} \cdot \frac{d^k(x^2 - 1)^k}{dx^k}. \tag{20}$$

To prove this, take the kth derivative of the $(r + 1)$th term in the binomial expansion of $(x^2 - 1)^k$, factor $(2k)!/k!$ from it, and observe that the result is the $(r + 1)$th term of (15). Hence, for positive integral values of k,

$$\frac{d^k(x^2 - 1)^k}{dx^k} = \frac{(2k)!}{k!} y_k. \tag{21}$$

From (21) and (19), equation (20) is easily derived.

If one carries out the differentiation indicated in (21) without removing the parentheses and observes that, when x is replaced by 1 in the result, only the term $[k! \; (2x)^k]_{x=1} = 2^k k!$ has a value different from zero, he concludes that

$$P_k(1) = \frac{1}{2^k \cdot k!} \, 2^k(k!) = 1. \tag{22}$$

This formula simplifies the use of Legendre polynomials and indicates the reason for the coefficient of y_k in (18).

A set of functions $f_r(x)$ continuous in the interval $a \leqq x \leqq b$ and having the property

$$\int_a^b f_r(x)f_s(x) \, dx = 0, \, r \neq s \tag{23}$$

is called an *orthogonal set*. The functions $f_r(x) = \sin rx$ form a simple orthogonal set since

$$\int_{-\pi}^{\pi} \sin rx \sin sx \, dx = 0, \, r \neq s.$$

This set is the basis of the very important Fourier series considered in §§111 and 112. The following proof shows that the Legendre functions constitute an orthogonal set in the interval $-1 \leqq x \leqq 1$ by showing that

$$\int_{-1}^{1} P_r(x) \, P_k(x) \, dx = 0, \, r \neq k. \tag{24}$$

Equation (11) may be written

$$\frac{d}{dx}[(1 - x^2)y'] + k(k + 1)y = 0.$$

In this replace y by the solution $P_k(x)$, multiply through by $P_r(x)$, and integrate to obtain

$$\int_{-1}^{1} P_r(x)\frac{d}{dx}[(1 - x^2)P_k'(x)]dx +$$

$$k(k + 1) \int_{-1}^{1} P_k(x)P_r(x)dx = 0. \tag{25}$$

Apply integration by parts to the first integral to get

$$\left[(1 - x^2)P_k'(x)P_r(x)\right]_{-1}^{1} - \int_{-1}^{1}(1 - x^2)P_r'P_k' \, dx +$$

$$k(k + 1) \int_{-1}^{1} P_k P_r \, dx = 0. \tag{26}$$

The first term of this vanishes. Now write (26) with r and k interchanged to obtain

$$-\int_{-1}^{1}(1 - x^2)P_k'P_r' \, dx + r(r + 1) \int_{-1}^{1}P_rP_k \, dx = 0. \quad (27)$$

Subtract (27) from (26), member by member, to get

$$(k - r)(k + r + 1)\int_{-1}^{1}P_rP_k \, dx = 0.$$

This shows that (24) holds true.

By using Rodrigues' formula (20) and repeated integration by parts, we can show that

$$\int_{-1}^{1}P_k^2(x) \, dx = \frac{2}{2k + 1}. \quad (28)$$

By using (24) and (28), a general method of expanding functions in a series of Legendre polynomials can be developed. The method is indicated in exercise 4 of the following list.

Exercises

1. Using the functions (19) show that (a) $P_0(1) = P_1(1) = P_2(1) = P_3(1) = 1$. (b) $\int_{-1}^{1} P_1(x)P_2(x)dx = \int_{-1}^{1}P_2(x)P_3(x)dx = 0$. (c) $\int_{-1}^{1} P_2^2(x)dx = [2/(2k + 1)]_{k=2} = 2/5$.

2. Find $P_6(x)$ by using (18) and show that $P_6(1) = 1$.

3. Check Rodrigues' formula (20) for $k = 3$.

4. Assuming that there are constants a_i such that

$$f(x) = a_0P_0(x) + a_1P_1(x) + \cdots + a_nP_n(x) + \cdots, \quad (a)$$

and that the series obtained by multiplying the right-hand member by $P_n(x)$ can be integrated, term by term, multiply both sides of (a) by $P_n(x)$, consider the integrals of all terms between the limits -1 and $+1$ and, remembering (24) and (28), obtain

$$a_n = \frac{2n + 1}{2} \int_{-1}^{1} f(x)P_n(x)dx.$$

5. Using a method suggested by exercise 4, expand x^4 in Legendre polynomials.

6. Find the first four terms of the expansion of e^x in Legendre polynomials.

90. The Bessel equation.

The Bessel equation, named after the German mathematician Friedrich Wilhelm Bessel, has the form

$$x^2D^2y + xDy + (x^2 - k^2)y = 0. \tag{29}$$

The theory developed in §§85 to 88 may be used to solve it. First get the indicial equation by substituting x^m for y in (29) and equating the coefficient of x^m to zero. This gives

$$m(m - 1) + m - k^2 = 0, \text{ or } m = \pm k. \tag{30}$$

Next substitute $\sum\limits_{n=0}^{\infty} c_r x^{m+r}$ for y in (29), equate the coefficient of x^{m+n} to zero, and solve for c_n to obtain

$$c_n = \frac{-c_{n-2}}{(m + n + k)(m + n - k)}. \tag{31}$$

Using this with $m = k$, we obtain as a solution of (29)

$$y_1 = x^k\left[1 - \frac{(x/2)^2}{1(1 + k)} + \frac{(x/2)^4}{1 \cdot 2 \cdot (1 + k)(2 + k)} - \cdots\right.$$

$$\left. + \frac{(-1)^r(k!)(x/2)^{2r}}{r!(r + k)!} + \cdots \right]. \tag{32}$$

Similarly, if k is not an integer, we obtain from (31) with $m = -k$

$$y_2 = x^{-k}\left[1 - \frac{(x/2)^2}{1(1 - k)} + \frac{(x/2)^4}{1 \cdot 2 \cdot (1 - k)(2 - k)} - \cdots\right.$$

$$\left. + \frac{(-1)^r(x/2)^{2r}}{r!(1 - k)(2 - k) \cdots (r - k)} + \cdots \right]. \tag{33}$$

In this case, the solution is

$$y = c_1y_1 + c_2y_2. \tag{34}$$

If k is an integer, (33) fails to give a solution and the method of §88 may be applied. Write

$$y_m = x^m\left[m + k + \sum_{r=1}^{\infty} \frac{(-1)^r (m + k)x^{2r}}{\prod\limits_{n=1}^{r} (m + 2n + k) (m + 2n - k)}\right], \tag{35}$$

where the sign Π indicates the product of the $2r$ factors obtained by replacing n in the denominator of (35) by the numbers $1, 2, \ldots, r$ in succession. Observe that, when $r \geqq k$, the factor $m + k$ cancels. Hence, taking the partial derivative of (35) with respect to m, replacing m by $-k$ in the result, multiplying by $(k-1)!$, and simplifying, we get

$$
\begin{aligned}
Y = \left(\frac{\partial Y_m}{\partial m}\right)_{m=-k} &= x^{-k} \log x \sum_{r=k}^{\infty} \frac{2(-1)^{r+k-1} (x/2)^{2r}}{r!(r-k)!} \\
&\quad + x^{-k} \sum_{r=0}^{k-1} \frac{(k-r-1)!(x/2)^{2r}}{r!} \\
&\quad + x^{-k} \sum_{r=k}^{\infty} \left[\frac{2(-1)^{r+k}(x/2)^{(2r)}}{r!(r-k)!} \sum_{n=1}^{r}\left(\frac{1}{2n} + \frac{1}{2(n-k)}\right)\right],
\end{aligned}
\tag{36}
$$

where the n in $n - k$ takes on all integral values from 1 to r except k, and $0! = 1$. The solution for the case when $k = 0$ cannot be obtained from (36) by replacing k by zero. This case will be considered in exercise 2. The general solution of (29), when k is any integer not zero, is

$$
y = c_1 y_1 + c_2 Y. \tag{37}
$$

Exercises

1. Write the solution of (29) when (a) $k = \frac{1}{2}$; (b) $k = 3$.

2. Find the general solution of (29) when $k = 0$.

3. If $J_k(x)$, $k = 0$ or a positive integer, is defined by

$$
J_k(x) = \frac{1}{2^k k!} y_1(x) = \frac{x^k}{2^k k!} \sum_{r=0}^{\infty} \frac{(-1)^r k! (x/2)^{2r}}{r!(r+k)!},
$$

show that the part of (36) represented by the first sum may be written in the form $-[(\log x)/2^{k-1}]J_k(x)$. *Hint:* Replace r by $R + k$ in the first sum of (36) and observe that the numbers on the summation sign will then be $R = 0$ to $R = \infty$.

4. Using the definition $J_k(x)$ from exercise 3, show that
(a) $J_0(x) + J_2(x) = (2/x) J_1(x)$; (b) $d/dx (J_0(x)) = J_1(x)$.

91. Approximate integration of differential equations.
There are many methods* of finding a result which approxi-

* J. B. Scarborough in his "Numerical Mathematical Analysis," pp. 219–283, considers four methods.

mates to any required degree of accuracy a solution of a given differential equation. The method is generally a step-by-step procedure which uses in each stage one or more of the results obtained in previous stages. Although the method usually requires a large amount of computation to obtain a particular result, it can often be applied when other methods fail and the result is given in considerable detail. It was formerly used extensively to compute the trajectories described by shells in long-range gunfire, requiring high angles of elevation. Two methods of obtaining approximations to a solution of a differential equation are considered in §§92 and 93.

92. Method of successive approximations. We shall illustrate the method by applying it to solve two examples.

Example 1. Find approximately the solution of

$$\frac{dy}{dx} = xy \tag{a}$$

which satisfies the initial conditions

$$y = 1, \text{ when } x = 0. \tag{b}$$

Solution. Taking $y = 1$ as a first approximation, substitute 1 for y in the right-hand member of (a) to obtain

$$\frac{dy}{dx} = x. \tag{c}$$

Integrating (c) and using initial conditions (b), we find, as a second approximation,

$$y = 1 + \frac{x^2}{2}. \tag{d}$$

Substituting y from (d) in the right-hand member of (a), integrating, and using the initial conditions (b), we obtain, as a third approximation,

$$y = 1 + \frac{x^2}{2} + \frac{x^4}{2^2 \cdot 2!}. \tag{e}$$

By continuing this step-by-step process, we could obtain, as the $(n + 1)$th approximation,

$$y = 1 + \frac{x^2}{2} + \frac{x^4}{2^2 \cdot 2!} + \cdots + \frac{x^{2n}}{2^n n!}. \qquad (f)$$

These happen to be the first $(n + 1)$ terms of the series solution satisfying conditions (b).   Hence it appears that *the limit of the nth approximation, as n becomes infinite, is the exact solution.*

Example 2.   Find approximately the solution of $\frac{d^2y}{dx^2} - \frac{2x}{dx}\frac{dy}{dx} = 2x$ which satisfies the initial conditions $y = 1$, $dy/dx = 0$, when $x = 0$.

Solution.   Writing $D = d/dx$, $z = dy/dx$, $Dz = d^2y/dx^2$ in the statement of the problem, we have the system

$$Dy = z, \quad Dz = 2x + 2xz \qquad (a)$$

and the initial conditions

$$y = 1, \quad z = 0, \text{ when } x = 0. \qquad (b)$$

The process to be performed repeatedly consists in substituting the approximations for y and z in terms of x in the right-hand members of (a), integrating the results and determining the constants of integration by using (b).

Substituting the first approximation $y = 1$, $z = 0$ in the right-hand member of (a), we get

$$Dy = 0, \quad Dz = 2x. \qquad (c)$$

Integrating these equations and determining the constants of integrating by using (b), we get

$$y = 1, \quad z = x^2 \qquad (d)$$

as the second approximation.   Substituting these values in the right-hand member of (a), integrating, and determining the constants, we get the third approximation,

$$y = 1 + \frac{x^3}{3}, \quad z = x^2 + \frac{x^4}{2}. \qquad (e)$$

The fourth approximation is

$$y = 1 + \frac{x^3}{3} + \frac{x^5}{5 \cdot 2!}, \quad z = x^2 + \frac{x^4}{2} + \frac{x^6}{3!}, \qquad (f)$$

and the $(n + 2)$nd $(n > 1)$ approximation for y is found to be

$$y = 1 + \frac{x^3}{3} + \frac{x^5}{5 \cdot 2!} + \cdots + \frac{x^{2n+1}}{(2n + 1)n!}. \qquad (g)$$

Here again the limit approached by the nth approximation, as n becomes infinite, is the series solution which satisfies the given initial conditions.

In general, the method applied to the system (a) of Example 2 may be applied to approximate a solution of any system of n first-order equations in $n + 1$ unknowns, provided the conditions of theorem II of §83 are satisfied for the system.*

Exercises

Solve each of the following differential equations by the method of this article and compare the results with the solution found by some other method:

1. $\dfrac{dy}{dx} = y + x$; $y = 1$, when $x = 0$

2. $\dfrac{dy}{dx} = xy + 1$; $y = 1$, when $x = 0$

3. $\dfrac{dx}{dt} = y$, $\dfrac{dy}{dt} = x + t$; $x = 1$, $y = -1$, when $t = 0$

4. $\dfrac{d^2y}{dx^2} = xy$, $y = 1$, $y' = 0$, when $x = 0$

Hint: Solve $\dfrac{dy}{dx} = z$, $\dfrac{dz}{dx} = xy$.

93. The Runge-Kutta method.

The method set forth in this article was devised by C. Runge about 1894 and extended by W. Kutta a few years later. It will serve as an illustration of a method based mainly on computation.

Let x_0 and y_0 be initial values of the variables x and y for a solution of the equation

$$\frac{dy}{dx} = f(x,y). \qquad (38)$$

* See Ince, E. L., "Ordinary Differential Equations," pp. 63–72.

A change h is made in x, and the corresponding change Δy in y is found by computing in order k_1, k_2, k_3, k_4, and Δy by means of the following formulas:

$$k_1 = f(x_0, y_0)\, h,$$
$$k_2 = f(x_0 + \frac{h}{2}, y_0 + \frac{k_1}{2})h,$$
$$k_3 = f(x_0 + \frac{h}{2}, y_0 + \frac{k_2}{2})h, \qquad (39)$$
$$k_4 = f(x_0 + h, y_0 + k_3)h,$$
$$\Delta y = \tfrac{1}{6}(k_1 + 2k_2 + 2k_3 + k_4).$$

This gives the values $x_1 = x_0 + h$, $y_1 = y_0 + \Delta y$. To find a third pair of values use the same formulas (39) with x_1 and y_1 taking the place of x_0 and y_0, respectively. When x_2 and y_2 are found, use (39) with x_0 and y_0 replaced by x_2 and y_2, and so on.

The error in the Runge-Kutta method is not easy to estimate. Roughly it is of the order of h^5. If $h = 0.1$, we expect an error in Δy affecting the fifth decimal place.*

The following example will illustrate the procedure.

Example. Find three pairs of values of x and y for the solution $dy/dx = -x + y$ by means of formulas (39) if the initial values of the variables are $x = 0$, $y = 2$.

Solution. The first value pair is $x = 0$, $y = 2$. Take $h = 0.1$, $x_0 = 0$, $y_0 = 2$ in (39), keep five decimal places during the computation, but round off the value of Δy to four decimal places. This gives:

$$k_1 = [-0 + 2]0.1 = 0.2,$$
$$k_2 = \left[-0 - \frac{0.1}{2} + 2 + \frac{0.2}{2}\right]0.1 = 0.205,$$
$$k_3 = \left[-0 - \frac{0.1}{2} + 2 + \frac{0.205}{2}\right]0.1 = 0.20525,$$
$$k_4 = [-0 - 0.1 + 2 + 0.20525]0.1 = 0.21053,$$
$$\Delta y = \tfrac{1}{6}[0.2 + 2(0.205) + 2(0.20525) + 0.21053] = 2.2052.$$

$$\text{Hence } \mathbf{x_1 = 0.1,\ y_1 = 2.2052.}$$

* See WILLERS, F. A., "Numerische Integration," pp. 91–92.

Substituting these values of x_1 and y_1, for x_0 and y_0 and 0.1 for h in (39), we obtain

$k_1 = 0.21052$, $k_2 = 0.21605$, $k_3 = 0.21632$, $k_4 = 0.22215$, and $\Delta y = \frac{1}{6}[k_1 + 2k_2 + 2k_3 + k_4] = 0.21624$.

Hence the third pair of values of x and y are

$$\mathbf{x_2 = 0.2, \; y_2 = 2.4214.}$$

The next pair of values could be computed by using x_2 and y_2 for x_0 and y_0 in (39).

Exercises

1. Check the values for x_2 and y_2 in the solution just given. Then compute $x_3 = 0.3$, $y_3 = 2.6499$ by using (39) with $x_0 = x_2$, $y_0 = y_2$ and $h = 0.1$. Finally compute y when $x = 0.4$.

2. Find three value pairs of x and y by using (39) for the solution of $dy/dx = xy + 1$ in which $y = 1$ when $x = 0$. Use $h = 0.1$.

3. The Runge-Kutta equations for solving two simultaneous equations of the type

$$\frac{dx}{dt} = f(t,x,y), \quad \frac{dy}{dt} = F(t,x,y)$$

are

$$k_1 = f(t_0,x_0,y_0)\Delta t,$$
$$l_1 = F(t_0,x_0,y_0)\Delta t,$$
$$k_2 = f\left(t_0 + \frac{\Delta t}{2},\, x_0 + \frac{k_1}{2},\, y_0 + \frac{l_1}{2}\right)\Delta t,$$
$$l_2 = F\left(t_0 + \frac{\Delta t}{2},\, x_0 + \frac{k_1}{2},\, y_0 + \frac{l_1}{2}\right)\Delta t,$$
$$k_3 = f\left(t_0 + \frac{\Delta t}{2},\, x_0 + \frac{k_2}{2},\, y_0 + \frac{l_2}{2}\right)\Delta t,$$
$$l_3 = F\left(t_0 + \frac{\Delta t}{2},\, x_0 + \frac{k_2}{2},\, y_0 + \frac{l_2}{2}\right)\Delta t,$$
$$k_4 = f(t_0 + \Delta t,\, x_0 + k_3,\, y_0 + l_3)\Delta t,$$
$$l_4 = F(t_0 + \Delta t,\, x_0 + k_3,\, y_0 + l_3)\Delta t,$$
$$\Delta x = \tfrac{1}{6}(k_1 + 2k_2 + 2k_3 + k_4),$$
$$\Delta y = \tfrac{1}{6}(l_1 + 2l_2 + 2l_3 + l_4).$$

In using these equations, first find k_1 and l_1, then k_2 and l_2, then k_3 and l_3, then k_4 and l_4, and finally Δx and Δy. Apply these equations to solve

$$\frac{dx}{dt} = y - t, \quad \frac{dy}{dt} = x + t$$

for the value sets x, y, t having $t = 0.1$, 0.2, and 0.3 if $x = 1$, $y = 1$, when $t = 0$.

CHAPTER XII

PARTIAL DIFFERENTIAL EQUATIONS OF THE FIRST ORDER

94. Solution of a partial differential equation. This chapter is concerned with partial differential equations, that is, equations containing partial derivatives. A solution or integral of such an equation is a relation among the variables involved that satisfies the equation. It is concerned with two or more independent variables and may or may not involve arbitrary constants and arbitrary functions. The following examples and exercises will illustrate these facts.

Example 1. Prove that

$$z = ax + a^2y^2 + b \qquad (a)$$

is a solution of

$$\frac{\partial z}{\partial y} = 2y\left(\frac{\partial z}{\partial x}\right)^2. \qquad (b)$$

Solution. Differentiating (a) partially with respect to x and with respect to y, we obtain

$$\frac{\partial z}{\partial x} = a, \frac{\partial z}{\partial y} = 2a^2y. \qquad (c)$$

Substitution from (c) in (b) gives the identity

$$2a^2y = 2ya^2.$$

Example 2. Prove that a solution of

$$\frac{\partial^2 y}{\partial t^2} = c^2\frac{\partial^2 y}{\partial x^2}^{*\cdot} \qquad (a)$$

* Equation (b) in Example 2 represents a motion compounded of two wave motions having equal wave lengths and periods but opposite directions. Because of this fact, equation (a) of Example 2 plays a very important role in mathematical physics, especially in the theory of sound and the theory of electricity and magnetism.

is

$$y = \varphi(ct - x) + \psi(ct + x), \tag{b}$$

where φ and ψ represent arbitrary functions.*

Solution. It will be convenient to use the notation

$$\frac{d\varphi}{d(ct - x)} = \varphi', \quad \frac{d^2\varphi}{[d(ct - x)]^2} = \varphi'',$$

$$\frac{d\psi}{d(ct + x)} = \psi', \quad \frac{d^2\psi}{[d(ct + x)]^2} = \psi''.$$

Partial differentiation of (b) gives

$$\left.\begin{array}{l} \dfrac{\partial y}{\partial t} = c\varphi' + c\psi', \quad \dfrac{\partial y}{\partial x} = -\varphi' + \psi', \\[2mm] \dfrac{\partial^2 y}{\partial t^2} = c^2\varphi'' + c^2\psi'', \quad \dfrac{\partial^2 y}{\partial x^2} = \varphi'' + \psi''. \end{array}\right\} \tag{c}$$

Substituting from (c) in (a), we obtain the identity

$$c^2\varphi'' + c^2\psi'' = c^2\varphi'' + c^2\psi''.$$

Note: Throughout the chapters on partial differential equations, we shall use the notation

$$p = \frac{\partial z}{\partial x}, \ q = \frac{\partial z}{\partial y}, \ r = \frac{\partial^2 z}{\partial x^2}, \ s = \frac{\partial^2 z}{\partial x \partial y}, \ t = \frac{\partial^2 z}{\partial y^2}. \tag{1}$$

Exercises

In the following exercises, φ and ψ represent arbitrary functions of the indicated variables. Verify the fact that each equation is a solution of the partial differential equation written opposite it:

1. $az = a^2x + y + b$ $pq = 1$
2. $2z = 2axe^y + a^2e^{2y} + b$ $q = xp + p^2$
3. $yz = ax + 2\sqrt{ay} + b$ $p = (yq + z)^2$
4. $6az = x^3y + x\,\varphi(y) + \psi(y)$ $ar = xy$
5. $z = x^n\,\varphi(y) + \psi(y)$ $xr = (n - 1)p$
6. $\varphi(x^2 - z^2, x^3 - y^3) = 0$ $y^2zp + x^2zq = x^2y^2$

* Throughout the chapters on partial differential equations, we shall assume that the arbitrary functions are continuous and possess such continuous partial derivatives as we may wish to use.

Hint: Let $u = x^2 - z^2, v = x^3 - y^3$. Then $\dfrac{\partial\varphi}{\partial x} = \dfrac{\partial\varphi}{\partial u}(2x - 2zp) + \dfrac{\partial\varphi}{\partial v}3x^2$
$= 0$, etc.

7. $z = e^{y/a}\varphi(x - y)$ $z = a(p + q)$
8. $z^2 = x^3y^2 + x\,\varphi(y) + \psi(y)$ $zr + p^2 = 3xy^2$
9. $x = \varphi(z) + \psi(y)$ $ps - qr = 0$
10. $2z = x^2y - 2xy + \varphi(y) + e^{-x}\psi(y)$ $p + r = xy$
11. $z = \varphi(y/x) + \psi(xy)$ $x^2r - y^2t = qy - px$
12. $z = \varphi(x + iy) + \psi(x - iy), i = \sqrt{-1}, r + t = 0$

95. Partial differential equation from integral.

In the case of ordinary differential equations, we were able to find a differential equation when its general solution was given (see §7, Chapter I). The same method will operate to find a partial differential equation satisfied by a given integral. The following examples will illustrate the process as well as the type of result to be expected.

Example 1. Find a partial differential equation whose integral is

$$z = ax + (a^2 + 3)y + b, \qquad (a)$$

if a and b are arbitrary constants.

Solution. Differentiating (a) partially with respect to x and y, we find

$$p = a, q = a^2 + 3. \qquad (b)$$

Elimination of a from equations (b) gives

$$\mathbf{q = p^2 + 3.}$$

Example 2. Find a partial differential equation whose integral is

$$z = ax^2 + by^2 + c, \qquad (a)$$

where a, b, and c are arbitrary constants.

Solution. Taking first and second partial derivatives of (a), we find

$$p = 2ax, q = 2by, r = 2a, s = 0, t = 2b. \qquad (b)$$

Here are six equations from which to eliminate three unknowns. Hence we obtain the three solutions

$$\mathbf{s = 0, p = rx, q = ty.} \qquad (c)$$

Example 3. Show that the partial differential equation of all spheres with centers in the xy-plane and radius 1 is

$$z^2(p^2 + q^2 + 1) = 1. \tag{a}$$

Solution. The equation of the spheres is

$$(x - h)^2 + (y - k)^2 + z^2 = 1. \tag{b}$$

Differentiating this partially with respect to x and to y, we get

$$2(x - h) + 2zp = 0, \; 2(y - k) + 2z(q) = 0. \tag{c}$$

Eliminating h and k between (b) and (c), we obtain (a).

Example 4. Find a partial differential equation whose integral is

$$\varphi(x^2 + y^2, \; x^2 - z^2) = 0, \tag{a}$$

where φ represents an arbitrary function.

Solution. Let $u = x^2 + y^2$ and $v = x^2 - z^2$. Partial differentiation of (a) gives

$$\left.\begin{array}{l} \dfrac{\partial \varphi}{\partial u} \dfrac{\partial u}{\partial x} + \dfrac{\partial \varphi}{\partial v} \dfrac{\partial v}{\partial x} = 2x \dfrac{\partial \varphi}{\partial u} + (2x - 2zp) \dfrac{\partial \varphi}{\partial v} = 0, \\[2mm] \dfrac{\partial \varphi}{\partial u} \dfrac{\partial u}{\partial y} + \dfrac{\partial \varphi}{\partial v} \dfrac{\partial v}{\partial y} = 2y \dfrac{\partial \varphi}{\partial u} - 2zq \dfrac{\partial \varphi}{\partial v} = 0. \end{array}\right\} \tag{b}$$

Eliminating $\dfrac{\partial \varphi}{\partial v} \div \dfrac{\partial \varphi}{\partial u}$ from (b), we find

$$\frac{-x}{x - zp} = \frac{y}{zq}, \text{ or } z(yp - xq) = xy.$$

Exercises

1. Find the partial differential equations of which the following are solutions:

(a) $z = ax + by$ (c) $z^2 = ax^2 + by^2$

(b) $z = a^2x - ay + b$ (d) $z = ax + f(a)y + b$

2. Find the partial differential equation of

(a) All planes through the origin not containing the z-axis.

(b) All planes having the sum of their intercepts on the coordinates axes unity.

(c) All spheres with centers in the xz-plane and radius 1.

(d) All spheres with centers on the line $x = y = z$.

(e) All right circular cones having the z-axis as axis.

(*f*) All spheres passing through the origin and having centers in the *xy*-plane.

3. Find the partial differential equations of which the following equations are solutions:

(*a*) $z = \varphi(x + y)$ (*e*) $z = \varphi(x) + \psi(y)$

(*b*) $z = x\varphi(x + y)$ (*f*) $y = \varphi(x + y) + \psi(z)$

(*c*) $y = z\varphi(x + y)$ (*g*) $z = \varphi(x + 2y) + \psi(x - y)$

(*d*) $y = \psi(z) + \varphi(x)$ (*h*) $z = \varphi(y/x) + \psi(xy)$

4. Show that for all cylindrical surfaces $\varphi(x,z) = 0$ having their elements parallel to the *y*-axis, $q = 0$.

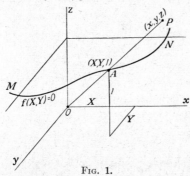

FIG. 1.

5. Find the partial differential equation of all conical surfaces with vertex at $(0,0,0)$. *Hint:* In Fig. 1, P represents any point on a conical surface, A the point where OP cuts plane $z = 1$, and curve MAN having equation $f(X,Y) = 0$, $z = 1$ the trace of the conical surface on plane $z = 1$. From Fig. 1

$$\frac{x - X}{X} = \frac{y - Y}{Y} = \frac{z - 1}{1}.$$

Solve these equations for X and Y and substitute in $f(X,Y) = 0$.

6. Show that the equation of all surfaces of revolution about the *z*-axis may be written

$$f(z, \sqrt{x^2 + y^2}) = 0, \text{ or } z = \varphi(x^2 + y^2),$$

and find the partial differential equation of these surfaces.

96. Equations easily integrable.

Some partial differential equations may be solved by inspection. Thus, the equation

$$\frac{\partial z}{\partial x} = x^2 + y \qquad (2)$$

evidently has as a solution

$$z = \frac{x^3}{3} + xy + \varphi(y), \tag{3}$$

where φ represents an arbitrary function. Since only differentiation with respect to x was indicated in (2), we got
(3) from it by integrating with respect to x while treating y
as a constant.

Again consider the equation

$$ys + p = 4xy, \tag{4}$$

where s and p have the meanings defined in **(1)** of §94.
Writing this in the form

$$y \frac{\partial p}{\partial y} + p = 4xy, \tag{5}$$

we see that it is an ordinary linear equation of the first degree in p and y if x is considered constant. Hence its solution is

$$py = 2xy^2 + \varphi(x). \tag{6}$$

Observe that the arbitrary function $\varphi(x)$ plays the role of a
constant since x was considered constant for the integration.
In (6) replace p by its equal $\partial z/\partial x$ and integrate again considering y as a constant to obtain

$$z = \int \left[2xy + \frac{1}{y} \varphi(x) \right] dx, \ (y, \text{ constant}),$$

or

$$z = x^2y + \frac{1}{y} \varphi_1(x) + \psi(y).$$

Here $\varphi_1(x)[= \int\varphi(x)dx]$ and $\psi(y)$ are arbitrary functions.

These illustrations indicate how a large class of partial
differential equations may be integrated by using the
methods of solving ordinary differential equations. It
is worthy of note that the constant of integration consists
of an arbitrary function of the variable considered constant
during the integration.

Exercises

1. $\dfrac{\partial z}{\partial x} = 3x^2 + y^2$

2. $y\dfrac{\partial z}{\partial y} + z = x^2$

3. $y\dfrac{\partial p}{\partial y} + p = 2x$

4. $r = f(x,y)$

5. $ys = x + ay$

6. $t - q = e^x + e^y$

7. $p + r = xy$

8. $xr + p = xy$

9. $r + p^2 = y^2$

10. $zp + z^2 = xy^2$

11. $pr + p^2 = a$

12. $\dfrac{\partial r}{\partial y} + \dfrac{\partial p}{\partial x} = 12$

13. $yt + 2q = 12x^2y^2$

97. Linear equations of the first order. The general linear partial differential equation of the first order in x, y, and z has the form

$$Pp + Qq = R, \qquad (7)$$

where P, Q, and R represent functions of x, y, and z, and p and q are defined in equation (1). The following method of solving this type of equation is due to the great French mathematician Lagrange; it is often referred to as *Lagrange's method*.

Let $u(x,y,z) = a$ be a solution of (7). Then

$$\frac{\partial u}{\partial x} + p\frac{\partial u}{\partial z} = 0, \; \frac{\partial u}{\partial y} + q\frac{\partial u}{\partial z} = 0, \qquad (8)$$

or

$$p = -\frac{\partial u/\partial x}{\partial u/\partial z}, \; q = -\frac{\partial u/\partial y}{\partial u/\partial z}. \qquad (9)$$

Substituting p and q from (9) in (7), we have, after slight simplification,

$$P\frac{\partial u}{\partial x} + Q\frac{\partial u}{\partial y} + R\frac{\partial u}{\partial z} = 0. \qquad (10)$$

Hence any solution of (7) is also a solution of (10).

Again let $u(x,y,z) = a$ be any solution of (10). Then

$$\frac{\partial u}{\partial x} = -\frac{\partial u}{\partial z}p, \; \frac{\partial u}{\partial y} = -\frac{\partial u}{\partial z}q. \qquad (11)$$

Substituting $\partial u/\partial x$ and $\partial u/\partial y$ from (11) in (10), we obtain, after slight simplification,

$$Pp + Qq = R.$$

Hence any solution of (10) is also a solution of (7).

Now consider the equations

$$\frac{dx}{P} = \frac{dy}{Q} = \frac{dz}{R}, \tag{12}$$

or

$$\frac{\dfrac{\partial u}{\partial x}dx}{P\dfrac{\partial u}{\partial x}} = \frac{\dfrac{\partial u}{\partial y}dy}{Q\dfrac{\partial u}{\partial y}} = \frac{\dfrac{\partial u}{\partial z}dz}{R\dfrac{\partial u}{\partial z}}. \tag{13}$$

Since the sum of the antecedents is to the sum of the consequents as any antecedent is to its consequent, we have

$$\frac{\dfrac{\partial u}{\partial x}dx + \dfrac{\partial u}{\partial y}dy + \dfrac{\partial u}{\partial z}dz}{P\dfrac{\partial u}{\partial x} + Q\dfrac{\partial u}{\partial y} + R\dfrac{\partial u}{\partial z}} = \frac{dx}{P} = \frac{dy}{Q} = \frac{dz}{R}. \tag{14}$$

If $u = a$ is an integral of (12), the numerator of the first fraction in (14) is zero and therefore its denominator must be zero. Hence any integral of (12) is also an integral of (10) and therefore of (7).

If $P = 0$ then x must be constant in (12) and x is considered as an integral of (12). If $P = 0$ in (7), it becomes $qQ = R$ and may be integrated by treating x as constant and using a function of x as the constant of integration. Similarly $y = 0$ is an integral of (12) if $Q = 0$, and z is an integral if $R = 0$.

If u and v represent functions of x, y, and z, and $\varphi(u,v)$ is an arbitrary function of u and v, then

$$d\varphi = \frac{\partial\varphi}{\partial u}\left(\frac{\partial u}{\partial x}dx + \frac{\partial u}{\partial y}dy + \frac{\partial u}{\partial z}dz\right) +$$
$$\frac{\partial\varphi}{\partial v}\left(\frac{\partial v}{\partial x}dx + \frac{\partial v}{\partial y}dy + \frac{\partial v}{\partial z}\,dz\right).$$

Hence, if u and v are integrals of (12), $d\varphi = 0$ and $\varphi(u,v) = 0$ is a solution of (10) and therefore of (7).

Letting $u = \psi(v)$ be the result of solving $\varphi(u,v) = 0$, for u in terms of v, we see that the general solution of (7) may be written $u = \psi(v)$.

In summary, if u(x,y,z) = a *and* v(x,y,z) = b *are two independent integrals of the ordinary differential equations*

$$\frac{dx}{P(x,y,z)} = \frac{dy}{Q(x,y,z)} = \frac{dz}{R(x,y,z)}, \quad (12)^*$$

then, either

$$\varphi(u,v) = 0, \text{ or } u = \psi(v) \tag{15}$$

is a general solution of

$$Pp + Qq = R. \tag{7}$$

The same line of reasoning shows that

$$\varphi(u_1, u_2, \ldots, u_n) = 0 \tag{16}$$

is the general solution of

$$P_1\frac{\partial z}{\partial x_1} + P_2\frac{\partial z}{\partial x_2} + \cdots + P_n\frac{\partial z}{\partial x_n} = R, \tag{17}$$

provided that

$$u_i(x_1, x_2, \ldots, x_n, z) = a_i, (i = 1, 2, \ldots, n)$$

are independent integrals of the differential equations

$$\frac{dx_1}{P_1} = \frac{dx_2}{P_2} = \cdots = \frac{dx_n}{P_n} = \frac{dz}{R}. \tag{18}$$

*From equation (12) we may write

$$\frac{l\,dx}{lP} = \frac{m\,dy}{mQ} = \frac{n\,dz}{nR} = \frac{l'\,dx}{l'P} = \frac{m'\,dy}{m'Q} = \frac{n'\,dz}{n'R} \tag{a}$$

where l, m, n, l', m', n' represent any expressions involving x, y, z. Hence, by the theory of proportion, we have

$$\frac{l\,dx + m\,dy + n\,dz}{Pl + Qm + Rn} = \frac{l'\,dx + m'\,dy + n'\,dz}{Pl' + Qm' + Rn'}. \tag{b}$$

In solving simultaneous differential equations, this equation (b) may be used to find a relation involving only two variables, or an integrable total differential equation.

Example 1.   Solve $(y + z)p + (x + z)q = x + y$.

Solution.   The first step is to find two integrals of

$$\frac{dx}{y + z} = \frac{dy}{x + z} = \frac{dz}{x + y}. \tag{a}$$

By the theory of proportion, we find from (a)

$$\frac{dx + dy + dz}{2x + 2y + 2z} = \frac{dx - dy}{-(x - y)} = \frac{dx - dz}{-(x - z)}. \tag{b}$$

Two integrals of (b) evidently are

$$\log (x + y + z) + 2 \log (x - y) = C_1, \text{ or}$$
$$(x + y + z)(x - y)^2 = c_1, \tag{c}$$

and

$$\log (x - y) - \log (x - z) = C_2, \text{ or } x - y = c_2(x - z). \tag{d}$$

Hence the solution required is

$$\varphi\left[(x + y + z)(x - y)^2, \ \frac{x - y}{x - z} \right] = 0,$$

or it may be written

$$\mathbf{x} - \mathbf{y} = (\mathbf{x} - \mathbf{z})\varphi[(\mathbf{x} + \mathbf{y} + \mathbf{z})(\mathbf{x} - \mathbf{y})^2].$$

Example 2.   Show how to use the method of this article to find an integrating factor of

$$M(x,y)dx + N(x,y)dy = 0. \tag{a}$$

Solution.   If $\mu(x,y)$ is an integrating factor of the given equation, then

$$\mu M \, dx + \mu N \, dy = 0 \tag{b}$$

is exact.   Hence, applying test (22) of §24, we have

$$\frac{\partial(\mu M)}{\partial y} = \frac{\partial(\mu N)}{\partial x}. \tag{c}$$

Performing the indicated differentiation and rearranging terms, we obtain

$$M\frac{\partial \mu}{\partial y} - N\frac{\partial \mu}{\partial x} = \mu\left(\frac{\partial N}{\partial x} - \frac{\partial M}{\partial y}\right). \tag{d}$$

Hence, any particular solution involving μ of

$$\frac{dx}{-N} = \frac{dy}{M} = \frac{d\mu}{\mu\left(\dfrac{\partial N}{\partial x} - \dfrac{\partial M}{\partial y}\right)} \qquad (e)$$

gives an integrating factor.

Exercises

1. $p + q = z$

2. $xp + yq = 2z$

3. $xp + zq = y$

4. $ap + bq = c$

5. $xp + zq + y = 0$

6. $xyq - x^2p = y^2$

7. $x^2p + y^2q = axy$

8. $yzp + xzq + 2xy = 0$

9. $xy^2p - y^3q + axz = 0$

10. $(x + y)(p - q) = z$

11. $xp + yq = 0$. *Hint:* $z = a$ is one required integral.

12. $zq = y$. *Hint:* $x = a$ is one required integral.

13. $(x + y)p = x - z$

14. $(x + y)p + (x - y)q = 0$

15. $yp + xq = x^2 - y^2 - z$

16. $\dfrac{\partial^2 z}{\partial x\, \partial y} + y\dfrac{\partial^2 z}{\partial x^2} = 4x$. *Hint:* First integrate with respect to x, treating y as constant. Observe that $\displaystyle\int^x \psi_1(ye^{-x})dx = \int^x \psi'(ye^{-x})$ $(-ye^{-x}\, dx) = \psi(ye^{-x}) + \varphi(y)$.

17. $x\dfrac{\partial^2 z}{\partial x^2} + y\dfrac{\partial^2 z}{\partial x\, \partial y} + \dfrac{\partial z}{\partial x} = 2x + y$

18. If u and v are functions of x, y, and z, and φ is an arbitrary function, prove that $\varphi(u,v) = 0$ satisfies a partial differential equation of the first order and first degree.

19. The solution of

$$py - qx = y \qquad (a)$$

is

$$\varphi(x^2 + y^2, z - x) = 0. \qquad (b)$$

Prove that any surface represented by (b) contains the curve

$$x^2 + y^2 = a^2 + b^2,\ z - x = c - a \qquad (c)$$

if (a,b,c) is a point on the surface. How many curves (c) lie on each surface defined by (b)?

20. Determine the equations of the surfaces that cut orthogonally the system of ellipsoids $\dfrac{x^2}{5} + \dfrac{y^2}{3} + z^2 = c^2$

21. Find an integrating factor of each equation by using (e) of Example 2 and solve:

  (a) $(2x + 2 + x^2 + y)dx - (x + 1)dy = 0$

  (b) $(4x^3 - y^2)dx + 2xy\,dy = 0$

  (c) $(2x^3y + y^3)dx - (x^4 + xy^2)dy = 0$

22. Using formula (e) of Example 2, find an integrating factor of

$$(y + y^2)dx - (x + y^2 + 2xy)dy = 0$$

23. Use formula (e) of Example 2 to find an integrating factor of

$$M\,dx + N\,dy = 0 \text{ if } \frac{\partial N}{\partial x} - \frac{\partial M}{\partial y} \text{ is equal to}$$

    (a) $Mf(y)$ (b) $Nf(x)$ (c) $k(xM - yN)/xy$

    (d) $\dfrac{2(Nx - My)}{x^2 + y^2}$ (e) $\dfrac{axM - byN}{xy}$

24. Use formula (e) of Example 2 to find an integrating factor of

$$[ay^n + by^m + Q(x)y]dx + [a(n - 1)y^{n-1} + b(m - 1)y^{m-1}]dy = 0$$

98. Determination of arbitrary function by means of initial conditions.

In the treatment of ordinary differential equations the arbitrary functions were determined by initial conditions consisting of corresponding particular values of the variables and their derivatives. The arbitrary functions in the solutions of partial differential equations are often determined by given functional relations among the variables and their derivatives. For example, the arbitrary function of a solution representing surfaces in space by means of a relation involving only one arbitrary function, might be determined by specifying that the surface contain a particular curve in the xz-plane. The equations of the curve would be the determining functional relations. The following example will serve to introduce the subject of boundary conditions, and applications later in the book will throw more light on the processes involving them.

  Example.   Find the solution of

$$yp + xq = z$$

representing a surface passing through the curve:

(I) $z = e^{x^2},\ y = 2.$

(II) $z = \dfrac{1}{1\cdot 2} + \dfrac{x}{2\cdot 3} + \dfrac{x^2}{3\cdot 4} + \cdots,\ y = 0.$

(III) $x + y + z = 3,\ z^2(x - y) = 2.$

Solution. The general solution of the equation, in accordance with §97 may be written

$$\varphi\left[\frac{z}{x+y}, z(x-y)\right] = 0. \qquad (a)$$

Let

$$\frac{z}{x+y} = u, \; z(x-y) = v. \qquad (b)$$

(I) In (b) replace y by 2 and solve for x and z in terms of u and v to obtain

$$x = \sqrt{4+\frac{v}{u}}, \; z = 2u + u\sqrt{4+\frac{v}{u}}. \qquad (c)$$

Now substitute these values for x and z in $z - e^{x^2} = 0$ to get

$$u\left(2 + \sqrt{4+\frac{v}{u}}\right) - e^{4+v/u} = 0.$$

In this, replace u and v by their values from (b) to get

$$\left(\frac{z}{x+y}\right)(2 + \sqrt{4+x^2-y^2}) - e^{4+x^2-y^2} = 0. \qquad (d)$$

Observe from (c) that the radical has the same sign as x. This result (d) is a solution since it is a special case of (a) and $z - e^{x^2} = 0$ is obtained from it by replacing y by 2.

(II) In (b) replace y by zero and solve the results for x and z in terms of u and v to obtain

$$x = \sqrt{\frac{v}{u}}, \; z = u\sqrt{\frac{v}{u}} = \sqrt{uv}. \qquad (e)$$

Substitute these values for x and z in

$$z = \frac{1}{1\cdot 2} + \frac{x}{2\cdot 3} + \cdots$$

and replace u and v in the result by their values from (b) to obtain after slight simplification

$$z = \sqrt{\frac{x+y}{x-y}}\left[\frac{1}{1\cdot 2} + \frac{\sqrt{x^2-y^2}}{2\cdot 3} + \frac{(\sqrt{x^2-y^2})^2}{3\cdot 4} + \cdots\right]. \qquad (f)$$

From (e) it appears that each radical takes the same sign as x.

(III) The plan of solution is to eliminate x, y, and z from the equations of the curve and (b), and replace u and v in the result by their values from (b). In $x + y + z = 3$ replace $x + y$ by z/u from (b) to obtain

$$z + \frac{z}{u} = 3. \tag{g}$$

In $z^2(x - y) = 2$, replace $z(x - y)$ by v to obtain

$$zv = 2. \tag{h}$$

Replace z in (g) by its value from (h) and in the result replace u and v by their values from (b) to obtain after slight simplification

$$\mathbf{2x + 2y + 2z = 3z^2(x - y).}$$

Exercises

1. Solve the example in §98 without reference to the given solution.

2. Find the solution of $xp + yq = z$ representing a surface containing the curve $z = \sin y$, $x = a$.

3. Show that a general solution of $p + q = z$ is

$$\varphi(ze^{-x}, x - y) = 0.$$

Find a surface represented by this solution and passing through the curve: (a) $z = \sin x$, $y = 0$. (b) $z = y^2$, $x = a$. (c) $x^2 + z^2 = a^2$, $y = 0$. (d) $x^2 - y^2 = 36$, $\log z = x - y$.

4. Find the equation of a surface for which

$$xyq - x^2p = y^2,$$

and find the particular solution satisfying the condition:

(a) $3q = 27y^2 + 8y$ when $x = 1$.   (b) $p = q$ when $x = 1$.

Hint: Write the solution in the form $z = y^2/3x + \varphi(xy)$.

5. Find the equation of a surface satisfying the condition $\partial^2 z/\partial x^2 = 0$, cutting the yz-plane in $z = y^2$, $x = 0$, and passing through curve $z = x$, $xy = 10$.

99. General, complete, singular solution.

Consider the general partial differential equation of the first order represented by

$$f(x,y,z,p,q) = 0. \tag{19}$$

A solution of (19) involving an arbitrary function will be referred to as a *general solution;* a solution having the form

$$\varphi(x,y,z,a,b) = 0, \tag{20}$$

where a and b are two arbitrary constants, will be called a *complete solution.*

The next article outlines the method of Lagrange and Charpit for finding a complete solution of a partial differential equation of the first order, and this article considers methods of finding the singular solution and a general solution from a complete solution.

Consider equation (20) as a known complete solution of (19). Then since z is a function of x and y, we have

$$dz = p \, dx + q \, dy, \tag{21}$$

where p and q are defined by

$$\frac{\partial \varphi}{\partial x} + \frac{\partial \varphi}{\partial z}p = 0, \frac{\partial \varphi}{\partial y} + \frac{\partial \varphi}{\partial z}q = 0. \tag{22}$$

From (20) other solutions of (19) may be obtained by treating a and b in (20) as functions of x and y. The following equations then take the place of (22):

$$\left. \begin{array}{l} \dfrac{\partial \varphi}{\partial x} + \dfrac{\partial \varphi}{\partial z}p + \dfrac{\partial \varphi}{\partial a}\dfrac{\partial a}{\partial x} + \dfrac{\partial \varphi}{\partial b}\dfrac{\partial b}{\partial x} = 0, \\[2mm] \dfrac{\partial \varphi}{\partial y} + \dfrac{\partial \varphi}{\partial z}q + \dfrac{\partial \varphi}{\partial a}\dfrac{\partial a}{\partial y} + \dfrac{\partial \varphi}{\partial b}\dfrac{\partial b}{\partial y} = 0. \end{array} \right\} \tag{23}$$

Comparing (23) and (22), we see that p and q will take values at any point (x,y,z) that will satisfy (19), if

$$\left. \begin{array}{l} \dfrac{\partial \varphi}{\partial a}\dfrac{\partial a}{\partial x} + \dfrac{\partial \varphi}{\partial b}\dfrac{\partial b}{\partial x} = 0, \\[2mm] \dfrac{\partial \varphi}{\partial a}\dfrac{\partial a}{\partial y} + \dfrac{\partial \varphi}{\partial b}\dfrac{\partial b}{\partial y} = 0. \end{array} \right\} \tag{24}$$

Equations (24) will be satisfied, if

$$\frac{\partial \varphi}{\partial a} = 0, \frac{\partial \varphi}{\partial b} = 0. \tag{25}$$

Elimination of a and b between (25) and (20) gives the equation of the envelope of the surfaces represented by (20). The equation of this envelope is called the *singular solution*.*

The condition that equations (24) be consistent is

$$\begin{vmatrix} \dfrac{\partial a}{\partial x} & \dfrac{\partial b}{\partial x} \\[2ex] \dfrac{\partial a}{\partial y} & \dfrac{\partial b}{\partial y} \end{vmatrix} = 0, \qquad (26)$$

and this is also the condition that b be a function of a,

$$b = \psi(a), \qquad (27)$$

where ψ represents an arbitrary function. If (27) holds, we have, from (24),

$$\frac{\partial \varphi}{\partial a} + \frac{\partial \varphi}{\partial b} \frac{d\psi}{da} = 0, \qquad (28)$$

and the result of eliminating a and b from (20), (27), and (28) is a solution. This last solution is the *general solution*, since it involves an arbitrary function. For each particular function $\psi_1(a)$, equations (20), (27), and (28) represent the envelope of $\varphi[x,y,z,a,\psi_1(a)] = 0$ and the general solution represents the total system of such envelopes.†

It now appears that, if we can find a complete solution

$$\varphi(x,y,z,a,b) = 0 \qquad (20)$$

---

* The equation of the envelope of a two-parameter family of surfaces $\varphi(x,y,z,a,b) = 0$, if there is one, is found generally by eliminating the parameters a and b from

$$\varphi(x,y,z,a,b) = 0, \quad \frac{\partial \varphi}{\partial a} = 0, \quad \frac{\partial \varphi}{\partial b} = 0.$$

Any factor of the eliminant used as a solution of a given differential equation should be tested by substitution in the equation.

† If the one-parameter family of surfaces represented by $\varphi(x,y,z,a) = 0$ has an envelope, it is generally found by eliminating the parameter a between $\varphi(x,y,z,a) = 0$, $\dfrac{\partial \varphi}{\partial a} = 0$.

of a partial differential equation

$$f(x,y,z,p,q) = 0, \tag{19}$$

then any singular solution that may exist can be found by eliminating a *and* b *from*

$$\varphi = 0, \frac{\partial \varphi}{\partial a} = 0, \frac{\partial \varphi}{\partial b} = 0, \tag{29}$$

and the general solution is represented by

$$\varphi_1[x,y,z,a] = \varphi[x,y,z,a,\psi(a)] = 0, \frac{\partial \varphi_1}{\partial a} = 0, \tag{30}$$

where ψ *represents an arbitrary function.*

Example.   Discuss the solutions of

$$z^2(p^2 + q^2 + 1) = 1. \tag{a}$$

Solution.   By substitution it is easy to show that

$$(x - a)^2 + (y - b)^2 + z^2 = 1 \tag{b}$$

is a complete solution of (a). Equating to zero the partial derivatives of (b) with respect to a and to b, we obtain

$$x - a = 0, y - b = 0. \tag{c}$$

Eliminating a and b from (b) and (c), we get

$$z = \pm 1,$$

as the singular solution of (b). It is the envelope of the spheres represented by (a). Obviously the spheres (b) have their centers in the xy-plane and, having 1 as radius, are tangent to the planes $z = \pm 1$. The general solution, in accordance with (30), is represented by

$$[x - a]^2 + [y - \psi(a)]^2 + z^2 = 1,$$
$$x - a + [y - \psi(a)]\psi'(a) = 0. \tag{d}$$

Observe that $\psi(a)$ is an arbitrary function. In general, to each function ψ there is associated a solution. Thus if $\psi(a) = 3$ in (d), we have from (d) $(x - a)^2 + (y - 3)^2 + z^2 = 1$, $x - a = 0$; that is,

$$(y - 3)^2 + z^2 = 1, \tag{e}$$

a right circular cylinder of radius 1 and axis through $(0,3,0)$ parallel to the X-axis. The cylinder (e) is the envelope of the spheres $(x - a)^2 + (y - 3)^2 + z^2 = 1$.

Exercises

1. Show that, if $\psi(a) = a$ in equation (d) of §99 the particular solution represented is the right circular cylinder $(x - y)^2 + 2z^2 = 2$.

2. Verify that the partial differential equation

$$z = px + qy + pq \qquad (A)$$

has $z = ax + by + ab$ as a complete solution. Show that the singular solution of (A) is $z = -xy$ and write the general solution in the form indicated by (30). Also find the particular solution corresponding to $\psi(a) = a$.

3. Show that $z = ax + by$, representing planes through $(0,0,0)$, is a complete solution of $z = px + qy$. Find the general solution in the form indicated by (30). Note that a is an arbitrary function of y/x and therefore that $z/x = a + \psi(a)\left(\dfrac{y}{x}\right) = \varphi(y/x)$.

4. Show that $2(x - a)^2 + 2(y - b)^2 + 2z^2 = a^2 + b^2$ is a complete solution of

$$z^2(p^2 + q^2 + 2) = x^2 + y^2 + 2z(px + qy).$$

Show that the singular solution is the cone $z^2 = x^2 + y^2$. Find the general solution in form (30), and find the particular solution corresponding to $\psi(a) = a$. Give a complete geometric interpretation.

5. Find a partial differential equation whose complete solution is $4(x - a)^2 + 4(y - b)^2 + z^2 = (b - a)^2$. Find its singular solution and its general solution. Give a complete geometric interpretation of the solutions.

100. General equation of the first order.
The object of this article is to explain the method, developed by Lagrange and Charpit, of solving an equation of the form

$$F(x,y,z,p,q) = 0. \qquad (31)$$

The variables p, q, and z are functions of x and y connected by the equations

$$p = \frac{\partial z}{\partial x}, \; q = \frac{\partial z}{\partial y}, \frac{\partial p}{\partial y} = \frac{\partial q}{\partial x}, \qquad (32)$$

and

$$dz = p\,dx + q\,dy. \tag{33}$$

The third equation of (32) is evidently the condition that (33) be integrable. It holds true whenever its members are continuous functions of x, y, and z.

The general method of solving (31) *consists in deriving another equation*

$$\varphi(x,y,z,p,q) = 0, \tag{34}$$

solving it simultaneously with (31) *for* p *and* q, *substituting the values thus found in* (33), *and integrating the resulting equation.**

It is important then to find a method of obtaining a relation having the form (34). By differentiating each of the equations (31) and (34) partially with respect to x and with respect to y, we obtain

$$\left.\begin{aligned}
\frac{\partial F}{\partial x} + \frac{\partial F}{\partial z}p + \frac{\partial F}{\partial p}\frac{\partial p}{\partial x} + \frac{\partial F}{\partial q}\frac{\partial q}{\partial x} &= 0, \\[4pt]
\frac{\partial F}{\partial y} + \frac{\partial F}{\partial z}q + \frac{\partial F}{\partial p}\frac{\partial p}{\partial y} + \frac{\partial F}{\partial q}\frac{\partial q}{\partial y} &= 0, \\[4pt]
\frac{\partial \varphi}{\partial x} + \frac{\partial \varphi}{\partial z}p + \frac{\partial \varphi}{\partial p}\frac{\partial p}{\partial x} + \frac{\partial \varphi}{\partial q}\frac{\partial q}{\partial x} &= 0, \\[4pt]
\frac{\partial \varphi}{\partial y} + \frac{\partial \varphi}{\partial z}q + \frac{\partial \varphi}{\partial p}\frac{\partial p}{\partial y} + \frac{\partial \varphi}{\partial q}\frac{\partial q}{\partial y} &= 0.
\end{aligned}\right\} \tag{35}$$

From these four equations we may eliminate the three quantities $\partial p/\partial x$, $\partial q/\partial y$, and $\partial p/\partial y = \partial q/\partial x$. Multiply the first equation by $-\partial\varphi/\partial p$, the second by $-\partial\varphi/\partial q$, the

---

* The equations represented by (31) and (34) can be solved for p and q in terms of x, y, and z provided that

$$\begin{vmatrix} \dfrac{\partial F}{\partial p} & \dfrac{\partial F}{\partial q} \\[8pt] \dfrac{\partial \varphi}{\partial p} & \dfrac{\partial \phi}{\partial q} \end{vmatrix}$$

is not identically zero.

third by $\partial F/\partial p$, and the fourth by $\partial F/\partial q$, add the four results, and rearrange terms to obtain

$$\frac{\partial F}{\partial p}\frac{\partial \varphi}{\partial x} + \frac{\partial F}{\partial q}\frac{\partial \varphi}{\partial y} - \left(\frac{\partial F}{\partial x} + p\frac{\partial F}{\partial z}\right)\frac{\partial \varphi}{\partial p} - \left(\frac{\partial F}{\partial y} + q\frac{\partial F}{\partial z}\right)\frac{\partial \varphi}{\partial q} +$$

$$\left(p\frac{\partial F}{\partial p} + q\frac{\partial F}{\partial q}\right)\frac{\partial \varphi}{\partial z} = 0. \quad (36)$$

This is an equation of the first order connecting the variables x, y, z, p, q, and φ. Consequently it may be solved by equating to zero an arbitrary function of integrals of

$$\frac{dp}{-\left(\dfrac{\partial F}{\partial x} + p\dfrac{\partial F}{\partial z}\right)} = \frac{dq}{-\left(\dfrac{\partial F}{\partial y} + q\dfrac{\partial F}{\partial z}\right)}$$

$$= \frac{dx}{\dfrac{\partial F}{\partial p}} = \frac{dy}{\dfrac{\partial F}{\partial q}} = \frac{dz}{p\dfrac{\partial F}{\partial p} + q\dfrac{\partial F}{\partial q}}. \quad (37)$$

Since any integral of (37) will be sufficient for our purposes, we choose the simplest one involving p, q, or both, and an arbitrary constant.

Example. Solve

$$pq = z. \quad (a)$$

Solution. Equation (37) for this case is

$$\frac{dx}{q} = \frac{dy}{p} = \frac{dp}{p} = \frac{dq}{q} = \frac{dz}{2pq}. \quad (b)$$

From the equality of the second and third fractions we find the integral

$$p = y + a. \quad (c)$$

Solving (a) and (c) for p and q, we have

$$p = y + a, \quad q = \frac{z}{y + a}. \quad (d)$$

Substitution of p and q from (d) in (33) gives

$$dz = (y + a)dx + \frac{z}{y + a}dy. \quad (e)$$

The solution of (e) is the complete integral*

$$z = (x + b)(y + a).$$

There is no singular solution, and the general solution is represented by

$$z = (y + a)[x + \varphi(a)], \quad x + (y + a)\frac{d\varphi}{da} + \varphi(a) = 0,$$

where φ represents an arbitrary function of a.

Exercises

1. To find a complete integral of $z = p + q$, use the first two ratios of (37) to get

$$\frac{dp}{-p} = \frac{dq}{-q}, \text{ or } p = aq.$$

Now substitute this value of p in $z = p + q$ and solve to find $q = z/(1 + a)$. Hence $p = az/(1 + a)$. Hence solve

$$dz = p\, dx + q\, dy = \frac{az}{1 + a}\, dx + \frac{z}{1 + a}\, dy$$

to get the complete solution $(1 + a) \log z = ax + y + b$.

2. Find a complete solution of

(a) $z = 5p + 6q$ \qquad\qquad (b) $z = pq$

3. Find a complete solution of $2xz = p + q$. *Hint:* Use the second and third ratios of (37). To integrate

$$dz = (2xz - ae^{x^2})dx + ae^{x^2}\, dy,$$

write it in the form

$$e^{-x^2}(dz - 2xz) = -a\, dx + a\, dy.$$

4. Find a complete solution of $px + qy = 0$. *Hint:* Use the first and third ratios of (37).

5. Using the first and second ratios of (37), show that $p = aq$ may be used in solving $f(z,p,q) = 0$. Find a complete solution of

(a) $z^2 = p + q$ \qquad\qquad (c) $z^2(p^2 + q^2 + 1) = c^2$
(b) $p^2 + q^2 = z$ \qquad\qquad (d) $z^{2n-2}(p^2 z^n + pq) = R^2$

6. $z = px + qy + f(p,q)$ is analogous to Clairaut's equation of §42. Show by direct substitution that $z = ax + by + f(a,b)$ is a solution of it. Find a complete solution of:

(a) $z = px + qy + pq$ \qquad\qquad (c) $z = px + qy$
(b) $z = px + qy - np^{1/n}\, q^{1/n}$ \qquad (d) $f(z - px - qy, p, q) = 0$

* See §81.

7. In solving a partial differential equation having the form $f(x,p) = \varphi(y,q)$, show that $f(x,p) = a$, $\varphi(y,q) = a$ may be used. Solve:

(a) $p + x = q - y$

(c) $p^2 y = q^2 x$

(b) $p^2 - q^2 = x - y$

(d) $p - \dfrac{df(x)}{dx} = q + \dfrac{dF(y)}{dy}$

8. Prove that $z = ax + by + c$ is a solution of $F(p,q) = 0$, provided that $F(a,b) = 0$. Solve:

(a) $pq = 1$

(c) $p = e^q$

(b) $3p^2 - 2q^2 = pq$

(d) $p + q^2 + 5q = 6$

9. Find a complete solution of:

(a) $p = 2xq^2$

(d) $z(p^2 - q^2) = x - y$

(b) $(p^2 + q^2)x = pz$

(e) $(2x - y)q^2 - p = 0$

(c) $(p^2 + q^2)y = z$

(f) $z = 2x^3 q^2 - px$

CHAPTER XIII

PARTIAL DIFFERENTIAL EQUATIONS OF ORDER HIGHER THAN THE FIRST

101. Definitions. The equation

$$\sum_{i=0,j=0}^{n,n} A_{ij}\frac{\partial^{i+j}z}{\partial x^i\,\partial y^j} = f(x,y),\ i + j \leqq n,\ \frac{\partial^0 z}{\partial x^\circ\,\partial y^\circ} = z, \quad (1)$$

where the quantities A_{ij} are functions of x and y or constants, being linear in the dependent variable z and its derivatives, is referred to as the *general linear partial differential equation*. If $i + j$ for every term in the left-hand member is equal to a constant n and $f(x,y) = 0$, the equation is called *homogeneous*.

In this chapter, we shall consider methods of solving equation (1) in case the A_{ij} are constant and also in case the equation is of the second order with the A_{ij} functions of x, y, z, p, and q.

102. Notation. Operators. As methods of procedure in solving linear partial equations are similar in many respects to those used in the case of ordinary linear differential equations, we shall use similar notation. Writing

$$D \text{ for } \frac{\partial}{\partial x},\ D' \text{ for } \frac{\partial}{\partial y}, \quad (2)$$

we define $F(D,D')z$ by the equation

$$\sum_{i=1,j=1}^{m,n} A_{ij}\frac{\partial^{i+j}z}{\partial x^i\,\partial y^j} + A_{00}z =$$

$$\sum_{i=1,j=1}^{m,n} A_{ij}D^i D'^j z + A_{00}z = F(D,D')z, \quad (3)$$

where the A_{ij} are constants and i and j are positive integers. Equation (1) may now be written

$$F(D,D')z = f(x,y), \qquad (4)$$

provided that the A_{ij} are constants. The student can show by the methods used in the case of operators for ordinary differential equations that

$$F(D,D')(z_1 + z_2 + \cdots) = F(D,D')z_1 + F(D,D')z_2 + \cdots, \quad (5)$$

and that

$$F(D,D')G(D,D')z = G(D,D') \cdot F(D,D')z. \qquad (6)$$

From (5) it appears that, when $z = z_1(x,y)$, $z = z_2(x,y)$, $\ldots$, are solutions of (4), then

$$z = z_1 + z_2 + \cdots \qquad (7)$$

is also a solution; that is, *the sum of any number of solutions of* (4) *is also a solution.* *Equation* (6) *indicates that when* $F(D,D')$ *is factored any order of the factors may be used.*

It is easy to verify that

$$(D - mD')\,[\varphi(y + mx)\psi(x)] = \varphi(y + mx)\frac{d\psi}{dx}. \qquad (8)$$

and, by applying (8) k times, in succession, that

$$(D - mD')^k[\varphi(y + mx)\psi(x)] = \varphi(y + mx)\frac{d^k\psi}{dx^k}. \qquad (9)$$

Similarly, the student may verify that

$$(D - mD' - n)[e^{nx}\varphi(y + mx)\psi(x)] =$$

$$e^{nx}\varphi(y + mx)\frac{d\psi}{dx}, \quad (10)$$

and then apply (10) repeatedly to obtain

$$(D - mD' - n)^k[e^{nx}\varphi(y + mx)\psi(x)] =$$

$$e^{nx}\varphi(y + mx)\frac{d^k\psi}{dx^k}. \quad (11)$$

103. Homogeneous partial differential equation. The general solution of the simplest type of homogeneous equation

$A_1 \dfrac{\partial z}{\partial x} + A_2 \dfrac{\partial z}{\partial y} = 0$, according to §97, is $z = \varphi\left(y - \dfrac{A_2 x}{A_1}\right)$ where φ represents an arbitrary function. This suggests that the more general equation

$$F(D,D')z = A_0 \frac{\partial^n z}{\partial x^n} + A_1 \frac{\partial^n z}{\partial x^{n-1} \partial y} + \cdots + A_n \frac{\partial^n z}{\partial y^n} = 0, \quad (12)$$

where the A's are constants, may have a solution of the form

$$z = \varphi(y + mx). \tag{13}$$

Substituting z from (13) in (12), we obtain

$$\varphi^{(n)} (A_0 m^n + A_1 m^{n-1} + \cdots + A_n) = 0, \tag{14}$$

where $\varphi^{(n)}$ is the nth derivative of $\varphi(y + mx)$ with respect to $y + mx$. If $\varphi^{(n)}$ is deleted from equation (14), the result is called the *auxiliary equation*. If m is a root of (14), evidently (13) is a solution of (12). Hence, if $m_1, m_2, \ldots, m_n$ are n distinct roots of

$$F(m, 1) = 0, \tag{15}$$

it appears that

$$z_1 = \varphi_1(y + m_1 x), z_2 = \varphi_2(y + m_2 x), \ldots \tag{16}$$

are solutions of (12) and therefore that

$$z = \varphi_1(y + m_1 x) + \varphi_2(y + m_2 x) + \cdots + \\ \varphi_n(y + m_n x) \tag{17}$$

is the general solution of (12).

Similarly by substituting $z = \varphi(x + ky)$ in (12) we get

$$\varphi^{(n)} (A_0 + A_1 k^1 + \cdots + A_{n-1} k^{n-1} + A_n k^n) = 0 \tag{18}$$

and, just as before, obtain the roots $k_1, k_2, \ldots, k_n$ and the corresponding solution

$$z = \psi_1(x + k_1 y) + \psi_2(x + k_2 y) + \cdots + \psi_n(x + k_n y). \tag{19}$$

The result of deleting $\varphi^{(n)}$ from (14) or (18) is referred to as an *auxiliary equation*.

The roots $k_1, k_2, \ldots$ of (18) are, as a whole, the reciprocals of the roots m_1, m_2, . . . of (14).* The arbitrary functions indicated by (17) or (19) may be used in a solution to correspond with non-zero roots of an auxiliary equation; but to a root $m = 0$ of (14) corresponds $\varphi(y)$ and to a root $k = 0$ of (18) corresponds $\psi(x)$ where φ and ψ represent arbitrary functions.

For example, to solve

$$\frac{\partial^2 z}{\partial x^2} + \frac{\partial^2 z}{\partial x\,\partial y} - 2\frac{\partial^2 z}{\partial y^2} = 0, \qquad (20)$$

write

$$m^2 + m - 2 = 0, \text{ or } m = -2, 1,$$

and as the corresponding solution

$$z = \varphi_1(y - 2x) + \varphi_2(y + x);$$

or write

$$1 + k - 2k^2 = 0, k = -\tfrac{1}{2}, 1$$

and, as the corresponding solution,

$$z = \psi(x - \tfrac{1}{2}y) + \psi_2(x + y).$$

In solving the equation

$$(D^2D' + DD'^2 - 6D'^3)z = 0,$$

we get, as the roots of the auxiliary equation,

$$m_1 = 2, m_2 = -3; k_1 = \tfrac{1}{2}, k_2 = -\tfrac{1}{3}, k_3 = 0,$$

and write the solution in the form

$$z = \varphi_1(y + 2x) + \varphi_2(y - 3x) + \psi(x).$$

The first two functions could have been written in the form $\psi_1(x + \tfrac{1}{2}y) + \psi_2(x - \tfrac{1}{3}y)$, but the last had to be an arbitrary function of x.

104. Auxiliary equation contains multiple roots. If a root of (15) is multiple, the sum of several of the arbitrary functions of (17) could be replaced by a single function and the solution would involve a smaller number of arbitrary func-

---

* If a root m of (14) is zero, the corresponding root k of (18) does not exist; conversely, if a root k is zero, the corresponding root m does not exist.

tions than n. Suppose that m is a p-fold multiple root of (15). The corresponding case of ordinary differential equations suggest that

$$z_p = \varphi_0(y + mx) + x\varphi_1(y + m_1x) + \cdots +$$
$$x^{p-1}\varphi_{p-1}(y + mx) \quad (21)$$

may be a solution. Substituting z from (21) in (12) and taking account of (9), we have

$$F(D,D')z_p = \psi(D,D')[(D - mD')^p \sum_{k=0}^{p-1} x^k\varphi_k(y + mx)] =$$
$$\psi(D,D')(0) = 0; \quad (22)$$

that is, (21) is the part of the general solution of (12) corresponding to a p-fold root of (15).

Similarly if the auxiliary equation $F(1, k) = 0$ has a root k repeated p times, the corresponding part of the solution may be written

$$z_p = \psi_0(x + ky) + y\psi_1(x + ky) + \cdots$$
$$+ y^{p-1}\psi_p(x + ky). \quad (23)$$

For example, an auxiliary equation of $(D - aD')D'^3z = 0$ is

$$(1 - ak)k^3 = 0, \text{ or } k = 1/a, 0, 0, 0,$$

and the solution of $(D - aD')D'^3z = 0$ is

$$z = \psi_1\left(x + \frac{y}{a}\right) + \psi_2(x) + y\psi_3(x) + y^2\psi_4(x).$$

105. Auxiliary equation contains imaginary roots. The part of a solution corresponding to a pair of complex roots $a \pm ib(i = \sqrt{-1})$ is

$$\varphi[y + (a + ib)x] + \psi[y + (a - ib)x]. \quad (24)$$

Since

$$f(x + iy) = \psi_1(x,y) + i\psi_2(x,y), \Big\}$$
$$f(x - iy) = \psi_1(x,y) - i\psi_2(x,y), \Big\} \quad (25)$$

where ψ_1 and ψ_2 represent *real* functions, it appears that

$$[f(x + iy) + f(x - iy)] \text{ and } [f(x + iy) - f(x - iy)]i$$

are real functions. Hence, the part of a solution corresponding to a pair of complex roots $a \pm ib$ of the auxiliary equation may be written

$$f_1(y + ax + ibx) + f_1(y + ax - ibx) + i[f_2(y + ax + ibx) - f_2(y + ax - ibx)]. \quad (26)$$

The form (26) is often inconvenient to use. Therefore another solution will be derived. Observe that

$$a_n[e^{ny+n(a+ib)x} + e^{ny+n(a-ib)x}] = a_n e^{n(y+a)} \cos nbx,$$

$$\frac{1}{i} b_n[e^{ny+n(a+ib)x} - e^{ny+n(a-ib)x}] = b_n e^{n(y+a)} \sin nbx, \quad (27)$$

are particular cases of (26). Since sums of the terms in (27) may be used, we may write as a solution of (12)

$$z = \sum^n e^{n(y+ax)}(a_n \cos nbx + b_n \sin nbx), \quad (28)$$

where a_n and b_n are arbitrary constants and (28) represents the sum of terms obtained by replacing n in succession by the values in any group of numbers. In particular, if n indicates the infinite series of integers 1, 2, . . . , (28) represents an infinite series.

In summary, the general solution of the homogeneous partial differential equation with constant coefficients $F(D,D')z = 0$ *is written*

$$z = z_d + z_m + z_c, \quad (29)$$

where z_d *for distinct roots,* z_m *for multiple roots, and* z_c *for complex roots represent sums of expressions having the forms indicated in* (16), (21), *and* (26) *or* (27), *respectively.*

By way of illustration, it appears that the auxiliary equation of $(D^5 - D^4D' + D^3D'^2 - D^2D'^3)z = 0$ has the roots, 0, 0, 1, $\pm i$. Hence the general solution is

$$z = \varphi_1(y) + x\varphi_2(y) + \varphi_3(y + x) + \sum^n e^{ny}(a_n \cos nx + b_n \sin nx).$$

Exercises

1. $D(D^2 - DD' - 2D'^2)z = 0$ 6. $(D^2 + a^2D'^2)z = 0$
2. $(D^4 + D'D^3)z = 0$ 7. $(D^2 - a^2D'^2)z = 0$
3. $D'^2(D - 2D')z = 0$ 8. $(D^4 - a^4D'^4)z = 0$
4. $D^2D'^2z = 0$ 9. $(D^3 - 8D'^3)z = 0$
5. $(D^2 - 4DD' + 13D'^2)z = 0$ 10. $D^n z = 0$

11. Find the solution of $(D^2 - D'^2)z = 0$ for which $z = 6x^2$, and $\partial z/\partial y = 6x^2 + 6$ when $y = 0$. *Hint:* Show that $z = \varphi(x + y) + \psi(x - y)$, $(z)_{y=c} = \varphi(x) + \psi(x) = 6x^2$, $\left(\dfrac{\partial z}{\partial x}\right)_{y=0} = \dfrac{\partial \varphi(x)}{\partial x} + \dfrac{\partial \psi(x)}{\partial x} = 12x$.

12. Find the solution of $D(D^2 - 4D'^2)z = 0$, for which $z = 8y^2$, $\partial z/\partial x = 0$, $\partial^2 z/\partial x^2 = 16$ when $x = 0$.

106. Linear equation with constant coefficients.   In this article, we shall deal with the general equation

$$F(D,D')z = \sum_{i=0,j=0}^{n,n} A_{ij}\frac{\partial^{i+j}z}{\partial x^i\,\partial y^j} = 0,\ i + j \leqq n, \qquad (30)$$

where the A_{ij} are constants.   To solve this, make the substitution

$$z = ce^{hx+ky} \qquad (31)$$

and, since $D^iD'^ie^{hx+ky} = h^ik^ie^{hx+ky}$, obtain

$$F(h,k)ce^{hx+ky} = 0.$$

In order that (31) be a solution, $F(h,k)$ must vanish.   Represent any linear factor of $F(h,k)$ by

$$h - mk - n. \qquad (32)$$

$F(h,k)$ will vanish if any one of its factors vanishes, that is, if $h = mk + n$.   Substitution of this value of h in (31) gives the solution

$$z = ce^{nx}e^{k(y+mx)}.$$

The numbers k and c are arbitrary, and, in accordance with (7), we can add together any number of terms like the right-hand member, to obtain

$$z = e^{nx}\sum^{k} c_k e^{k(y+mx)}, \qquad (33)$$

where c_k is an arbitrary constant and the sum extends over any group of numbers for k. Equation (33) suggests that

$$z = e^{nx}\varphi(y + mx), \qquad (34)$$

where φ represents an arbitrary function, may be a solution of (30). Since $F(D,D') = F_1(D,D')(D - mD' - n)$, we have

$$F_1(D,D')\{(D - mD' - n)[e^{nx}\varphi(y + mx)]\}$$
$$= F_1(D,D')(0) = 0;$$

that is, (34) is a solution of (30). Since there are n factors of the form (32), there will be n terms like (34) and the general solution will be

$$z = \sum_{j=1}^{n} e^{n_j x}\varphi_i(y + m_i x), \qquad (35)$$

where $h - m_j k - n_j$, $j = 1, 2, \ldots, n$ are the factors of $F(h,k)$.

If $(h - mk - n)^p$ is a factor of $F(h,k)$, the corresponding part of the general solution may be shown, by using (11), to be

$$e^{nx}[\varphi_0(y + mx) + x\varphi_1(y + mx) + \cdots + x^{p-1}\varphi_{p-1}(y + mx)]. \quad (36)$$

For a factor of $F(h,k)$ having the form $k - Mh - N$, $F(h,k)$ would be zero when $k = Mh + N$, the corresponding solution would be

$$z = ce^{hx+(Mh+N)y} = ce^{Ny}e^{h(x+My)}, \qquad (37)$$

and, just as before, we would derive the solution

$$z = e^{Ny}\psi(x + My) \qquad (38)$$

and then find the general solution in the form

$$z = \sum_{j=1}^{n} e^{N_j y}\psi_i(x + M_i y). \qquad (39)$$

If m_i or M_i for the factor of $F(h,k)$ is not zero, the corresponding term of the solution may be written in the form (34) or the form (38). But, corresponding to a factor having the form $h - n$, the form $e^{nx}\varphi(y)$ must be used in the solution, and corresponding to a factor $k - N$, the form $e^{Ny}\psi(x)$ must be used.

Example 1. Solve $(D + D' - 3) (D - 2) (D' + 4)z = 0$.
Solution. In this case
$$F(h,k) = (h + k - 3)(h - 2)(k + 4) = 0.$$
In the first factor $m = -1$, $n = 3$ and the corresponding part of the solution, by (34), is $e^{3x}\varphi_1(y - x)$. In the second factor $m = 0$, $n = 2$ and the corresponding part of the solution, by (34), is $e^{2x}\varphi_2(y)$. In the third factor $M = 0$, $N = -4$ and the corresponding part of the solution, by (39), is $e^{-4y}\psi(x)$. Hence the required solution is
$$\mathbf{z} = \mathbf{e^{3x}}\varphi_1 \ (\mathbf{y} - \mathbf{x}) + \mathbf{e^{2x}}\varphi_2(\mathbf{y}) + \mathbf{e^{-4y}} \ \psi(\mathbf{x}).$$
Example 2. Solve $(D + D' + 2)^2 (D - D')z = 0$.
Solution. In this case
$$F(h,k) = (h + k + 2)^2(h - k) = 0.$$
For the first factor $m = -1$, $k = -2$, and since the factor is repeated the corresponding part of the solution is
$$e^{-2x}[\varphi_1(y - x) + x\varphi_2(y - x)].$$
Corresponding to the second factor we have $e^{0x}\varphi_3(y + x)$, and the required solution is
$$\mathbf{z} = \mathbf{e^{-2x}}[\varphi_1(\mathbf{y} - \mathbf{x}) + \mathbf{x}\varphi_2(\mathbf{y} - \mathbf{x})] + \varphi_3(\mathbf{y} + \mathbf{x}).$$

107. $F(h,k)$ cannot be reduced to a product of linear factors. When $F(h,k)$ for an equation of type (30) is not reducible to factors linear in h and k, the solution can be expressed as sums of powers of e. For example, consider
$$(D^3 - D')(D + D'^2 + 1)z = 0. \tag{40}$$
Substitute ce^{hx+ky} for z in this to obtain
$$c(h^3 - k)(h + k^2 + 1)e^{hx+ky} = 0.$$
It now appears that ce^{hx+ky} will be a solution of (40) if $k = h^3$ or if $h = -k^2 - 1$. Also a sum of such terms will satisfy (40). Accordingly, a solution may be written

$$z = \sum_{}^{h} c_h e^{hx+h^3y} + \sum_{}^{k} c_k e^{-(k^2+1)x+ky},$$

where c_h and c_k represent arbitrary constants and h and k may assume the values in any sequence of numbers.

This solution illustrates a general process. If the factors of $F(h,k)$ are

$$h = \varphi_1(k),\ h = \varphi_2(k),\ \ldots,\ h = \varphi_m(k)$$

a solution of $F(D,D')z = 0$ may be written in the form

$$z = \sum_{}^{k} \sum_{j=1}^{m} a_{jk} e^{\varphi j(k)x+ky}, \tag{41}$$

where the A_{kj} represent arbitrary constants and k assumes the values in any sequence of numbers.

Exercises

1. By using (11) prove that the expression (36) when substituted for z in $F(D,D')z = 0$ will satisfy it provided that $(h - mk - n)^p$ is a factor of $F(h,k)$.

Solve the following equations:

2. $(D + D' + 3)(D - D')z = 0$

3. $(D + 2)(D - D' - 3)z = 0$

4. $(2D + 3D' - 3)(D' + 4)z = 0$

5. $(D + D' + 1)^3 z = 0$

6. $D(D' + 2D - 3)^2 z = 0$

7. $(D' + D + 1)(D' - 4)z = 0$

8. $(D' - 4)(D' + 4)z = 0$

9. $(D + a)(D'^2 - a^2)z = 0$

10. $(D^3 + D')z = 0$

11. $(D^3 + D')(D + D'^2)z = 0$

12. $(D^2 - DD' + D' - 1)z = 0$

13. $(DD' + aD + bD' + ab)z = 0$

14. $(D'^2 + DD' + D - 1)z = 0$

15. $(D'^2 - 3DD' + 2D^2 + D' - D)z = 0$

16. Show that the solution of $(D^2 + D'^2 + 1)z = 0$ may be written in the form

$$z = \sum^{k} e^{ky}(A_k \cos \sqrt{k^2 + 1}\, x + B_k \sin \sqrt{k^2 + 1}\, x)$$

17. Prove that a solution of $[(D + aD' + m)^2 + b^2D'^2]z = 0$ may be written in the form

$$z = e^{-mx} \overset{k}{\Sigma}(A_k \sin bk\, x + B_k \cos bk\, x)e^{k(y-ax)}$$

18. $[(D + aD' + m)^2 + n^2]z = 0$

19. $(D^2 + 2DD' + D'^2 + 4D + 4D' + 4)z = 0$

20. $(D^2 + 2DD' + D'^2 + 1)z = 0$

21. $(D^3 - 8D'^2)z = 0$

108. Right-hand member not zero. Consider the linear partial differential equation

$$F(D,D')z = f(x,y), \tag{42}$$

where the coefficients of the derivatives are constants. The solution of (42), $z = z_c + z_p$ consists of two parts, z_c the integral of $F(D,D')z = 0$, and z_p any particular integral of (42). In this article a few methods of finding a particular integral are considered.

When $F(D,D')$ can be factored into expressions linear in D and D', the method of §97 can be employed repeatedly to obtain a particular solution. Let $F(D,D')z = (aD + bD' + c) \cdot \varphi(D,D')z$. Then, letting $u = \varphi(D,D')z$, write the equation in the form

$$(aD + bD' + c)u = f(x,y), \tag{43}$$

and solve this for u in terms of x and y by the method of §97 to obtain

$$u = \varphi(D,D')z = f_1(x,y). \tag{44}$$

The simplest solution $f_1(x,y)$, *generally obtained by omitting arbitrary functions, should be used.* Evidently this same process may be applied repeatedly, once for each linear factor, until a solution is obtained. An illustration will indicate the general procedure.

Consider the equation

$$(D - D' - 2)(D - 2D' - 4)z = 96xye^{-2y}. \tag{a}$$

Let $u = (D - 2D' - 4)z$ so that (a) becomes

$$\frac{\partial u}{\partial x} - \frac{\partial u}{\partial y} = 96xye^{-2y} + 2u. \tag{b}$$

Now using the method of §97, write

$$\frac{dx}{1} = \frac{dy}{-1} = \frac{du}{96xye^{-2y} + 2u}. \qquad (c)$$

From the first equation of (c), $x + y = c$. In the equation of the second and third ratios of (c) replace x by $c - y$ and solve the resulting equation for u to obtain $u = (-48cy^2 + 32y^3)e^{-2y}$ or, replacing c by its equal $x + y$ and simplifying,

$$u = (D - 2D' - 4)z = -(48xy^2 + 16y^3)e^{-2y}. \qquad (d)$$

Observe that we could have used a general solution of (b) instead of (d), but this would have led to unnecessary complication. To solve (d) write

$$\frac{dx}{1} = \frac{dy}{-2} = \frac{dz}{-(48xy^2 + 16y^3)e^{-2y} + 4z}$$

and, proceeding as before, obtain

$$z = (8xy^3 + 3y^4)e^{-2y}. \qquad (e)$$

This is a particular solution of (a). Its general solution is

$$z = e^{2x}\varphi_1(y + x) + e^{4x}\varphi_2(y + 2x) + e^{-2y}(8xy^3 + 3y^4). \qquad (f)$$

The method of undetermined coefficients, used in the corresponding case of ordinary differential equations, may often be used to advantage. If there is a term in the right-hand member having the form ce^{ax+by}, the corresponding part of the particular solution is easily found by substituting $z = Ae^{ax+by}$ in the equation to obtain

$$AF(a,b)e^{ax+by} = ce^{ax+by}. \qquad (45)$$

This shows that the corresponding part of the particular solution is

$$\left[\frac{c}{F(a,b)}\right]e^{ax+by}. \qquad (46)$$

Similarly, for a term of the form $\sin(ax + by)$ or $\cos(ax + by)$ in the right-hand member, substitute

$$z = A\sin(ax + by) + B\cos(ax + by) \qquad (47)$$

in the equation, equate coefficients of like terms, and solve the resulting equations to find A and B.

Consider, for example,

$$(D^2 - D'^2 + D - D')z = 2e^{x+2y} - 3\sin(2x - y). \quad (g)$$

The part of z_p of the particular solution corresponding to $2e^{x+2y}$ is

$$\frac{2}{1 - 2^2 + 1 - 2}e^{x+2y} = -\frac{1}{2}e^{x+2y}. \quad (h)$$

Next substitute $z = A\sin(2x - y) + B\cos(2x - y)$ in $F(D,D')z = -3\sin(2x - y)$ to find

$$(-3A - 3B)\sin(2x - y) + (3A - 3B)\cos(2x - y)$$
$$= -3\sin(2x - y).$$

Therefore $-3A - 3B = -3$, $3A - 3B = 0$. Hence $A = \frac{1}{2}$, $B = \frac{1}{2}$, and the corresponding part of the particular solution is

$$\tfrac{1}{2}\sin(2x - y) + \tfrac{1}{2}\cos(2x - y). \quad (i)$$

The complete solution of (g) is

$$z = z_c + z_p = \varphi_1(y + x) + e^{-x}\varphi_2(y - x) - \tfrac{1}{2}e^{x+2y} +$$
$$\tfrac{1}{2}\sin(2x - y) + \tfrac{1}{2}\cos(2x - y). \quad (j)$$

Finally, consider an equation

$$F(D,D')z = P(x,y),$$

where $P(x,y)$ is a polynomial of the nth degree in x and y. Let $D^l D'^m_z$ be a term of the lowest order in $F(D,D')z$. Then an *effective trial integral is generally obtained by equating z to the product of* x^{l}y^m *and the general polynomial of degree* n *in two variables with general constants for coefficients.* For example, an effective trial integral for

$$(D + D' + 1)(D - D')z = 3x^2 + 2y - 4 \quad (k)$$

is

$$z = x(Ax^2 + Bxy + cy^2 + Dx + Ey + F). \quad (l)$$

By substituting this value for z in (k), equating the coefficients of like terms in the two members of the result, and solving for the constants, the student may obtain the particular solution,

$$z = x^3 + 2xy - 2x^2.$$

It is to be observed that there generally exist an infinite number of particular integrals. For example, the use of the trial integral $z = y(Ax^2 + Bxy + cy^2 + Dx + Ey + F)$ in (k) leads to the particular solution

$$z = -3x^2y - 3xy^2 - y^3 + 6xy + 2y^2.$$

Exercises

1. Use (45) and (46) to find a particular solution of
$$(D^2 - D'^2)z = e^{2x-y}.$$

2. Use (47) to find a particular solution of
(a) $[(D + D')^2 - a^2]z = \sin 2ay$.   (b) $(D^3 - DD'^2)z = \sin x + \cos x$.

3. Solve $(D - D')(D - D' - 2)z = 4xe^{-2y}$ by letting $u = (D - D' - 2)z$ and solving the resulting equation by the method of §97, and then replacing u by $(D - D' - 2)z$ and solving the result for z.

4. Solve $(D + D')(D + 4)z = 24xy$ by using as trial integral $z = y(Ax^2 + Bxy + cy^2 + Dx + Ey + F)$.

5. Solve $(D^2 - 3DD' + 2D'^2) = 2x$.

6. Solve $D'(D - D')^2z = 1/x^2$ by solving a succession of linear equations of the first order.

7. Solve $(D^2 - 4D'^2 + 2D + 1)z = xy + 24e^{x-2y}$.

8. Solve, $(D + D')(D - D')z = 2y - 12x + 6 \sin (x + 2y)$.

9. $(D + D')^2z = 2e^{x-y}$. *Hint:* Since the general integral has the form $\varphi(x - y) + y\psi(x - y)$, an integral of type Ae^{x-y} or Aye^{x-y} would satisfy $(D + D')^2z = 0$ and be ineffective. Hence, use as trial integral $z = Ay^2e^{x-y}$.

10. $(D^2 + a^2D'^2)z = \sin(y - ax)$

11. $(D^2 + DD' - 2D'^2)z = xe^{x-y}$

12. Prove that the substitution $X = \log x$, $Y = \log y$ will reduce an equation having the form
$$\sum_{i=0,\,j=0}^{n,\,n} A_{ij}x^iy^j \frac{\partial^{i+j}z}{\partial x^i \partial y^j} = f(x,y), \; A_{ij} \text{ constants}$$
to the linear equation with constant coefficients.

109. Special types of second-order equations.
In §96 partial differential equations that could be integrated by the

methods of ordinary differential equations were considered. In the process only two quantities were considered as variables for a particular integration, and the constant of integration generally took the form of an arbitrary function of the variable treated as constant. In this article, the same method and also the method of Lagrange discussed in §97 will be used. The notation of equations (1) in §94 will be employed.

Evidently equations of the types

$$r = \varphi(x,y), \; s = \psi(x,y), \; t = \chi(x,y) \qquad (48)$$

may be solved by two successive integrations. The student may review the process by solving the equation

$$s = \frac{\partial^2 z}{\partial x \, \partial y} = 12x^2 + y^{-\frac{1}{2}}$$

to get as a solution

$$z = 4x^3y + 2xy^{\frac{1}{2}} + \varphi(y) + \psi(x).$$

Methods of ordinary differential equations apply to solve equations having one of the forms

$$Rr + Pp + Zz = V, \; Tt + Qq + Zz = V,$$

where the capital letters represent functions of x and y. For example, to solve

$$t + 2q - 3z = 9x^2y, \qquad (49)$$

write

$$\frac{\partial^2 z}{\partial y^2} - 2\frac{\partial z}{\partial y} - 3z = 9x^2y,$$

and, treating x as a constant, and using functions of x as constants of integration, solve the equation as though it were an ordinary differential equation in z and y. The solution is

$$z = \varphi(x)e^{3y} + \psi(x)e^{-y} - 3x^2y + 2x^2. \qquad (50)$$

Finally, consider the types of equations represented by

$$R_1r + S_1s = V_1, \; S_2s + T_2t = V_2, \qquad (51)$$

where R_1, S_1, and V_1 are functions of x, y, and p, and S_2, T_2, and V_2 are functions of x, y, and q. To solve the first equation of (51), write it in the form

$$R_1\frac{\partial p}{\partial x} + S_1\frac{\partial p}{\partial y} = V_1, \tag{52}$$

and using the method of Lagrange in §97 solve (52) for p in terms of x and y; then replace p by $\partial z/\partial x$ and complete the solution for z by an integration in which y is considered as constant. The following example will illustrate the method.

Example. Solve

$$2xr - ys + 2x + 2p = 0. \tag{a}$$

Solution. Equation (a) may be written

$$2x\frac{\partial p}{\partial x} - y\frac{\partial p}{\partial y} = -2x - 2p. \tag{b}$$

Then, applying Lagrange's method, write

$$\frac{dx}{2x} = \frac{dy}{-y} = \frac{dp}{-2x - 2p}, \tag{c}$$

find the integral $xy^2 = c_1$ from the first two ratios and $2px + x^2 = c_2$ from the first and third ratios; then derive from these integrals

$$p = -\frac{1}{2}x + \frac{1}{2x}c_2 = -\frac{1}{2}x + \frac{1}{2x}\varphi(xy^2). \tag{d}$$

Now, observing that

$$\int\frac{1}{x}\varphi(xy^2)dx \; (y, \text{constant}) =$$

$$\int\frac{1}{xy^2}\varphi(xy^2)y^2 \, dx = \varphi_1(xy^2), \tag{e}$$

replace p in (d) by $\partial z/\partial x$ and, treating y as constant, derive

$$\mathbf{z} = -\tfrac{1}{4}\mathbf{x}^2 + \varphi_1(\mathbf{xy}^2) + \psi(\mathbf{y}).$$

Exercises

Solve the following partial differential equations:

1. (a) $t = 12xy$ (b) $s = 6xe^{-3y}$

2. (a) $r + p - 6z = 0$ (c) $t + 4z = x^2$

    (b) $t + q - 2z = 0$ (d) $r - yp - 2y^2z = 2xy^2$

3. (a) $xr - ys = 2y$
   (b) $xr + ys = 0$
   (c) $xs - yt = 2x$

4. (a) $pr = xy^2$
   (b) $r - ys = 0$
   (c) $xr + 2ys = p + x$
   (d) $2r + 3p - 5z = 25xy$
   (e) $xs - 2yt = 2q + x$

   (d) $s = 6x + p$
   (e) $xs - yt + q = 12xy$
   (f) $xs - 2x^2t = q$
   (f) $t - 2q = 3x^2$
   (g) $r + ys = p$
   (h) $xr + s + p = 0$
   (i) $x^2r + xp + z = xy$
   (j) $qs - pt = 0$

Hint to (i): Let $w = \log x$. Then $\dfrac{\partial z}{\partial x} = \dfrac{\partial z}{\partial w}\dfrac{\partial w}{\partial x} = \dfrac{\partial z}{\partial w}\dfrac{1}{x}$.

Hint to (j): consider $\dfrac{\partial}{\partial y}(p/q)$.

110. Equation $Rr + Ss + Tt = V$. Gaspard Monge applied the method of this article to solve the equation

$$Rr + Ss + Tt = V, \tag{53}$$

where R, S, T, and V represent functions of p, q, x, y, and z, and r, s, and t have the usual meanings.

Since z, p, and q are functions of x and y, we have

$$dz = p\, dx + q\, dy, \tag{54}$$
$$dp = r\, dx + s\, dy, \tag{55}$$
$$dq = s\, dx + t\, dy. \tag{56}$$

Solving (55) and (56) for r and t, respectively, substituting the results in (53) and collecting the terms containing s in the left-hand member and the others in the right, we find

$$s\left(R\frac{dy}{dx} - S + T\frac{dx}{dy}\right) = R\frac{dp}{dx} + T\frac{dq}{dy} - V. \tag{57}$$

Evidently this equation will be satisfied if each member vanishes, that is, if

$$R\, dy^2 - S\, dx\, dy + T\, dx^2 = 0, \tag{58}$$
$$R\, dp\, dy + T\, dq\, dx - V\, dx\, dy = 0. \tag{59}$$

The equations (54), (58), and (59) are three total differential equations in five unknowns; ordinarily four equations are required for a determinate system. Hence integrals of

(54), (58), and (59) can be found only when certain conditions are satisfied.

Let α and β be the two values obtained by solving (58) for y'. The system to be solved may then be written

$$\frac{dy}{dx} = \alpha, \frac{dy}{dx} = \beta, \tag{60}$$

$$R\, dp\, dy + T\, dq\, dx - V\, dx\, dy = 0, \tag{61}$$

$$dz = p\, dx + q\, dy. \tag{62}$$

One method consists in combining one of the equations (60) with (61) to obtain a relation among the variables x, y, p, q,

$$\varphi(x,y,p,q) = 0, \tag{63}$$

and then solving this equation. The result is a solution of the original equation. When the relation (63) is linear in p and q, Lagrange's method, considered in §97, may be used.

In some cases two relations like (63) may be obtained, one by using the first of (60) with (61) and the other by using the second of (60) with (61). When these two relations are solved for p and q and the results substituted in (62) to obtain

$$dz = p(x,y)dx + q(x,y)dy, \tag{64}$$

the result is integrable* and the solution of (64) is the required solution.

It should be observed that only a small class of equations of type (53) can be solved. Other methods† than those indicated above may be employed but their field of application is closely limited.

Example 1. Solve

$$r - 2xs + x^2t = q + 6x. \tag{a}$$

---

* The proof that (64) will be integrable is omitted here. It is given in "Differential Equations" by Max Morris and Orley Brown, pp. 273, 274.

† See, for example, "Partial Differential Equations" by Frederic H. Miller, pp. 182–194.

Solution.   Equations (58) and (59) give in this case
$$dy^2 + 2x\,dx\,dy + x^2\,dx^2 = 0, \qquad (b)$$
$$dp\,dy + x^2\,dq\,dx - (q + 6x)\,dx\,dy = 0. \qquad (c)$$
One factor of (b) is $dy + x\,dx$.   Hence
$$dy = -x\,dx, \text{ or } 2y + x^2 = c. \qquad (d)$$
Divide (c) by dy and use (d) to obtain
$$dp - (x\,dq + q\,dx) - 6x\,dx = 0$$
or
$$p - qx = 3x^2 + \varphi(2y + x^2). \qquad (e)$$
Note that, because of (d), the constant of integration could be taken in the form $\varphi(2y + x^2)$.   Now, applying Lagrange's method of §97 to (e), write
$$\frac{dx}{1} = \frac{dy}{-x} = \frac{dz}{\varphi(2y + x^2) + 3x^2}. \qquad (f)$$
From the first two fractions (f) deduce
$$2y + x^2 = c. \qquad (g)$$
Using (g) and the first and third ratios of (f), write
$$dz = [\varphi(c) + 3x^2]dx. \qquad (h)$$
Hence,
$$\mathbf{z} = \varphi(\mathbf{c})\mathbf{x} + \mathbf{x}^3 + \mathbf{c_1} = \mathbf{x}\varphi(\mathbf{2y} + \mathbf{x}^2) + \mathbf{x}^3 + \psi(\mathbf{2y} + \mathbf{x}^2). \ (i)$$

Example 2.   Solve
$$q(2 + q)r - 2(p + q + pq)s + p(2 + p)t = 0. \qquad (a)$$
Solution.   Equations (58) and (59) give in this case
$$q(2 + q)dy^2 + 2(p + q + pq)dy\,dx + p(2 + p)dx^2 = 0, \qquad (b)$$
$$q(2 + q)dp\,dy + p(2 + p)dq\,dx = 0. \qquad (c)$$
Factoring (b), we find
$$[p\,dx + q\,dy][(p + 2)dx + (q + 2)dy] = 0. \qquad (d)$$
Equating the first factor to zero, we get
$$p\,dx + q\,dy = 0. \qquad (e)$$
Equation (e) combined with (54) gives
$$dz = 0, \text{ therefore } z = c, \qquad (f)$$

and (e) combined with (c) gives

$$(p + 2)dq - (q + 2)dp = 0, \text{ therefore } p + 2 = (q + 2)c. \quad (g)$$

Hence, from (f)

$$p + 2 = (q + 2)\varphi(z), [\varphi(z), \text{ an arbitrary function}]. \quad (h)$$

Using the method of §97 to integrate this, we write

$$\frac{dx}{1} = \frac{dy}{-\varphi(z)} = \frac{dz}{2\varphi(z) - 2}. \quad (i)$$

Hence

$$2\,dx + 2\,dy + dz = 0, \text{ or } 2x + 2y + z = c,$$

and, from the last two fractions of (i),

$$y = \int \frac{-\varphi\,dz}{2\varphi - 2} + c_2, \text{ or } \mathbf{y} = \psi(\mathbf{z}) + \lambda(\mathbf{2x + 2y + z}).$$

Exercises

1. $xr + 2xs + xt = p + q$

2. $yr - 2ys + yt = (p - q)(x + y)$

3. $x^2r + 2xys + y^2t = 0$

4. $x^2r - xys + yq = 0$. *Hint:* Write (58) and (59) for this equation. Then use $x\,dy + y\,dx = 0$ in the equation from (59) to get $-x\,dp + q\,dy = 0$. Now replace $q\,dy$ by $dz - p\,dx$ and integrate the result to obtain $z - px = \varphi(xy)$.

5. $qxr - (px - qy)s - pyt = 0$. *Hint:* Read the solution of Example 2 of this article.

6. $x^2r - y^2t = qy - px$. *Hint:* To find an integral from $x^2\,dp\,dy - y^2\,dq\,dx = (qy - px)dx\,dy$ and $x\,dy - y\,dx = 0$, first obtain

$$x\,dp - y\,dq = (qy - px)\frac{dy}{y},$$

then replace $x\,dp - y\,dq$ by its equal $d(xp - yq) - p\,dx + q\,dy$ and simplify to get $d(xp - yq) = 0$.

7. $x^2r - 2xys + y^2t + 2px = 0$

8. $r + ys - 2y^2t = 2qy$

9. $(y + 1)r - (y^2 - 1)s - y(y + 1)t = p + q$

10. $x(r - 2s + t) = p - q$

11. $x(x + y)r + (x^2 - y^2)s - (x + y)yt = (x - y)(p + q)$

12. $(x^2 - xy)r + (y^2 - x^2)s + (xy - y^2)t = (x + y)(p - q)$

13. $x^2r - y^2t = qy - px$

14. $y^2r - 2ys + t = 6y + p$

15. $q^2r - 2pqs + p^2t = 0$

16. $ps - qr = 0$. *Hint:* Applying (54), (58), and (59), show that $z = c$, $p = c_1 = 1/\phi'(z)$.

17. $(a + fq)^2r - 2(a + fq)(e + fp)s + (e + fp)^2t = 0$

CHAPTER XIV

APPLICATIONS OF PARTIAL DIFFERENTIAL EQUATIONS

111. Fourier series. Because Fourier series play a very important role in many applications of partial differential equations, a brief discussion of them will be given.

A series having the form

$$a_0 + a_1 \cos x + a_2 \cos 2x + \cdots + a_n \cos nx + \cdots$$
$$+ b_1 \sin x + b_2 \sin 2x + \cdots + b_n \sin nx + \cdots \quad (1)$$

is called a *Fourier series*. If there is a Fourier series that represents $f(x)$ in the interval $-\pi < x < \pi$ and if the term-by-term integration of this series used in the following development is permissible, then the values of the coefficients a_i and b_i are easily determined. Formulas for finding these constants will now be derived.

By direct evaluation of integrals, we get

$$\int_{-\pi}^{\pi} \sin mx \, dx = 0, \quad \int_{-\pi}^{\pi} \cos mx \, dx = 0,$$

$$\int_{-\pi}^{\pi} \sin mx \cos nx \, dx = 0, \, m \neq n, \quad (2)$$

$$\int_{-\pi}^{\pi} \sin^2 mx \, dx = \int_{-\pi}^{\pi} \cos^2 mx \, dx = \pi, \quad (3)$$

where m and n represent integers. Writing $f(x)$ equal to the series (1) gives

$$f(x) = a_0 + a_1 \cos x + a_2 \cos 2x + \cdots$$
$$+ b_1 \sin x + b_2 \sin 2x + \cdots. \quad (4)$$

Multiplying (4) through by dx, equating the definite integrals of the two members for the limits $-\pi$ and π, and taking account of (2) and (3), we get

$$\int_{-\pi}^{\pi} f(x)\ dx = 2\pi a_0, \text{ or } a_0 = \frac{1}{2\pi}\int_{-\pi}^{\pi} f(x)\ dx. \qquad (5)$$

Next multiply both members of (4) by $\cos mx\ dx$, equate the definite integrals of the two members for the limits $-\pi$ and π, and take account of (2) and (3) to obtain

$$\int_{-\pi}^{\pi} f(x)\ \cos mx\ dx = \int_{-\pi}^{\pi} a_m \cos^2 mx\ dx = \pi a_m,$$

or

$$a_m = \frac{1}{\pi}\int_{-\pi}^{\pi} f(x)\ \cos mx\ dx. \qquad (6)$$

Similarly, by using (4) multiplied through by $\sin mx\ dx$, obtain

$$b_m = \frac{1}{\pi}\int_{-\pi}^{\pi} f(x)\ \sin mx\ dx. \qquad (7)$$

It has been proved* that if $f(x)$ is single-valued and finite in the interval $-\pi < x < \pi$ and has only a finite number of discontinuities and of maxima and minima in this interval, then the Fourier series resulting from (4) by substituting in it from (5), (6), and (7)

$$\left. \begin{array}{l} \mathbf{a_0} = \dfrac{1}{2\pi}\displaystyle\int_{-\pi}^{\pi} \mathbf{f}(\alpha)\ \mathbf{d}\alpha, \ \mathbf{a_m} = \dfrac{1}{\pi}\displaystyle\int_{-\pi}^{\pi} \mathbf{f}(\alpha)\ \cos \mathbf{m}\alpha\ \mathbf{d}\alpha, \\[4mm] \mathbf{b_m} = \dfrac{1}{\pi}\displaystyle\int_{-\pi}^{\pi} \mathbf{f}(\alpha)\ \sin \mathbf{m}\alpha\ \mathbf{d}\alpha, \ \mathbf{m} = \mathbf{1, 2, \cdots} \end{array} \right\} \qquad (8)$$

is equal to $f(x)$ for all values of x in the interval $-\pi < x < \pi$,

* Expansion in Fourier series is explained in books on advanced calculus. Also consult:

BYERLY, W. E., "Fourier's Series and Spherical Harmonics."

CARSLAW, H. S., "Introduction to the Theory of Fourier's Series and Integrals."

excepting at points of discontinuity. At a point of discontinuity where $x = a$, the value of the series is

$$\tfrac{1}{2} \lim_{\epsilon \to 0} \left[f(a - \epsilon) + f(a + \epsilon) \right]. \tag{9}$$

When $x = -\pi$ and when $x = \pi$, the value of the series for $f(x)$ is

$$\tfrac{1}{2}[f(-\pi) + f(\pi)]. \tag{10}$$

Both $\sin mx$ and $\cos mx$ have the period 2π since $\sin m(x + 2k\pi) = \sin mx$, and $\cos m(x + 2k\pi) = \cos mx$ where

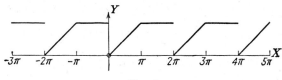

Fɪɢ. 1.

m and k are integers. Hence the values assumed by series (1) in the interval $-\pi < x < \pi$ are assumed by it in any other interval $(2k - 1)\pi < x < (2k + 1)\pi$. Figure 1 indicates this situation by showing the graph of a function from $-\pi$ to π and repetitions of it.

The Fourier series representing $\int f(x) \, dx$ *may be obtained by integrating, term by term, the Fourier series for* $f(x)$; *but, only under certain conditions,* * *will the Fourier series for* $df(x)/dx$ *be obtained by differentiating the Fourier series for* $f(x)$, *term by term.*

Example. Find a Fourier series equal to π for values of x

* From a theorem of calculus relating to the differentiation of series term by term, it follows that if a series of the form (1) converges to $f(x)$ in the interval $a \leqq x \leqq b$ and if the series of derivatives obtained from (1)

$$\sum_{n=1}^{\infty} na_n \sin nx + \sum_{n=1}^{\infty} nb_n \cos nx$$

is uniformly convergent in $a \leqq x \leqq b$, then the series of derivatives converges to $f'(x)$.

between $-\pi$ and 0 and equal to x for values of x between 0 and π.

Solution. Figure 1 represents the function. Using formulas (8), we get

$$a_0 = \frac{1}{2\pi}\int_{-\pi}^{0} \pi\, dx + \frac{1}{2\pi}\int_{0}^{\pi} x\, dx = \frac{\pi}{2} + \frac{\pi^2}{4\pi} = \frac{3\pi}{4},$$

$$a_m = \frac{1}{\pi}\int_{-\pi}^{0} \pi \cos mx\, dx + \frac{1}{\pi}\int_{0}^{\pi} x \cos mx\, dx$$

$$= \frac{-2}{\pi m^2}\ (m,\ \text{odd}),\ = 0\ (m,\ \text{even}),$$

$$b_m = \frac{1}{\pi}\int_{-\pi}^{0} \pi \sin mx\, dx + \frac{1}{\pi}\int_{0}^{\pi} x \sin mx\, dx = \frac{-1}{m}.$$

Substituting these values in (4), we obtain

$$f(x) = \frac{3\pi}{4} - \frac{2}{\pi}\left(\frac{\cos x}{1^2} + \frac{\cos 3x}{3^2} + \frac{\cos 5x}{5^2} + \cdots\right)$$
$$- \left(\sin x + \frac{\sin 2x}{2} + \frac{\sin 3x}{3} + \cdots\right). \tag{11}$$

A few observations may be of interest.

When $x = 0$, the series (11) in accordance with (9) will take the value $\pi/2$. Hence,

$$\frac{\pi}{2} = \frac{3\pi}{4} - \frac{2}{\pi}\left(\frac{1}{1^2} + \frac{1}{3^2} + \frac{1}{5^2} + \cdots\right),\ \text{or}$$

$$\frac{1}{1^2} + \frac{1}{3^2} + \frac{1}{5^2} + \cdots = \frac{\pi^2}{8}.$$

The term-by-term integral with limits $-\pi$ and x of the series (11) represents the area under the graph of $f(x)$, that is, $\pi(\pi + x)$ when $-\pi < x \leqq 0$ and $\pi^2 + \frac{1}{2}x^2$ when $0 < x \leqq \pi$.

Exercises

1. Assuming that a series of type (1) exists for the expansion of $f(x)$ and that term-by-term integration is permissible, derive formulas (8).

2. Expand $f(x) = x$ in a Fourier series by using (4) and (8). Replace x by $\pi/2$ in the result to show that $1 - \frac{1}{3} + \frac{1}{5} - \frac{1}{7} + \cdots = \pi/4$.

3. Find a Fourier series which will be equal to zero in the interval $-\pi < x < 0$, and equal to 1 in the interval $0 < x < \pi$. In the result let $x = \pi/2$ to check the sum of the series in exercise 2. Also check that the series has the sum zero when $x = -\pi/2$.

4. Find a Fourier series for $f(x)$ where $f(x) = \frac{1}{2}$ when $-\pi < x < 0$, and $f(x) = x/\pi$ when $0 < x < \pi$.

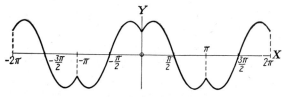

Fig. 2.

112. Cosine series. Sine series. If a function $f(x)$ is even, that is, if $f(x) = f(-x)$, then b_m from (8) will be zero since, in one kind of defining sum, each element $\sin mx_i f(x_i)\Delta x_i$ will cancel an element $\sin(-mx_i)f(-x_i)\Delta x_i = -\sin(mx_i)f(x_i)\Delta x_i$. Moreover a_n will be equal to twice the value of $(1/\pi)\int_0^\pi f(x) \cos mx\, dx$. Hence, an even function may be expanded by using (4) with

$$a_0 = \frac{1}{\pi}\int_0^\pi f(x)\, dx, \quad a_m = \frac{2}{\pi}\int_0^\pi f(x) \cos mx\, dx, \quad b_m = 0. \quad (12)$$

Figure 2 shows a function represented by a Fourier expansion from $-\pi$ to π by means of (4) and (12). Note that the graph is symmetrical to the y-axis.

It also appears that any function $f(x)$ can generally be expanded by using (4) and (12); for expansion of a function $\varphi(x)$ where $\varphi(x) = f(x)$ in $0 < x < \pi$ and $\varphi(x) = f(x)$ in $-\pi < x < 0$ by means of (4) and (8) will give the same result as expansion by means of (4) and (12).

Similarly if $f(x)$ is an odd function, that is, if $f(-x) = -f(x)$, it may be expanded by (4) with

$$a_0 = 0, \ a_m = 0, \ b_m = \frac{2}{\pi} \int_0^\pi f(x) \sin mx \ dx. \qquad (13)$$

Figure 3 indicates the type of function represented by a Fourier sine series. Note that it is symmetrical with respect to the origin. In general, formula (13) may be used to expand a function in the interval $0 < x < \pi$. Each of the expansions using (8), (12), and (13) will represent $f(x)$ between

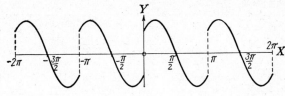

Fig. 3.

0 and π but will generally represent different functions outside this interval.

A Fourier series representing $f(x)$ in the interval between $-c$ and c can be obtained by replacing x in $f(x)$ by xz/π,

$$x = \frac{cz}{\pi} \qquad (14)$$

expanding $f(cz/\pi)$ by using (4) and (8), and then replacing z by $\pi x/c$ in the result. The substitution (14) may be employed in connection with (12) and (13) to obtain an expansion relating to the interval $0 < x < c$.

Example 1. Expand $f(x) = 1$ in a sine series by using (4) and (13).

Solution. Using (13), we get

$$a_0 = 0, \ a_m = 0, \ b_m = \frac{2}{\pi} \int_0^\pi \sin mx \ dx = \frac{2(1 - \cos m\pi)}{m\pi}.$$

Substituting these values in (4), we obtain

$$1 = \frac{4}{\pi} \left(\sin x + \frac{\sin 3x}{3} + \frac{\sin 5x}{5} + \cdots \right). \qquad (15)$$

Example 2. By using (4) and (12) expand x in a cosine series valid for the interval $0 < x < c$.

Solution. Let $x = cz/\pi$ and apply (12) to obtain

$$a_0 = \frac{1}{\pi}\int_0^\pi \frac{c}{\pi}z\,dz = \frac{c}{2}, \quad a_m = \frac{2}{\pi}\int_0^\pi \frac{cz}{\pi}\cos mz\,dz =$$

$$\frac{2c}{\pi^2 m^2}(\cos m\pi - 1), \quad b_m = 0.$$

Substitute these values in (4) to get

$$\frac{cz}{\pi} = \frac{c}{2} + \frac{2c}{\pi^2}\left(\frac{-2\cos z}{1^2} - \frac{2\cos 3z}{3^2} - \frac{2\cos 5z}{5^2} - \cdots\right),$$

or, replacing z by $\pi x/c$ and simplifying slightly,

$$x = \frac{c}{2} - \frac{4c}{\pi^2}\left(\frac{1}{1^2}\cos\frac{\pi x}{c} + \frac{1}{3^2}\cos\frac{3\pi x}{c} + \cdots\right). \tag{16}$$

Exercises

1. (a) Use (4), (13), and (14) to expand x in a sine series valid for the interval from 0 to c. (b) Using integration with the result and the fact that $a_0 = (1/\pi)\int_0^\pi (c^2 z^2/\pi^2)dz = c^2/3$, obtain an expansion of x^2 in a series of cosines. (c) In the result of part (b) set $x = c$ and then deduce that $1/1^2 + 1/2^2 + 1/3^2 + \cdots = \pi^2/6$.

2. Using (4), (12), and (14), expand x^2 in a cosine series valid for the interval $0 < x < c$.

3. Integrate series (15) to obtain all terms except the constant term of (16) with $c = \pi$. Determine the constant term by using the value $\pi/2$ for x.

4. Show that, for the interval $0 < x < L$,

$$mx(L - x) = \frac{8L^2 m}{\pi^3}\left(\frac{1}{1^3}\sin\frac{\pi x}{L} + \frac{1}{3^3}\sin\frac{3\pi x}{L} + \frac{1}{5^3}\sin\frac{5\pi x}{L} + \cdots\right)$$

5. Expand x^2 in a sine series valid for the interval $0 < x < c$.

6. Expand $h + kx$ in a sine series valid for the interval $0 < x < c$.

113. Vibrations of a string. Figure 4 represents a string L units long fastened at A and B. Assume that the vibrations are so small that the tension T in the string may be considered constant, that the weight of the string is small in comparison with T, that the length of the string may be considered as a constant L for each of its positions, and that each point in the string moves parallel to the y-axis. Consider the motion of a small piece PQ (see Fig. 4) of the string Δx units long. Two forces of magnitude T act at its ends, one inclined θ and the other $\theta + \Delta\theta$ to the x-axis. Since θ is small, $\sin\theta$

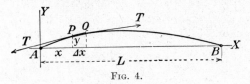

FIG. 4.

$= \tan\theta = \partial y/\partial x$, approximately. Therefore, applying Newton's law parallel to the y-axis, we get

$$T[\sin(\theta + \Delta\theta) - \sin\theta] = T\left[\frac{\partial y(x + \Delta x, t)}{\partial x} - \frac{\partial y(x,t)}{\partial x}\right]$$

$$= \frac{\rho\,\Delta x}{g}\frac{\partial^2 y}{\partial t^2}, \quad (17)$$

where ρ is the weight per unit length of the string. Dividing (17) through by $\rho\,\Delta x/g$ and equating the limits of its members, we have

$$a^2\frac{\partial^2 y(x,t)}{\partial x^2} = \frac{\partial^2 y}{\partial t^2}, \; a^2 = \frac{Tg}{\rho}. \quad (18)$$

Example. A string is stretched along the x-axis to which it is attached at $x = 0$ and at $x = L$. Find y in terms of x and t, assuming that $y = mx(L - x)$ when $t = 0$.

Solution. To get solutions of (18) substitute in it

$$y = Xe^{j\omega t}, \quad (a)$$

where X is a function of x only and $j = \sqrt{-1}$. This gives

$$a^2 X'' e^{j\omega t} = -\omega^2 X e^{j\omega t}. \quad (b)$$

Dividing $e^{j\omega t}$ from (b) and solving the result, we get

$$X = c_1 \sin\frac{\omega}{a}x + c_2 \cos\frac{\omega}{a}x. \quad (c)$$

Hence, since $e^{j\omega t} = \cos \omega t + j \sin \omega t$,

$$y = \left(c_1 \sin \frac{\omega}{a}x + c_2 \cos \frac{\omega}{a}x\right)(\cos \omega t + j \sin \omega t). \quad (d)$$

Since both the real and the imaginary part of (d) satisfy (18) for each constant c_1 and c_2, it appears that solutions of (18) can be made up of sums of terms having any one of the forms

$$A \cos \frac{\omega}{a}x \cos \omega t, \; B \cos \frac{\omega}{a}x \sin \omega t,$$

$$C \sin \frac{\omega}{a}x \cos \omega t, \; B \sin \frac{\omega}{a}x \sin \omega t. \qquad (e)$$

The initial conditions are

$$y = 0, \text{ when } x = 0, \text{ and } y = 0, \text{ when } x = L, \quad (f)$$
$$y = mx\,(L - x) \text{ when } t = 0. \qquad (g)$$

Conditions (f) will be satisfied, provided we take

$$\omega = \frac{n\pi a}{L}, \; (n, \text{ an integer}) \qquad (h)$$

and restrict ourselves to terms having the form of those in the last line of (e). From exercise 4, §112, we have

$$mx(L - x) = \frac{8L^2m}{\pi^3}\left(\sin \frac{\pi x}{L} + \frac{1}{3^3} \sin \frac{3\pi x}{L} + \right.$$

$$\left. \frac{1}{5^3} \sin \frac{5\pi x}{L} + \cdots \right). \quad (i)$$

Hence conditions (18), (f), and (g) are satisfied by

$$y = \frac{8L^2m}{\pi^3}\left[\frac{1}{1^3}\cos \frac{a\pi t}{L} \sin \frac{\pi x}{L} + \frac{1}{3^3}\cos \frac{3\pi a t}{L} \sin \frac{3\pi x}{L} + \cdots\right]. \quad (j)$$

Problems

1. If the string of the illustrative example is 3 ft. long and weighs $\frac{1}{30}$ lb., if $T = 10$ lb., and if $m = 0.01$, find the equation of the moving string. Find the time frequency of the first harmonic, that is, of the first term.

2. If, when $t = 0$, $y = A \sin (2\pi x/L)$ for the string of the illustrative example, find y in terms of x and t.

3. If, when $t = 0$, the particles of the string of the illustrative example have velocities defined by $\left(\dfrac{\partial y}{\partial t}\right)_{t=0} = A \sin \dfrac{n\pi x}{L}$, find the displacement $y(x,t)$ of the string.

4. If, when $t = 0$, the particles of the string of the illustrative example have velocities defined by $\left(\dfrac{\partial y}{\partial t}\right)_{t=0} = mx(L - x)$, find the corresponding displacement function $y(x,t)$.

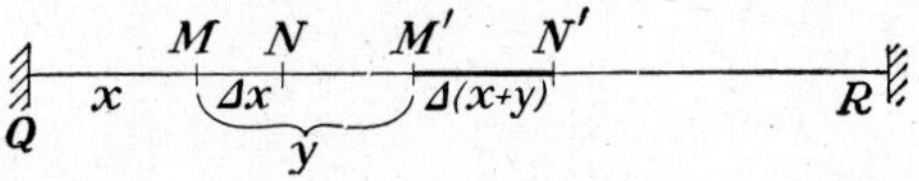

FIG. 5.

114. Vibrations of a rod. Figure 5 represents a straight, elastic, homogeneous rod of density ρ, modulus of elasticity E, length L, and cross-sectional area A. It is fixed at Q and R, but the particles of the rod between Q and R move along the line QR. It is assumed that the pressure on any cross section is uniformly distributed and that all particles on any cross section have the same velocity. Let y be the displacement at time t of a particle that is distant x from Q when the rod is at rest. Then Δy is the change in length of the part of the rod marked Δx in Fig. 5. Now, by Hooke's law,

$$E = \frac{P}{A(l_1/L)}, \text{ or } l_1 = \frac{PL}{AE}, \tag{19}$$

where l_1 is the amount that a rod of length L and cross-sectional area A is stretched by force P. Applying this equation to the piece MN in Fig. 5, we obtain

$$\Delta y = \frac{P(x_1, t)}{AE}\Delta x, \tag{20}$$

where x_1 satisfies $x < x_1 < x + \Delta x$. Dividing by Δx and equating the limits of the two members, we get

$$\frac{\partial y(x,t)}{\partial x} = P(x,t)/AE. \tag{21}$$

Now apply Newton's law of motion to the part $M'N'$ of the rod. This gives

$$P(x + \Delta x, t) - P(x,t) = \frac{A\rho \, \Delta x}{g} \frac{\partial^2 y_1}{\partial t^2},$$

where y_1 satisfies $y < y_1 < y + \Delta y$. Now divide by Δx and equate limits to get

$$\frac{\partial P}{\partial x} = \frac{A\rho}{g} \frac{\partial^2 y}{\partial t^2}, \tag{22}$$

and eliminate P between (21) and (22) to obtain

$$a^2 \frac{\partial^2 y(x,t)}{\partial x^2} = \frac{\partial^2 y(x,t)}{\partial t^2}, \quad a^2 = \frac{Eg}{\rho}. \tag{23}$$

Note that this equation has the same form as (18) in §113 and therefore has the solutions marked (e) in §113.

Exercises

1. For each of the following sets of conditions find the corresponding solution of (23):

(a) $y(0,t) = 0$, $y(L,t) = 0$, $y(x, 0) = A \sin \dfrac{2\pi x}{L}$

(b) $y(0,t) = 0$, $y(L,t) = 0$, $y(x,0) = A \sin \dfrac{m\pi x}{L} + B \sin \dfrac{n\pi x}{L}$

(c) $y(0,t) = 0$, $y(L,t) = 0$, $y(x,0) = Ax(L - x)$

In solving part (c) use the result in exercise 4 of §112.

2. For a steel rod $\rho = 490$ lb./ft.^{3}, $E = 4.3 \times 10^9$ lb./ft.^{2}, $g = 32$ ft./sec.^{2} Using the initial conditions $y(0,t) = 0$, $y(3,t) = 0$, $y(x,0) = 0.0001x(3 - x)$, find the corresponding solution of (23) and give the frequency of the harmonic represented by the first term.

115. Flow of heat. Let $\theta(x,y,z,t)$ represent the temperature at any point in space at time t and assume that the heat flows in the direction of decreasing temperature and that the rate across any small square is proportional to the area of the square and to $\partial\theta/\partial s$ where s is measured normal to the square. Also assume that the quantity of heat in a small body is proportional to its mass and to its temperature θ.

To get the partial differential equation of heat flow, express in mathematical symbols the relation that rate at which heat enters the small block of Fig. 6 minus the rate at which it leaves is equal to the rate of increase of heat in the block. The rate at which heat leaves is $k\,[\partial\theta(x, y_1, z_1, t)/\partial x]\,\Delta y\,\Delta z$ where k is a constant and point (x,y_1,z_1) is a certain point in face AB. Similarly, the rate at which heat enters through face CD is approximately $k[\partial\theta\,(x + \Delta x, y_1, z_1, t)/\partial x]\Delta y\,\Delta z$. Hence the rate at which heat enters through the faces of the block perpendicular to the x-axis is

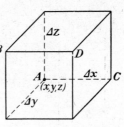

Fig. 6.

$$k\left[\frac{\partial\theta(x + \Delta x, y_1,z_1,t)}{\partial x} - \frac{\partial\theta(x,y_1,z_1,t)}{\partial x}\right]\Delta y\,\Delta z. \qquad (24)$$

Similarly, the rate at which heat enters the block through faces perpendicular to the y-axis is

$$k\left[\frac{\partial\theta(x_2,y + \Delta y,z_2,t)}{\partial y} - \frac{\partial\theta(x_2,y,z_2,t)}{\partial y}\right]\Delta x\,\Delta y, \qquad (25)$$

and the rate for the faces perpendicular to the z-axis is

$$k\left[\frac{\partial\theta(x_3,y_3,z + \Delta z,t)}{\partial x} - \frac{\partial\theta(x_3,y_3,z,t)}{\partial y}\right]\Delta y\,\Delta z. \qquad (26)$$

The rate of increase of heat in the block is

$$c\rho\,\Delta x\,\Delta y\,\Delta z\frac{\partial\theta(x_4,y_4,z_4,t)}{\partial t} \qquad (27)$$

where ρ is the density and (x_4,y_4,z_4) is a certain point in the block. Equating the sum of expressions (24), (25), and (26) to expression (27), dividing the result through by $\Delta x\,\Delta y\,\Delta z$, and equating the limits of the two members as Δx, Δy, and Δz approach zero, we get

$$k\left[\frac{\partial^2\theta}{\partial x^2} + \frac{\partial^2\theta}{\partial y^2} + \frac{\partial^2\theta}{\partial z^2}\right] = c\rho\frac{\partial\theta}{\partial t}. \qquad (28)$$

To get the equation of heat flow in a plate with insulated surfaces, omit $\partial^2\theta/\partial z^2$ from (28) to obtain

$$k\left(\frac{\partial^2\theta}{\partial x^2} + \frac{\partial^2\theta}{\partial y^2}\right) = c\rho\frac{\partial\theta}{\partial t}, \qquad (29)$$

and to get the equation for the flow in an insulated rod, leave $\partial^2\theta/\partial y^2$ from (29) to get

$$k\frac{\partial^2\theta}{\partial x^2} = c\rho\frac{\partial\theta}{\partial t}. \qquad (30)$$

After heat has flowed until the temperature at any point is constant, the steady state is reached. *To obtain the equations for flow of heat in the steady state, replace $\partial\theta/\partial t$ by zero in* (28), (29), *and* (30). Thus for steady-state flow we get from (28)

$$\frac{\partial^2\theta}{\partial x^2} + \frac{\partial^2\theta}{\partial y^2} + \frac{\partial^2\theta}{\partial z^2} = 0. \qquad (31)$$

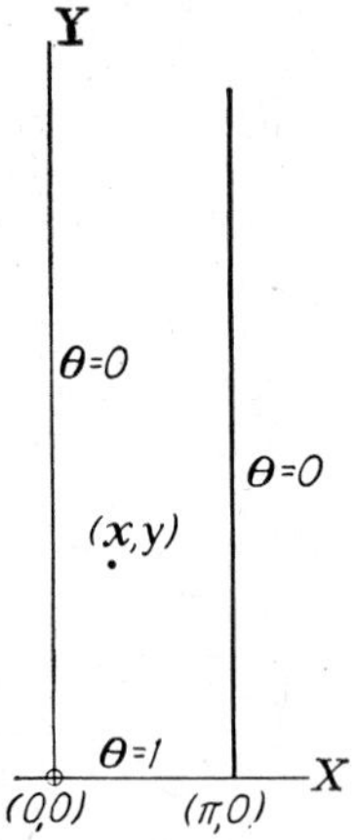

FIG. 7.

Example. Fourier's problem is to find the temperature θ at any point (x,y) of a thin plate (see Fig. 7), π units wide and infinitely long, assuming (a) the steady state so that

$$\frac{\partial^2\theta}{\partial x^2} + \frac{\partial^2\theta}{\partial y^2} = 0, \qquad (a)$$

from (29) with $\partial\theta/\partial t = 0$; (b) perfectly insulated surfaces; (c) the short edge constantly at temperature unity; (d) the long edges at temperature zero.

Solution. Taking the Y-axis along an infinite edge and the x-axis along the short edge, we have the boundary conditions: (α) temperature $\theta = 0$, when $x = 0$; (β) $\theta = 0$, when $x = \pi$; (γ)$\theta = 0$, when $y = \infty$; (δ)$\theta = 1$, when $y = 0$.

To solve (a) substitute $\theta = Y(y)e^{i\omega x}$ in it to obtain

$$(-\omega^2 Y + Y'')e^{i\omega x} = 0,$$

or

$$Y = c_1 e^{\omega y} + c_2{}^{-\omega y},$$

and
$$\theta = (c_1 e^{\omega y} + c_2 e^{-\omega y})(\cos \omega x + j \sin \omega x). \qquad (b)$$

Since c_1, c_2, and ω are arbitrary and since both the real part and the pure imaginary part must satisfy (a), any one of the terms

$$A e^{\omega y} \sin \omega x, \; B e^{\omega y} \cos \omega x, \; C e^{-\omega y} \sin \omega x, \; G e^{-\omega y} \cos \omega x \qquad (c)$$

is a solution of (a), and any sum of such terms is a solution. It remains to choose such a sum that the initial conditions will be satisfied by it. Conditions (α) and (β) will be satisfied by

$$\theta = \sum_{\omega=1}^{\infty} (c_{1\omega} e^{\omega y} + c_{2\omega} e^{-\omega y}) \sin \omega x, \qquad (d)$$

and condition (γ) will also be satisfied by (d) if $c_{1\omega} = 0$. The expansion of unity in a Fourier series is

$$1 = \frac{4}{\pi}(\sin x + \tfrac{1}{3} \sin 3x + \tfrac{1}{5} \sin 5x + \cdots). \qquad (e)$$

Hence conditions (α), (β), (γ), and (δ) are satisfied by

$$\theta = \frac{4}{\pi}\left(\frac{1}{1}e^{-y} \sin x + \frac{1}{3}e^{-3y} \sin 3x + \frac{1}{5}e^{-5y} \sin 5x + \cdots\right).$$

Exercises

1. Solve the problems obtained from the illustrative example by replacing condition (c) by (I) the short edge has temperature $\theta(x,0) = A \sin 3x$; (II) $\theta(x,0) = Ax$.

2. Find the temperature $\theta(x,y)$ for the plate of Fig. 7 assuming the steady state and $\theta(0,y) = m$, $\theta(\pi,y) = m$, $\theta(x,\infty) = m$, and $\theta(x,0) = m \sin 3x + m$. *Hint:* Use a solution having the form
$$\theta = A + B e^{-3y} \sin 3x.$$

3. Find the temperature in the plate of Fig. 7 assuming the steady state, $\theta(0,y) = m$, $\theta(\pi,y) = m$, $\theta(x,\infty) = m$, and $\theta(x,0) = 1$. *Hint:* Use a solution having the form $\theta = B + C\varphi(x,y)$ where $\varphi(x,y)$ is the solution of the illustrative example.

4. Find the solution of $\dfrac{\partial^2 y}{\partial t^2} = \dfrac{a^2 \partial^2 y}{\partial x^2}$ satisfying the conditions $y = 0$ when $x = 0$, $y = 0$ when $x = c$, $y = gx$ for $0 < x < c/2$ and $t = 0$, and $y = g(c - x)$ for $c/2 < x < c$ and $t = 0$.

5. Find the temperature $\theta(x,y)$ at any point of the plate of Fig. 7 under the conditions: $\theta(0,y) = 10$, $\theta(\pi,y) = 100$, $\theta(x,0) = 40$, $\theta(x,\infty) = 10 + 90\ x/\pi$, and the steady state.

Suggestion: Observe that $\theta = A + Bx$ satisfies equation (a) of the example. Hence, let

$$\theta(x,y) = A + Bx + \varphi(x,y)$$

where $\varphi(0,y) = 0$, $\varphi(\pi,y) = 0$. Then from the initial conditions we have

$$10 = A + \varphi(0,y) = A,$$
$$100 = A + \pi B + \varphi(\pi,y) = A + \pi B,$$
$$40 = A + BX + \varphi(x,0)$$

Hence $A = 10$, $B = 90/\pi$, $\varphi(x,0) = 30 - 90x/\pi$.

116. One-dimensional heat flow.

The temperature θ in an insulated rod through which heat is flowing parallel to the axis of the rod satisfies equation 30 in §115, namely,

$$a^2\frac{\partial^2\theta(x,t)}{\partial x^2} = \frac{\partial\theta(x,t)}{\partial t},\ a^2 = \frac{k}{c\rho}. \tag{32}$$

To find solutions of (32), substitute in it

$$\theta = T(t)e^{j\omega x}, \tag{33}$$

where T is a function of t only, ω is a constant, and $j = \sqrt{-1}$. From this result obtain

$$-a^2\omega^2 T e^{j\omega x} = T'e^{j\omega x}.$$

Divide out $e^{j\omega x}$ and solve for T to obtain

$$T = Ae^{-a^2\omega^2 t}.$$

Substituting this in (33) and considering that both the real part of θ and the pure imaginary part must satisfy (32), we find that terms having either of the forms

$$Ae^{-a^2\omega^2 t}\sin\ \omega x,\ Be^{-a^2\omega^2 t}\cos\ \omega x, \tag{34}$$

and therefore sums of such terms, will satisfy (32).

The following example will illustrate a method of solving simple problems relating to the flow of heat.

Example. A rod L cm. long with insulated lateral surface is initially at temperature 20°C. throughout. If one end is kept at 10°C. and the other at 100°C., find the temperature θ as a function of time t and distance x from the end at 10°C.

Solution. The boundary conditions are

$$\theta(0,t) = 10, \; \theta(L,t) = 100, \; \theta(x,0) = 20. \qquad (a)$$

A sum $\varphi(x,t)$ of terms having the first form of (34) will satisfy the condition $\varphi(0,t) = 0$, $\varphi\left(\dfrac{k\pi}{\omega},t\right) = 0$, k an integer. Also $\theta = A + Bx$ satisfies (32). Now let the required solution be

$$\theta(x,t) = A + Bx + \varphi(x,t), \qquad (b)$$

where

$$\varphi(x,t) = \sum_{k=1}^{\infty} A e^{-a^2 k^2 \pi^2 t/L^2} \sin \frac{k\pi}{L}x. \qquad (c)$$

Using the conditions (a) with (b) and (c), we obtain

$$10 = A + \varphi(0,t) = A, \; 100 = A + BL + \varphi(L,t) =$$
$$A + BL, \; 20 = A + Bx + \varphi(x,0). \qquad (d)$$

Solve (d) for A, B, and $\varphi(x,0)$ to get

$$A = 10, \; B = \frac{90}{L}, \; \varphi(x,0) = 10 - \left(\frac{90}{L}\right)x. \qquad (e)$$

Next expand $\varphi(x,0)$ in a Fourier series for the interval $0 < x < L$, to obtain

$$\varphi(x,0) = 10 - \frac{90x}{L} = -\frac{4}{\pi}\left[\frac{35}{1}\sin\frac{\pi x}{L} - \frac{45}{2}\sin\frac{2\pi x}{L}\right.$$
$$\left. + \frac{35}{3}\sin\frac{3\pi x}{L} - \frac{45}{4}\sin\frac{4\pi x}{L} + \cdots \right]. \qquad (f)$$

To form $\varphi(x,t)$ write in front of the 1st, 2d, $\ldots$, terms in (f) the respective results of setting $k = 1, 2, \ldots$, in $e^{-k^2 a^2 \pi^2 t/L}$. Then $\theta(x,t)$ from (b) is given by

$$\theta(x,t) = 10 + \frac{90x}{L} - \frac{4}{\pi}\left(\frac{35}{1}e^{-a^2\pi^2 t/L^2}\sin\frac{\pi x}{L}\right.$$
$$\left. - \frac{45}{2}e^{-4a^2\pi^2 t/L^2}\sin\frac{2\pi x}{L} + \cdots \right). \qquad (g)$$

Exercises

1. What is the steady-state equation for the flow of heat in the rod of the illustrative example?

2. Find the expression $\theta(x,t)$ for temperature in the rod of the illustrative example if $\theta(0,t) = 0$, $\theta(L,t) = 100$, $\theta(x,0) = 0$.

117. Telephone, telegraph, and radio equations. Figure 8 represents a long line carrying electricity. The current goes out through AB and returns through the ground from C to D. Let L (henrys/mile) be the inductance of the line AB, let R(ohms/mile) be its resistance, let C(farads/mile) be its

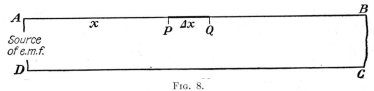

Fig. 8.

capacitance to ground, and let G(mhos/mile) be the leakage of current or conductance to ground. Let $e(x,t)$ and $i(x,t)$ represent the voltage and current at a point in the line AB x miles from A, and derive relations between e and i by considering the flow of electricity in a small portion PQ of the cable having length Δx. The drop Δe in potential along PQ will be approximately

$$\Delta e = -R\,\Delta x i(x_1,t) - L\,\Delta x\,\frac{\partial i(x_1,t)}{\partial t}, \qquad (35)$$

where $x < x_1 < x + \Delta x$. Dividing this equation through by Δx and equating the limits approached by its members as Δx approaches zero, we get

$$\frac{\partial e}{\partial x} = -Ri(x,t) - L\frac{\partial i(x,t)}{\partial t}. \qquad (36)$$

Here changes in e due to leakage and capacitance to ground are of second order and therefore have nothing to do with equation (36).

Similarly, the drop in current along PQ is approximately

$$\Delta i = -G \, \Delta x e(x_1,t) - C \, \Delta x \frac{\partial e(x_1,t)}{\partial t}.$$

Dividing this through by Δx and equating the limits approached by its members as Δx approaches zero, we obtain

$$\frac{\partial i}{\partial x} = -Ge - C\frac{\partial e}{\partial t}. \tag{37}$$

Equations (36) and (37) are basic equations. Three important sets will be derived from them.

Eliminate i between (36) and (37) by equating the partial derivatives with respect to x of the two members of (36), replacing $\partial i/\partial x$ in the result by its value from (37) and $\partial^2 x/(\partial x \, \partial t)$ by its value obtained from (37) by partial differentiation with respect to t, and simplifying; the result is

$$\frac{\partial^2 e}{\partial x^2} = RGe + (RC + LG)\frac{\partial e}{\partial t} + LC\frac{\partial^2 e}{\partial t^2}. \tag{38}$$

Similarly eliminate e between (36) and (37) to get

$$\frac{\partial^2 i}{\partial x^2} = RGi + (RC + LG)\frac{\partial i}{\partial t} + LC\frac{\partial^2 i}{\partial t^2}. \tag{39}$$

The equations (36), (37), (38), and (39) are known as the *telephone equations*.

In many applications to telegraph signaling, G and L are negligible. Replacing G and L by 0 in equations (36), (37), (38), and (39) we obtain the telegraph equations which follow:

$$\begin{aligned}
\frac{\partial e}{\partial x} &= -Ri \\[4pt]
\frac{\partial i}{\partial x} &= -C\frac{\partial e}{\partial t}, \\[4pt]
\frac{\partial^2 e}{\partial x^2} &= RC\frac{\partial e}{\partial t}, \\[4pt]
\frac{\partial^2 i}{\partial x^2} &= RC\frac{\partial i}{\partial t}.
\end{aligned} \tag{40}$$

For high frequencies we may place $G = R = 0$ in (36), (37), (38), and (39) to obtain the radio equations which follow:

$$\frac{\partial e}{\partial x} = -L\frac{\partial i}{\partial t},$$

$$\frac{\partial i}{\partial x} = -C\frac{\partial e}{\partial t}, \tag{41}$$

$$\frac{\partial^2 e}{\partial x^2} = LC\frac{\partial^2 e}{\partial t^2},$$

$$\frac{\partial^2 i}{\partial x^2} = LC\frac{\partial^2 i}{\partial t^2}.$$

Exercises

1. Substitute $e = X(x)\,e^{j\omega t}$ in the third radio equation (41), show that X has the form $c_1 \sin \omega x + c_2 \cos \omega x$, and then deduce that the third radio equation is satisfied by the expressions for e

$$\cos \omega\sqrt{LC}\,x \cos \omega t, \quad \cos \omega\sqrt{LC}x \sin \omega t, \tag{42}$$
$$\sin \omega \sqrt{LC}\,x \sin \omega t, \quad \sin \omega\sqrt{LC}\,x \sin \omega t.$$

If i and e are to satisfy the four radio equations (41) and $e = A \sin \omega\sqrt{LC}\,x \cos \omega t$, show that i must have the form $i = -A\sqrt{C/L} \cos \omega\sqrt{LC}\,x \sin \omega t + B$, where B is a constant.

2. If $i = A \cos \omega\sqrt{LC}\,x \sin \omega t$, find e so that i and e satisfy the radio equation (41).

3. Substitute $e = \epsilon^{j\omega x}T(t)$ in the third equation of (40) and, from the result, deduce that some solutions of that equation have the form

$$A\epsilon^{-(\omega^2/RC)t} \cos \omega x, \quad B\epsilon^{-(\omega^2/RC)t} \sin \omega x. \tag{43}$$

4. (a) If $e = A\epsilon^{-(\omega^2/RC)t} \cos \omega x$, find a corresponding function $i(x,t)$ such that e and i satisfy (40). (b) If $i = A\epsilon^{-(\omega^2/RC)t} \sin \omega x$, find $e(x,t)$ such that i and e will satisfy (40).

5. In a steady-state condition for which i and e are functions of x only, solve (40). Since i and e depend on x only, $\partial i/\partial t$ and $\partial e/\partial t$ are zero.

6. In Fig. 8 take L miles as the length of AB and solve the corresponding telegraph equations (40). Use as initial conditions $e(0,t) = 0$, $e(L,t) = 0$, $e(x,0) = 2 + 3x/L$. Results in exercise 2 of this article and in exercise 6 of §112 may be used to shorten the work.

7. Solve the third radio equation (41) by the method of §103 to obtain

$$e = \varphi_1\left(x + \frac{1}{\sqrt{LC}}\, t\right) + \varphi_2\left(x - \frac{1}{\sqrt{LC}}\, t\right).^*$$

Substitute this in the second of equations (41) and integrate to obtain

$$i = -\sqrt{\frac{C}{L}}\left[\varphi_1\left(x + \frac{1}{\sqrt{LC}}t\right) - \varphi_2\left(x - \frac{1}{\sqrt{LC}}t\right)\right] + \psi(t).$$

Now substitute these values of e and i in the first equation of (41) and deduce that $\psi(t)$ is a constant.

8. A line is called distortionless if $LG = RC$, or $G/C = R/L$. Make the substitution

$$e = E(x,t)\epsilon^{-Gt/C},\ i = I(x,t)\epsilon^{-Gt/C}$$

in (36), (37), (38), and (39) to obtain equations having the form (41) of the radio equations for a distortionless line. Also check directly that (38) is satisfied by

$$e = A\epsilon^{-Gt/C} \sin \omega\sqrt{LC}\, x \cos \omega t,$$

when $G/C = R/L$, and find the corresponding $i(x,t)$ to satisfy (36) and (37).

118. Fluid motion.

Because of the importance of fluid motion, as exemplified by the flow of air over airplane wings and the flow of water near ships, and because the solution of fluid-motion problems involves partial differential equations, a brief introduction to the subject will be given.

Consider the motion of a homogeneous fluid with continuous structure and no viscosity.† In this case all forces exerted by the fluid on a surface will be normal to the surface. For simplicity, think of a fluid moving between two parallel planes and assume that any particle remains in a plane parallel to the bounding planes and that the motions in all such planes are the same. The flow will then be two-dimensional.

---

* An equation of the form $e = \varphi(x - \omega t)$ represents a wave motion because the value of e associated with any point in the line at any instant is taken on at each point as the time t increases. If $e = m$ at point x_1 and time t_1, then e will equal m provided $x - \omega t = x_1 - \omega t_1$, that is, as x varies with the time, the condition $e = m$ moves along the line like the crest of a wave. Observe that $e = \varphi\ (x + \omega t)$ represents waves moving in a direction opposite to that of the motion represented by $e = \varphi(x - \omega t)$.

† All fluids are viscous but many, water for example, are only slightly viscous.

The motion of the fluid will be due to pressure in the fluid and a force proportional to the mass like the pull of gravity. Thus the pressure p in the fluid will be a function of x,y, and t, and the force per unit mass will have components $X(x,y,t)$ and $Y(x,y,t)$ parallel to the co-ordinate axes. Also let $u(x,y,t)$ and $v(x,y,t)$ be the x and y components of the velocity at time t.

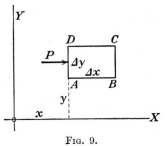

Fig. 9.

From calculus, we have for the x and y components of acceleration

$$a_x = \frac{du}{dt} = \frac{\partial u}{\partial x} u + \frac{\partial u}{\partial y} v + \frac{\partial u}{\partial t},$$

$$a_y = \frac{dv}{dt} = \frac{\partial v}{\partial x} u + \frac{\partial v}{\partial y} v + \frac{\partial v}{\partial t}. \tag{44}$$

Now apply Newton's law of motion to the element of fluid represented by $ABCD$ in Fig. 9. The forces at time t on the faces represented by AD and BC may be expressed as an average pressure multiplied by the area $h \, \Delta y$, where h is the distance between the bounding planes. Accordingly we write as the total force due to pressure on the surfaces represented by AD and BC,

$$h \, \Delta y p(x,y_1,t) - h \, \Delta y p(x + \Delta x,y_1,t), \text{ where } y < y_1$$
$$< y + \Delta y. \tag{45}$$

Also the force proportional to mass acting on the element in the x-direction may be expressed by

$$\frac{h}{g} \, \Delta y \, \Delta x \, \bar{\rho} X \left(\frac{x_2,y_2,t}{g} \right), \tag{46}$$

where $\bar{\rho}$ is the average density of the fluid in the element and (x_2,y_2) is a point properly chosen in the element. Hence we have

$$h \, \Delta y p(x,y_1,t) \, - \, h \, \Delta y \, p(x + \Delta x, y_1, t) + \frac{h}{g} \, \Delta y \, \Delta x \bar{\rho} X \; (x_2, y_2, t)$$

$$= \frac{\bar{\rho} h \, \Delta y \, \Delta x}{g} \frac{du(x_3, y_3, t)}{dt}. \quad (47)$$

where (x_3, y_3) is a properly chosen point in the element. Dividing through by $\Delta x \, \Delta y$, equating the limits of the two members as Δx and Δy approach zero, and simplifying slightly we get

$$\frac{du}{dt} = X - \frac{g}{\rho} \frac{\partial p}{\partial x}. \quad (48)$$

Applying Newton's law parallel to the y-axis, we obtain in a like manner

$$\frac{dv}{dt} = Y - \frac{g}{\rho} \frac{\partial p}{\partial y}. \quad (49)$$

Finally express the condition that the rate of change of amount of fluid in the element is the rate at which fluid enters minus the rate at which it leaves. The rate of change of the quantity is

$$\frac{\partial}{\partial t}[h \, \Delta x \, \Delta y \, \rho(x_1, y_1, t)] = h \, \Delta x \, \Delta y \frac{\partial \bar{\rho}_1}{\partial t}. \quad (50)$$

The rate of entering minus the rate of leaving is approximately

$$h \, \Delta y (\overline{\rho u}_{x,y_1,t} - \overline{\rho u}_{x+\triangle x, y_1, t}) + h \, \Delta x (\overline{\rho v}_{x_1,y,t} - \overline{\rho v}_{x_1, y+\Delta y, t}). \quad (51)$$

Equating the limit of (51) divided by $\Delta x \, \Delta y$ as Δx and Δy approach zero to the limit of (50) divided by $\Delta x \, \Delta y$, we get

$$- \frac{\partial(\rho u)}{\partial x} - \frac{\partial(\rho v)}{\partial y} = \frac{\partial \rho}{\partial t}. \quad (52)$$

Equations (48), (49) and (52) are the differential equations of fluid flow for the special case considered.

To understand the simplest case, the idea of *rotation* will be required. Figure 10 shows positions $A'B'C'D'$ after Δt units of time of four fluid particles originally at points A, B, C, and

D of Fig. 9. ϵ_x and ϵ_y represent infinitesimals of higher order than Δx, Δy, and Δt. Disregarding infinitesimals of

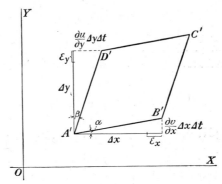

Fig. 10.

higher order than the first, we get for the angular velocity ω_x of $A'B'$,

$$\omega_x = \frac{\dfrac{\partial v}{\partial x}\,\Delta x\,\Delta t}{\Delta t\,\Delta x} = \frac{\partial v}{\partial x}, \tag{53}$$

and for the angular velocity ω_y of $A'D'$

$$\omega_y = \frac{-\dfrac{\partial u}{\partial y}\,\Delta y\,\Delta t}{\Delta t\,\Delta y} = -\frac{\partial u}{\partial y}. \tag{54}$$

One-half the sum of the velocities ω_x and ω_y is called the *rotation* of the fluid, that is,

$$\text{Rotation} = \frac{1}{2}\left(\frac{\partial v}{\partial x} - \frac{\partial u}{\partial y}\right). \tag{55}$$

Now consider the motion of a fluid for which the rotation is zero, that is

$$\frac{\partial v}{\partial x} = \frac{\partial u}{\partial y}; \tag{56}$$

the fluid is incompressible, that is,

$$\rho = \text{constant}; \tag{57}$$

the fluid is in the steady state, that is, u and v are functions of x and y only; and the force is conservative, that is, there exists a force function $U(x,y)$ such that

$$\frac{\partial U}{\partial x} = X, \frac{\partial U}{\partial y} = Y. \tag{58}$$

From (44) and the fact that the steady state exists

$$\frac{du}{dt} = \frac{\partial u}{\partial x}u + \frac{\partial u}{\partial y}v. \tag{59}$$

Hence, taking account of (56), (57), (58), and (59), we may write (48) in the form

$$u\frac{\partial u}{\partial x} + v\frac{\partial u}{\partial y} = \frac{\partial U}{\partial x} - \frac{g}{\rho}\frac{\partial p}{\partial x}. \tag{60}$$

The integral of (60) is

$$\frac{u^2 + v^2}{2} = U - \frac{g}{\rho}p + C. \tag{61}$$

Exercises

1. From (56) deduce that in steady-state irrotational fluid motion there is a *velocity potential* $\varphi(x,y)$ such that

$$\partial\varphi/\partial x = u, \quad \partial\varphi/\partial y = v.$$

The curves $\varphi(x,y) = c$ are called *curves of constant velocity potential*.

2. A streamline of a fluid in motion is a curve at each of whose points the direction of the velocity is the same as that of the curve. Hence along streamlines $dy/dx = v/u$ or

$$v\,dx - u\,dy = 0.$$

Show that, for steady-state irrotational motion of an incompressible fluid, this equation is exact because of (52), which, for the case in question, simplifies to $\partial u/\partial x + \partial v/\partial y = 0$. Hence show that there are streamlines represented by

$$\psi(x,y) = C, \quad \partial\psi/\partial x = v, \quad \partial\psi/\partial y = -u.$$

Also show that the streamlines $\psi(x,y) = C$ are the orthogonal trajectories of the velocity potential curves considered in exercise 1.

3. If $f(z) = v(x,y) + iu(x,y)$, where u and v are real functions of x and y, is analytic then

$$\frac{\partial v}{\partial x} = \frac{\partial u}{\partial y}, \quad \frac{\partial u}{\partial x} = -\frac{\partial v}{\partial y}.$$

These are equivalent to (56) and (52) for steady-state irrotational motion of an incompressible fluid.

(a) Using $f(z) = (x + iy)^2 = x^2 - y^2 + 2ixy$, take $v = x^2 - y^2$, $u = 2xy$, find the corresponding equations of the streamlines and curves of constant velocity potential. Also assuming that $X = 0$, $Y = -g$, find p in terms of x and y. (b) Carry out the same process for $f(z) = 1/z$, assuming $X = 0$, $Y = -g$.

INDEX

ANSWERS

1. (a) 2,2. (b) 3,1. (c) 2,1. (d) 2,2. (e) **1,3.** (f) 2,2. **2.** (13) 1,1. (14) 1,1. (15) 1,1. (16) 2,1. (17) 2,1.

1. $y' = y$. **2.** $2xy' = y$. **3.** $xy'' = y'$. **4.** $y'' + y' - 2y = 0$. **5.** $xyy'' + xy'^2 = yy'$. **6.** $y'' = 0$. **7.** $y''' = 0$. **8.** $x + yy' = 0$. **9.** $y = xy' + 3y'^2 - 4y'$. **10.** $y'' + 9y = 0$. **11.** $y'(2x - y + 4) + x - 2y + 5 = 0$. **12.** $y'' - 5y' + 6y = 12$. **13.** $xy' = x^2 + y^2 + y$. **14.** $y'^2 = yy''$. **15.** $y'^2 + yy'' + 1 = 0$. **16.** $(1 + y'^2)^3 = 25y''^2$. **17.** (a) $y^2(1 + y'^2) = 1$. (b) $x + yy' = 0$. (c) $y = xy'$. (d) $(1 + y'^2)^3 = 16y''^2$. (e) $xyy'^2 + (x^2 - y^2 - 4)y' - xy = 0$. (f) $y'' = 0$. (g) $y'''(1 + y'^2) = 3y'y''^2$. **18.** $yy' = 1 + xy'^2$.

1. $x^2 + y^2 = c$. **2.** $y - x = cxy$. **3.** $y = cx$. **4.** $(1 + x^2)(1 + y^2)^2 = c$. **5.** $1 + y = c(2 - x)$. **6.** $\rho = ce^\theta$. **7.** $i = ce^{-\frac{R}{L}t}$. **8.** $2x - y^2 = \log(cy)^2$. **9.** $y[x + \sqrt{1 + x^2}] = c$. **10.** $\log(y + \sqrt{1 + y^2}) = \sin^{-1}x + c$. **11.** $xy^2 = c(2 - x)$. **12.** $\sqrt{x^2 + a^2} = \log(cy)$. **13.** $x^2y^2 = c(1 - x^2)$. **14.** $y = c(x + a)(1 - ay)$. **15.** $3e^{7y} + 7e^{-3x} = c$. **16.** $y = c(1 + y)e^x$. **17.** $x^2 + y^2 = 13$. **18.** $y = 6x$. **19.** $\rho = 2e^\theta$. **20.** $y + 2\sqrt{1 + x^2} = 0$. **21.** $xy^2 = x^2 + x - 1$. **22.** $y\sqrt[4]{x + 2} + \sqrt[4]{3}(x - 2) = 0$. **23.** $5\sqrt{1 - y^2} + 5\sqrt{1 - x^2} = 7$. **24.** $1 + 2y = 2e^{2/x}$. **25.** $2x - 1 = 5e^{-2y}$. **26.** $\tan y (1 + e^x)^3 = 27$. **27.** $r(3 - 5\sin\theta) = 2$.

1. (a) $y = (x - 1)^2$. (b) $y^3 = 3x + 55$. (c) $3y = 4x$. (d) $16y^2 - 9x^2 = 175$. (e) $(x + 1)^2 + (y - 1)^2 = 25$. **3.** (a) $xy = c$. (b) $y = cx$. (c) $y^2 + 2x^2 = c$. (d) $x^2 + 5y^2 = c$. (e) $x^2 + 3y = c$. **4.** Each curve in the original family would cross at right angles only the family of curves in the derived system corresponding to the same value of c. **5.** $y^2 = cx$; $y^{a+b} = cx^b$. **6.** (a) $x^2 + 2y^2 = c$. (b) $ax^2 + by^2 = c$. **7.** $x^2 = \pm y^2 + c$. **8.** $y(c - x) = 2k$. **9.** $y^2 = 2kx + c$.

1. (a) $y^2 = 10x - 51$. (b) $y = 10e^{x/3}$. **2.** $y^n = cx$. **3.** (a) $y = ce^{kx}$.

(b) $y^2 = kx^{n+1} + c$.　**4.** (a) $\rho = ce^{k\theta}$.　(b) $\rho = c - k\cos\theta$.　**5.** (a) $\rho = ce^{\theta/k}$.　(b) $\rho = ce^{\pm\sqrt{k}\theta}$.　**6.** (a) $\rho = c\cos\theta$. (b) $4\rho^{-1} = 2\theta + \sin 2\theta + c$. (c) $\rho^2 + \theta^2 = c\rho^2\theta^2$. (d) $\rho = c\csc^4\theta$. (e) $\rho = c\cos^9\dfrac{\theta}{3}$. (f) $\rho = c(1 + \cos\theta)$. **7.** $\rho = ae^{\theta\cot\alpha}$. **8.** (a) $\rho = c\sin\theta$. (b) $\rho = c\sin^2\tfrac{1}{2}\theta$, $\rho = c\csc^4\left(135° - \dfrac{\theta}{4}\right)$. **9.** $y = Re^{x/k}$ **10.** $y(c - \pi x) = k$.

§12, pages 24, 25

1. $y = cx$, $xy^3 = c$. **2.** $ky = \pm\sqrt{1 - k^2}\,x + c$. **3.** $\rho = ce^{\pm\frac{\sqrt{1-k^2}}{k}\theta}$. **4.** $y = \tfrac{2}{3}x^2$, $2y = x^2 + 3$. **5.** (a) $x^2 + y^2 = a^2$. (b) $\pm x = \sqrt{a^2 - y^2} + a\log\dfrac{\sqrt{a^2 - y^2} - a}{y}$ **7.** (a) $\rho = c\cos\theta$. (b) $\rho(\theta + c) = \pm\left(\sqrt{a^2 - \rho^2} + \rho\sin^{-1}\dfrac{\rho}{a}\right)$.

§15, pages 28, 29

1. 4 min. 42 sec. **2.** 10 min. **3.** 15.85 years. **4.** 6.18 per cent. **5.** $i = 30\left(\tfrac{11}{30}\right)^{100t}$. **6.** 0.0208 sec. **7.** \$42,511. **8.** $p = 14.7e^{-0.0000375h}$, 8.37 lb./in.²

§16, pages 31, 32

1. $v = \tfrac{20}{61}$ ft./sec., $v = 20\,e^{-0.35}$. **2.** $v = 3t^2$, $s = t^3$. **3.** (a) $v = 7.5(1 - e^{-0.161t})$. (b) 6 ft./sec. (c) 7.5 ft./sec. **4.** (a) $v = \tfrac{1}{2}(15 + 29e^{-0.161t})$. **5.** (a) $v = 3.75(1 - e^{-0.322t})$. **6.** (a) $v = 20(1 - e^{-0.00322t})$. (b) 20 ft./sec. (c) 11 min. 55 sec. **7.** 32,000 ft./sec., or about 6 mi./sec. **8.** $t = \dfrac{2000wm^n}{pg}\displaystyle\int_{\frac{1}{2}m}^{\frac{1}{4}m}\dfrac{dv}{m^n - v^n}$

§17, pages 33, 34

1. (a) 172.9 lb.; 200 lb.; (c) 34.7 min. **2.** 54.4 lb. **3.** 30.5 min. **4.** $a = -0.02$, $b = 4$. **5.** 0.531 gal.

§18, pages 34, 36

1. $Q = 150 - 100e^{-0.02t}$. **2.** $v = 20 - 160e^{-5t}$. **3.** $i = (E/R)(1 - e^{-Rt/L})$. **4.** $y^2 - x^2 = 16$. $3y^2 - 2x = 69$. **5.** $pv^k = c$. **6.** $x^2 + (y - c)^2 = 2k$. **7.** (a) $\rho = c\sin\theta$, $\rho = c\csc\theta$. (b) $\rho = a\sec(\theta + c)$. (c) $\rho = \dfrac{c}{1 + \cos\theta} = c/2\,\sec^2\theta/2$. (d) $\rho\cos\theta = c$, $\rho\sec\theta = c$. (e) $\rho = c\csc\theta e^{\frac{1}{2}\theta/k}$. **8.** $\rho^3\sec 3\theta = c$. $\rho^3 = c\sec 3\theta$. **10.** $v = 173\left(1 - e^{-\frac{g}{173}t}\right)$ 151 ft./sec. **11.** (a) 1.37×10^8 cal. (b) 1.66×10^6 cal. **12.** 9.33×10^5 cal., 7.21×10^4 cal.; 1.17×10^5 cal. **13.** (a) 1 min. 44 sec. (b) 1 min 48 sec. **14.** 26 min. 28 sec. **15.** 7 min. 59 sec.

§19, pages 38, 39

1. $(x + y - 2)^2 = -4x + c.$ **2.** $x^2y^2 = 3y^4 + c.$ **3.** $(cx + 2)(x^2 + y^2) - x = 0.$ **4.** $(st - 2)^3 t = cs.$ **5.** $(x - 2y)^2 + 10(x - 2y) + 2y = c.$
6. $x + y + 3 \log (2x + y + 3) = c.$ **7.** $x^2 + 3 = c[3 - (x + y)^2].$
8. $s^2 = t^2(c + 2 \log t).$ **9.** $\theta^3\rho^3(c - e^\theta) = 1.$ **10.** $\csc (\theta^2\rho) - \cot (\theta^2\rho) = c\theta.$ **11.** $x^3 y = x^3 + c.$ **12.** $(2y + cx)(x + y)^2 + x = 0.$ **13.** $x^2 y^2 = c(x^2 + y^2).$ **14.** $\rho - m \tan^{-1}\left(\dfrac{\rho + \theta}{m}\right) = c.$

§20, pages 41, 42

2. $m = n = l + 2k.$ **3.** $x^2 + 2xy - y^2 = c.$ **4.** $x(x^2 + 3y^2) = c.$
5. $2xy + x^2 = c.$ **6.** $x(5x^2 - 21y^2) = c.$ **7.** $\rho^2 - 2\rho\theta - \theta^2 = c.$ **8.** $2x^2 + 2xy + y^2 = c.$ **9.** $2y = cx^2 - \dfrac{1}{c}.$ **10.** $y^3 = x^3 \log cx^3.$ **11.** $y = ce^{-\sqrt{x/y}}.$
12. $\sin (y/x) + \log cx = 0.$ **13.** $x \sin (y/x) = c.$ **14.** $\log cx = \sin (y/x).$
15. $y = (x^3 + c)\sqrt{x^2 + y^2}.$ **17.** $x^2 + y^2 = cy.$ **18.** $\log c\sqrt{x^2 + y^2} \pm \tan^{-1} (y/x) = 0.$ **19.** $x^3 y = c(3x - 2y).$

§21, page 43

1. $(x + y - 1)^3 = c(x - y + 3).$ **2.** $(2x + y - 4)^2 = c(x + y - 1).$

3. $\log (y^2 - 2xy + 2x^2 - 2x + 1) + 2 \tan^{-1} \dfrac{y - x}{x - 1} = c.$

4. $\tan^{-1}\dfrac{y + 2}{2x + 2} + \log [4(x + 1)^2 + (y + 2)^2] = c.$ **5.** $5x - 10y + \log (10x + 5y - 2) = c.$ **6.** $x + 2y + \log (2x - y) = c.$

§22, pages 43, 44

1. (a) $(3x^2 - y^2 - 8xy)dx - (2xy + 4x^2)dy.$ (b) $\dfrac{5}{xy} (x\,dx + y\,dy).$
(c) $(4x^3 y^4 + \cos x)dx + 4x^4 y^3 \, dy.$ **2.** (a) $3x^2 y \, dx + (x^3 - 2y)dy = 0.$
(b) $2x\,dx - \left(2y + \dfrac{3}{y}\right)dy = 0.$ (c) $(2ax + by)dx + bx\,dy = 0.$
4. (a) $x^2 + xy - y^2 + c.$ (b) $x^2 + xy - y^3 - 3y + c.$ (c) $x^3 - x^2 y + y^4 + 3y + c.$ (d) $x^2 + x \tan y - y^3 + c.$

§24, page 47

1. $x^2 - 2xy + y^2 + 10x = c.$ **2.** $x^2 - 3y^2 + 2x \tan y = c.$ **3.** $2x^3 + 6xy^2 + 9y^2 - 6y = c.$ **4.** $\sec x + \sec y + y(2 - x) = c.$ **5.** $y^3 + 3xy^2 + 3x^2 y - 3a^2 x = c.$ **6.** $ax^2 + bxy + cy^2 + gx + ey + h = 0.$ **7.** $x + y \log y = y(c - x^2).$ **8.** $x^2 y + xy^2 + \log y = c.$ **9.** $y(x^4 + c) + 4x = 0.$
10. $x + \sqrt{x^2 + y^2} = c.$ **11.** $x^2 y^2(x^2 - y^2) = c.$ **12.** $(m + 1)x^{n+1} - (n + 1)x^{m+1} y^{n+1} = cy^{n+1}.$

§25, pages 50, 51

1. $y = x^2 + cx + 3$. **2.** $xy = ce^{x^3}$. **3.** $x^2 + y^2 = ce^{2y^3}$. **4.** $(m - n + 1)$ $xy = (1 - n)x^n y^{m+1} + cx^n y^n$. **5.** $4x^3 y = x^4 + c$. **6.** $x = ce^{y^3/3x^3}$. **7.** $y = x \tan(\log\sqrt{x^2 + y^2} + c)$. **8.** $y = x \tan[\frac{1}{4}(x^2 + y^2)^2 + c]$. **9.** (a) $x = ce^{x/y}$. (b) $y^3 + 3x^3 \log cx = 0$. (c) $2x^2 \log cx + 2xy - y^2 = 0$. **10.** (a) $x^3 y^2 = Re^x$. (b) $x^3 y^4 + 2 = cx^3 y^2$. (c) $x^4 y^6 + cx^{10}y^6 = 3$. (d) $x^3 = y^{11} + cy^4$. **13.** $x^{\frac{1}{2}}(7y^4 + x^3) = c$. **14.** $x^2 y^2 = ce^{-2x} - 3$. **15.** $2x^3 y^3 + 2y^3 + 9y^2 = c$. **16.** (a) $\log\left(\dfrac{y^2}{x^2}\right) + x^2 y^2 = c$. (b) $x^2 y^2 - 2 \log y = c$. (c) $cxy + 1 = xy \log\left(\dfrac{x^2}{y}\right)$.

§26, pages 53, 54

1. $10xy = 2x^5 - 15x^2 + c$. **2.** $15x^2 y = 3x^5 + 10x^3 + c$. **3.** $y = x^2 \log x - x + 2x^2$. **4.** $y \cos x + 3e^{-\sin x} = 7$. **5.** $4x^3 y + 2x \cos 2x = c + \sin 2x$. **6.** $2xy^{-4} = 7 + y^2$. **7.** $y = 4e^{x^2/2} + e^{x^2}$. **8.** $2x + 4y = 1 - 5e^{-2x}$. **9.** $y = ax + 2a\sqrt{1 + x^2}$. **10.** $(3xy + ax^2 + 2a)\sqrt{1 - x^2} = c$. **11.** $\rho = \sin\theta - 1 + ce^{-\sin\theta}$. **12.** $y = x^2(1 + ce^{1/x})$. **13.** $y(1 + x) = ce^x - a$. **14.** $i = \dfrac{E}{R^2 + L^2\omega^2}(R \sin\omega t - L\omega \cos\omega t + L\omega e^{-\frac{R}{L}t})$. **15.** $i = \left(\dfrac{EC\omega}{1 + \omega^2 R^2 C^2}\right)\left(\cos\omega t + RC\omega \sin\omega t - e^{-\frac{1}{RC}t}\right)$.

§27, pages 55, 56

1. $xy^{-2} + x^5 = c$. **2.** $x^{-3}y^{-3} + x^2 = c$. **3.** $y^{-1} + 12e^{2x} = ce^x$. **4.** $y^3(x + 1) = (x + 1)^3 + c$. **5.** $y^{\frac{1}{2}} = 2e^{3x^2} + ce^{x^2}$. **6.** $y(x^2 + 1) = 2x$. **7.** $xy(1 - \log^2 x) = 2$. **8.** $y(2 \sin x + 1) = 2 \sec x + 2 \tan x$. **9.** $x^{-1} = 2 - y^2 - e^{-\frac{1}{2}y^2}$. **10.** $2x^{-2} = m(1 - 2y) + ce^{-2y}$.

§28, pages 57, 58

1. $x = t^2 + c_1$, $y = c_1 t + c_2$. **2.** $x = c_1 e^{-t} + c_2$, $y = (t + c_1)e^{-t}$. **3.** $x = 1000t + c_1$, $y = 500t - 8t^2 + c_2$. **4.** $\rho = \frac{1}{2}e^t + c_1 e^{-t}$, $\theta = \frac{1}{2}e^t - c_1 e^{-t} + c_2$. **5.** $x = 6t^2 + 2c_1 t$, $y = -2t^3 + (6 - c_1)t^2 + 2c_1 t + c_2$. **6.** $x = t + c_1 t^{-1}$, $y = c_1 \log t - t - c_1 t^{-1} + c_2$. **7.** $x^2 = t^2(2 \log t + c_1)$, $2y = t^3(2 \log t + c_1 - 1) + c_2 t$. **8.** $x = 4e^t(t - 1) + 2e^{2t} + c_1$, $y = 4e^t - e^{2t}(2t - 1) + c_2$. **9.** $\rho = c_1 t$, $\theta = (c_1 + 1)t \log t + c_2 t$. **10.** $x = c_1 \cos(at + c_2)$, $y = c_1 \sin(at + c_2)$.

§29, pages 59 to 61

1. $xy \log\left(\dfrac{cx}{y}\right) = x + y$. **2.** $3y(x^2 + 3) + 5x^3 = c$. **3.** $\log x + \tan^{-1}\left(\dfrac{y + x}{2x}\right) = c$. **4.** $4x - 2y = \log\dfrac{c(x + y - 1)}{x + y + 1}$. **5.** $y \sec^3 x =$

$2 \tan x + c$. **6.** $2x = y(c - x^2)$. **7.** $x^3 + x^2y + \sin y = c$. **8.** $y = x(1 + \log y)$. **9.** $x + y = \log(cxy)$. **10.** $y \log(cx) = \pm 1$. **11.** $y = cx$, $y^2 - 2x^2 = c$. **12.** $2x^3 + xy^2 = 2x \log y + 5x - 2$. **13.** $xy + 1 = 4.946e^{-x/y}$. **14.** $5y^2 = 8 \cos x + 4 \sin x - 4e^{\pi - 2x}$. **15.** $x^3y = 8xy - 16$. **16.** $x + y + c = 4 \log(2x + 3y + 7)$. **17.** $5xy^2 = 18(y^2 - x^2)$. **18.** $xy = 3(x^2 - 1)^3 - 21(x^2 - 1)$. **19.** $6x^2y + 6xy^2 + a^2y + b^2x = c$. **20.** $\log xy + y \log \dfrac{x - 1}{x + 1} = c$. **21.** $(x + y + 5)^2 = 16x + 20$. **22.** $(2x + y - 5)^2 = (3x + 2y - 2)^2 + c$. **23.** $(x^2 - y)^4 = 3\sqrt{x^2 - y^2} + c$. **24.** (a) $(x^2 - xy)e^{\frac{1}{2}y^2} = c$. (b) $6x^2y + 2x - 1 = ce^{-2x}$. (c) $x(xy + 1)e^y = c$. (d) $e^{6x}(2x^2y + y^2) = c$. **25.** $xy(y - x) = c(y + x)$. **26.** $4y = \log \dfrac{c(4x - 3y - 3)}{4x - 3y + 1}$. **27.** $25y^3 + 8(1 + 2y)^2(1 - y)e^{\frac{3}{2}x^2} = 0$. **28.** $x^2 + y^2 + c = \log(3x^2 + 4y^2 - 2)$. **29.** $y(\sec x + \tan x) = x + c$. **30.** $xy(x^2 + y^2 - 1) + 1 = 0$. **31.** $y^2 + x(\log x - 4) = 0$. **32.** $y = x + x \log\left(\dfrac{x + y}{4}\right)$. **33.** $(x + y - 3)^3 = 125(x - y - 1)$. **34.** $3x^2 + 2xy - y^2 = c$. **35.** $6\rho\theta - 2\rho^3 + 3 \sin^2 \theta = c$. **36.** $x(x + y)^3 = 3my + cx$. **37.** $(y - x^2 - xy)(x + y)^3 = c(y + 2x^2 + 2xy)$. **38.** $(3x + 2x^2 + 2y^2)\sqrt{x^2 + y^2} = c$. **39.** $xy(x^2 - xy + y^2) = c$. **40.** (a) $\log cx^2y + xy = 0$. (b) $x^n \sin xy = c$. **41.** (a) $x^2\sqrt{y} + \log cx = 0$. (b) $\sqrt{y} + x \sin\left(\dfrac{\sqrt{y}}{x}\right) = c$. **42.** (a) $x^3y^2 + 4x^{\frac{3}{2}}y^{\frac{1}{2}} = c$. (b) $2x^5y^3 + x^2y^4 = c$. **43.** $x^{\frac{3}{2}}(x^2 + y^2) + y^{\frac{3}{2}} = c$. **46.** $x[c - (y - 2x)^2] = 2y - 10x \tan^{-1}\left(\dfrac{y}{x}\right)$. **47.** $x = (t + 3c_1)e^{3t}$, $9y = (12t + 36c_1 - 1)e^{3t} + c_2$. **48.** $x - y = t + c_1$, $x \log x - y = c_2x$. **49.** $xy = t^2 + c_1$, $x + y = \log(2t^2 + c_1) + c_2$. **50.** $y^2 = 2x + c_1$, $y\sqrt{y^2 + 1} + \log(y + \sqrt{y^2 + 1}) \pm 10t = c_2$.

§30, pages 62, 63

1. $4x^3 + 12xy^2 - 3y^4 = 204$. **2.** $x^2 + y^2 = cx$. **3.** $\sqrt{\rho^2 - a^2} - a \sec^{-1}\left(\dfrac{\rho}{a}\right) = c \pm a\theta$. **4.** $x^2 + y^2 = cx$. **6.** $t \log 0.75 = 300 \log\left(\dfrac{6 - 15x}{6 - 10x}\right)$. **7.** $x = ka(a - x)t$. **8.** $y^2 + x^2 \log x^2 \pm y\sqrt{y^2 - x^2} \mp x^2 \log\left(\dfrac{y + \sqrt{y^2 - x^2}}{x}\right) = c$. **9.** $c\rho^2 = \rho \sin \theta - 3$.

§31, pages 65, 66

1. $x = (t + 1)^2$, $y = 2(t + 1)$. **4.** $x = 50{,}000(1 - e^{-0.032t})$, $y = 81{,}250(1 - e^{-0.032t}) - 1000t$. **5.** $66\frac{2}{3}$ lb. **6.** 256 lb. **7.** 222 lb. **9.** $x = y = ce^{4t}$.

§32, pages 67, 68

1. (a) $q = (q_0 - CE)e^{-t/CR} + CE$, $i = \left(\dfrac{CE - q_0}{CR}\right)e^{-t/CR}$.

(b) 0, CE. **2.** (a) $q = -CRI_0 e^{-t/CR} + CE$, $i = I_0 e^{-t/CR}$, (b)　No.

4. (a) $i = \left(I_0 - \dfrac{E}{R}\right)e^{-Rt/L} + \dfrac{E}{R}$. (b) $i = \dfrac{E}{R}(1 - e^{-Rt/L})$.

6. $q = q_0 \cos\left(\dfrac{t}{\sqrt{LC}}\right)$, $i = -\dfrac{q_0}{\sqrt{LC}} \sin\left(\dfrac{t}{\sqrt{LC}}\right)$.

§33, page 69

1. 1.05 lb./in.² **2.** $(p_0^{\frac{2}{3}} - \frac{2}{7}k^{-\frac{2}{7}}h)^{3.5}$, $\frac{7}{2}p_0^{\frac{2}{7}}k^{\frac{5}{7}}$. **3.** 98,000 ft.

§34, pages 69-72

1. $2nk\rho^{n-2} = (n - 2)\theta + c$. **2.** 67.2 lb. **3.** $y = x \tan (ky + c)$.

4. $x^2y^2 - 2cy + 9 = 0$. **5.** $\log \sqrt{x^2 + y^2} \pm 2 \tan^{-1} \dfrac{y}{x} = c$. **7.** $T(1 + \mu^2)$

$= \rho a[(1 - \mu^2) \sin \varphi - 2\mu \cos \varphi] + ce^{\mu\varphi}$. **8.** Straight line. **9.** $a\rho^{-1} =$
$\sin \theta + ce^{\theta \cot \alpha}$. **10.** $c\rho^2 = a - \rho \sin \theta$. **11.** 66.2 lb./ft.³ **12.** $R = 1000$ ft.
13. $\sqrt{3}x = \sinh (4\sqrt{3}t + 1.317)$, $2y = \cosh (4\sqrt{3}t + 1.317)$. **14.** $2x =$
$t + \dfrac{25}{t}$, $2y = t - \dfrac{25}{t}$. **15.** $\sqrt{l^2 - y^2} + l \log \left(\dfrac{l - \sqrt{l^2 - y^2}}{y}\right) =$
$c - x$. **16.** A parabola.

§37, pages 76, 77

1. (a) $y^2 = 16x$. (b) $y^4 = 4x^3$. (c) $x^2 + y^2 = 9$. (d) $y^2 - x^2 = 9$.
2. (a) $x = 1 + 3c^2$, $y = 2c^3$. (b) $x = \alpha \sin \alpha + \cos \alpha$, $y = \alpha \cos \alpha -$
$\sin \alpha$.

§38, pages 80, 81

5. $y = 1$.

§39, page 82

1. $(x^2y - c)(xy - c) = 0$. **2.** $(2y - x^2 - c) \times (y + x - 1 - ce^{-x}) = 0$.
3. $(3y - x^3 - c)(2 \log y - x^2 - c)(1 + xy - cy) = 0$. **4.** $(2y + bx^2 - c)$
$\times [x - a \sin (y + c)] = 0$. **5.** $2cy = c^2x^2 - 1$. **6.** $(y - c)(y + x - c)$
$(x^2 + xy + y^2 - c) = 0$. **7.** $[(y + c)^2 - x^2][y - 2x - c] = 0$. **8.** Each
family of the new system will be the orthogonal trajectories of one
family of the original system.

§40, pages 84, 85

1. (a) $2cy = c^2x^2 + 3$, $y^2 = 3x^2$. (b) $xy = c^2x + c$, $4x^2y + 1 = 0$.
2. (a) $x = 2p + cp^{-2}$, $y = p^2 + 2cp^{-1}$. (b) $x = 3p + 2cp^{-\frac{1}{2}}$, $y = \frac{3}{2}p^2 -$
$cp^{\frac{3}{2}}$. **3.** $y^2 = cx^2 + c^2$. **4.** $x(4cx + 1)^2 = (4cx + 1)(x + 6cy) - c(x +$
$6cy)^2$, $y = 0$.

§41, page 86

1. (a) $x = y + \log(1 + ce^{-y})$. (b) $y^2 = 2cx + c^2$. (c) $(x + c)^2 = 2cy - c^2$, $x^2 + 2xy - y^2 = 0$. **2.** (a) $x = c - 2p - 2\log(p - 1)$. $y = c - p^2 - 2p - 2\log(p - 1)$. (b) $x = \dfrac{c(1 + a^2p^2)}{4p\sqrt[3]{p(3 - a^2p^2)}}, y = \dfrac{c}{\sqrt[3]{p(3 - a^2p^2)}}$.
3. (a) $y = c(c - x)^2$, $27y = 4x^3$, $y = 0$. (b) $y = cx + c^{-1}$, $y^2 = 4x$.
(c) $c^3y = cxy + 1$, $4y^2x^3 = 27$. **4.** (a) $2cx = y^2 + a^2c^2$, $x = \pm ay$.
(b) $x^2c^2 = 1 + cy^2$. **5.** $x^2c^2 = 1 + 2cy$.

§42, pages 87, 88

1. (a) $y = cx + c^2$, $x^2 + 4y = 0$. (b) $y = cx + c^3$, $27y^2 + 4x^3 = 0$.
(c) $y = cx + a\sqrt{1 + c^2}$, $x^2 + y^2 = a^2$. **2.** $y - cx = \sin(y - cx) + c^2$.
3. $e^y = cx - 3c^2$, $x^2 = 12e^y$. **4.** $y^2 = 2cx + c^3$, $27y^4 = -32x^3$. **5.** $xy - c = 0$, $y = cx + c^2$, $x^2 + 4y = 0$. **6.** (a) $x = -3p^2 - 4p^3$, $y = -2p^3 - 3p^4$. (b) $x = -\dfrac{2p^2 + 1}{\sqrt{p^2 + 1}}, y = \dfrac{-p^3}{\sqrt{p^2 + 1}}$. (c) $x = -\dfrac{1 + 3p}{2p^{\frac{1}{2}}}, y = \frac{1}{2}(1 - p)p^{\frac{1}{2}}$. **7.** (a) $y = px + 1/4p$. (b) $y = px \pm r\sqrt{1 + p^2}$. (c) $y = px \pm \sqrt{4mp}$. (d) $y = px \pm \frac{2}{3}p^{\frac{3}{2}}$. (e) $y = px + (1 - n)\left(\dfrac{p}{n}\right)^{n/(n-1)}$.

§43, pages 90, 91

1. (a) $(x - c)^2 + y^2 = 1$, $y = \pm 1$. (b) $x^2 + (y - c)^2 = 1$, $x = \pm 1$.
(c) $c^2x = cy - 1$, $y^2 = 4x$. (d) $y = cx + 3\sqrt{1 + c^2}$, $x^2 + y^2 = 9$.
(e) $(x - 2c)^2 + y^2 = c^2$, $x = \pm\sqrt{3}y$. (f) $(x - c)^2 + y^2 = c^2\sin^2\alpha$, $y = \pm x\tan\alpha$. (g) $(y + c)^2 = x(x - a)^2$, $x = 0$. (h) $y = c(x - c)^2$, $y = \frac{4}{27}x^3$, $y = 0$. (i) $y = cx - c^3$, $y^2 = \frac{4}{27}x^3$. (j) $(y + c)^2 = x^3$, none.
(k) $ay^2 = (x - c)^3$, $y = 0$. (l) $a^3x + cxy + c^2 = 0$, $xy^2 = 4a^3$, (m) $y = cx + \sin^{-1}c$, $\pm y = \sqrt{x^2 - 1} + \sin^{-1}\left(\dfrac{\sqrt{x^2 - 1}}{x}\right)$. **2.** $x = \dfrac{k}{(c - 1)^2}$, $y = \dfrac{c^2k}{(c - 1)^2}$, or $(x + y - k)^2 = 4xy$. **3.** (a) $(y + x - k)^2 + 4kx = 0$.
(b) $2xy = a^2$. (c) $x^2 = 4(1 - y)$. (d_1) $y^2 = 2kx + k^2$. (d_2) $(k - a^2)(k - y^2) = kx^2$. (d_3) $4(x^2 + y^2) = k^2$. (d_4) $(k + a^2)(k - y^2) = kx^2$.
(d_5) None. **5.** (a) $x^2 + (y + m)^2 = A^2$. (b) $(x - n)^2 + (y + m)^2 = A^2$.
(c) $b^2x^2 + a^2y^2 = a^2b^2$. **6.** (a) $27y^2 = 4(x - 2)^3$. (b) $8y^3 = 27x^2$. (c) $3x = p^{-\frac{2}{3}}(1 + 4p^2)$, $6y = p^{-\frac{2}{3}}(5 + 2p^2)$. (d) $x = \pm\dfrac{1}{(1 + 2p^2)^{\frac{3}{2}}}, y = \pm\dfrac{2p^3}{(1 + 2p^2)^{\frac{3}{2}}}$. **7.** $y = \frac{1}{2}p^2 - 1 + c(1 + p^2)^{-\frac{1}{2}}$, $x = p - cp(1 + p^2)^{-\frac{1}{2}}$.

§44, pages 93, 94

1. (a) $5e^{3x}$. (b) $-39 \cos 3x + 26 \sin 3x$. (c) $8x^2 - 8x - 4$. **2.** (a) $9e^{3x}$;
(b) 0. (c) $-(a^2 + b^2) \sin bx$. (d) $(b^2 + a^2)^2 \cos bx$. (f) 0. **3.** (a) $2e^{-x}$.
(b) $64e^{3x}$. (c) 0. **4.** (a) $\dfrac{x^2}{2} + c$. (b) $x^3 + c_1x + c_2$. (c) $\dfrac{x^5}{60} + c_1x^2 +$
$c_2x + c_3$. (d) $\dfrac{x^5}{10} + c_1x^3 + c_2x^2 + c_3x + c_4$. **5.** $2/a^2$. **6.** (a)
$\dfrac{1}{am + b} e^{mx}$. (b) $-\tfrac{1}{17}(\sin 2x + 4 \cos 2x)$. **7.** $-(x^3 + 3x^2 + 6x + 6)$.

§45, page 95

1. (a) $-e^{-2x}$. (b) $32a^5e^{ax}$. (c) 0. (d) $-3e^{-2x}$. (e) 0. (f) $120e^{-3x}$.
2. (a) 0. (b) $24xe^{2x}$. (c) $\sin xe^{-x}$. (d) $\cos xe^{-2x}$. (e) $-192e^{-3x}$. **4.** (a)
$e^{3x} (\cos 2x - 14 \sin 2x)$. (b) $e^{-x} (-9 \sin 2x - 2 \cos 2x)$. (c) e^{-2x}
$(24x - 10x^4)$. (d) $e^{-x}(16^n + 1) \cos 2x$. **5.** (a) $e^{-x}(12x^3 - 36x^2 + 24x)$.
(b) $e^x(\sin x - 6 \cos x)$. (c) $2e^{3x} \tan^3 x$. **7.** $-31 \sin 2x, 288 \cos 3x$.

§47, page 98

1. $y = c_1e^x + c_2e^{2x}$. **2.** $y = c_1e^x + c_2e^{-x} + c_3e^{3x}$. **3.** $y = c_1e^{kx} +$
c_2e^{-kx}. **4.** $y = c_1e^x + c_2e^{2x} + c_3e^{-3x}$. **5.** $y = c_1 + c_2e^x + c_3e^{-x}$.
6. $y = e^{\frac{1}{2}x}\left(c_1e^{\frac{\sqrt{13}}{3}x} + c_2e^{-\frac{\sqrt{13}}{3}x}\right)$. **7.** $y = c_1 + c_2e^{\frac{\sqrt{5}x}{2}} + c_3e^{-\frac{\sqrt{6}}{2}x}$.
8. $y = c_1 + c_2e^{3x} + e^{-x}\left(c_3e^{\sqrt{2}x} + c_4e^{-\sqrt{2}x}\right)$.

§49, page 100

1. $y = c_1 + (c_2 + c_3x)e^x$. **2.** $y = c_1e^{-x} + (c_2 + c_3x)e^x$. **3.** $y =$
$e^x(c_1 + c_2x + c_3x^2)$. **4.** $y = c_1 + c_2x + c_3x^2$. **5.** $y = c_1 + c_2x +$
$(c_3 + c_4x)e^{2x} + (c_5 + c_6x)e^{-2x}$. **6.** $y = c_1 + c_2x + c_3e^{-4x} + (c_4 + c_5x)e^{2x}$.
7. $y = (5 - 14x)e^x$. **8.** $y = 2x + 4e^{-x}$. **9.** $y = c_1 + (c_2 + c_3x)e^{2x}$,
$y = 1 + 2xe^{2x}$. **10.** $y = e^{-x} + (2x - 1)e^x$. **11.** $y = x + e^x - e^{-x}$.

§50, pages 101, 102

1. $y = e^x(c_1 \sin x + c_2 \cos x)$. **2.** $y = c_1 + c_2 \sin kx + c_3 \cos kx$.
3. $y = (c_1 + c_2x) \sin 2x + (c_3 + c_4x) \cos 2x$. **4.** $y = c_1e^{ax} + c_2e^{-ax} +$
$c_3 \sin ax + c_4 \cos ax$. **5.** $y = c_1 + c_2x + (c_3 + c_4x) \sin \sqrt{3}x +$
$(c_5 + c_6x) \cos \sqrt{3}x$. **6.** $y = c_1e^{-x} + c_2e^{3x} + e^{-x}(c_3 \sin \sqrt{5}x + c_4$
$\cos \sqrt{5}x)$. **7.** $y = c_0e^{-ax} + e^{\frac{a}{2}x}\left[c_1 \sin\left(\dfrac{\sqrt{3}}{2}ax\right) + c_2 \cos\left(\dfrac{\sqrt{3}}{2}ax\right)\right]$. **8.** y
$= 1 + e^x \sin x$. **9.** $y = 4e^x \sin x - 2e^{-2x}$. **10.** $y = 3 \sin 10x + 4$
$\cos 10x$.

§51, pages 103, 104

1. $y = c_1 e^{2x} + c_2 e^{-4x} - 8x - 2$. **2.** $y = c_1 e^{2x} + c_2 e^{-x} - 3e^x$.
3. $y = c_1 \sin ax + c_2 \cos ax + x$. **4.** $y = c_1 e^{ax} + c_2 e^{-ax} - 1 - (1/2a^2)$
$\sin ax$. **5.** $y = c_1 e^{ax} + c_2 e^{-ax} + c_3 \sin ax + c_4 \cos ax - (x^3/a^4)$.
6. $y = c_1 e^{-x} + c_2 e^{-3x} + xe^x - \frac{3}{4} e^x - 2$. **7.** $y = 2e^{2x} - 2x \sin 2x -$
$\cos 2x$. **9.** $y = e^{2x} - 2 \sin x - 2x^2 - 2x + 3$. **10.** $y = -\frac{1}{4}(10 + 7e^{2x} + 3e^{-2x}) + e^x + 2e^{-x}$.

§52, page 105

1. $y = c_1 + c_2 x + c_3 x^2 + c_4 e^{-x} + x^4 + 4x^3$. **2.** $y = (c_1 + c_2 x + \frac{1}{2} x^2)e^x$
$+ 3$. **3.** $y = c_1 + c_2 x + c_3 e^{-x} - 6x^2 + 2x^3$. **4.** $y = c_1 + c_2 e^{-2x} - 2e^{-x} + x^2$. **5.** $y = c_1 \sin x + c_2 \cos x - \frac{1}{2} x \cos x$. **6.** $y = c_1 e^{-x} + c_2 e^{-3x} + \frac{1}{2} xe^{-x} + x - \frac{4}{3}$. **7.** $y = c_1 + c_2 \sin 2x + c_3 \cos 2x + x - x \cos 2x$. **8.** $y = c_1 + e^x(c_2 \cos 2x + c_3 \sin 2x) + 2x + \dfrac{15 \sin 2x + 60 \cos 2x}{34}$. **9.** $y = c_1 e^x + c_2 xe^x + x^3 e^x$. **10.** $y = e^x(c_1 \sin x + c_2 \cos x) - \frac{1}{2} xe^x \cos x$.

§53, page 108

1. $y = (c_1 + x) \sin x + (c_2 + \log \cos x) \cos x$. **2.** $y = \sin 2x[c_1 + \frac{1}{2} \log (\csc 2x - \cot 2x)] + \cos 2x[c_2 + \frac{1}{2} \log (\sec 2x + \tan 2x)]$. **3.** $y = e^{2x}\left[c_1 + c_2 x + \dfrac{x^{n+2}}{(n+1)(n+2)}\right]$, $(n \neq -1 \text{ or } -2)$, $y = e^{2x}[c_1 + c_2 x + x \log x]$, $(n = -1)$, $y = e^{2x}[c_1 + c_2 x - \log x]$, $(n = -2)$.
4. $y = e^{-2x}(c_1 + c_2 x - \log x)$. **5.** $y = c_1 \sin x + c_2 \cos x + \sin x \log (\csc x - \cot x) - \cos x \log (\sec x + \tan x)$. **6.** $y = e^x[c_1 \sin x + c_2 \cos x + \sin x \log (\csc x - \cot x) - \cos x \log (\sec x + \tan x)]$.
7. $y = e^x [c_1 + c_2 \cos x + c_3 \sin x + \log (\sec x + \tan x) + \sin x \log \cos x - x \cos x]$.

§54, page 111

1. $y = e^x(c_1 + c_2 x + \frac{1}{4·2} x^7)$. **2.** $y = e^{-x}[c_1 + c_2 x + c_3 x^2 + \log (2x + 3)]$. **3.** $y = c_1 e^{-2x} + c_2 e^{-4x} + 4e^x(e^{-2x} - 3e^{-3x} + 3e^{-4x})$. **4.** $y = x^n e^x$.
6. $y = (1 - x + x^2/2)e^{-2x}$. **7.** $4y = 4e^x \cos x + (\sin x - \cos x)e^{2x}$.
8. $y = e^x(\cos x + 2x \sin x)$. **9.** $y = x^2(e^x + e^{2x})$.

§55, page 114

1. $x = c_1 e^{4t} - c_2 e^{3t}$, $y = 3c_1 e^{4t} + c_2 e^{3t}$. **2.** $x = c_1 e^t + c_2 e^{-t} + c_3 \sin t + c_4 \cos t - 1$, $y = c_1 e^t + c_2 e^{-t} - c_3 \sin t - c_4 \cos t$. **3.** $x = c_1 e^{3t} + c_2 e^{-t} + 0.4 \sin t - 0.2 \cos t$, $y = -2c_1 e^{3t} + 2c_2 e^{-t} + 0.2 \sin t + 0.4 \cos t$.
4. $x = (2c_1 + 2c_2 t)e^t + (2c_3 + 2c_4 t)e^{-t}$, $y = (c_2 - c_1 - c_2 t)e^t - (c_3 + c_4 + c_4 t)e^{-t}$. **5.** $x = (6c_2 - 2c_1 - 2c_2 t)e^t - \frac{1}{3}(c_3 e^{-\frac{3}{2}t} + 2)$, $y = (c_1 + c_2 t)e^t + c_3 e^{-\frac{3}{2}t} - t$. **6.** $x = c_1 - 3c_2 e^{2t} - 3c_3 e^{-2t}$, $y = -2c_2 e^{2t} + 2c_3 e^{-2t}$,

$z = c_2e^{2t} + c_3e^{-2t} + c_1$. **7.** $x = c_1e^{2t} + c_2e^{-t} + \frac{1}{2}$, $y = c_1e^{2t} - 2c_2e^{-t} +$
$t - \frac{1}{2}$, $z = -2c_1e^{2t} + c_2e^{-t}$. **8.** $y = c_1e^{\sqrt{3}t} + c_2e^{-\sqrt{3}t} + c_3 \sin \left(\frac{t}{\sqrt{3}} \right) +$
$c_4 \cos \left(\frac{t}{\sqrt{3}} \right) + 2e^t$, $x = 16\,e^t + (5D - 3D^3)y$. **9.** $2x = (23 - 13t)e^t +$
$(23 + 13t)e^{-t} - 46$, $4y = (-36 + 13t)e^t - (36 + 13t)e^{-t} + 72$.
10. $x = c_1e^t + c_2e^{-t} + \frac{1}{4}\,te^t$, $2y = -c_1e^t + (c_3 - c_2)e^{-t} - \frac{1}{4}\,te^t$,
$z = c_1e^t - (c_2 + c_3)e^{-t} + \frac{1}{4}\,te^t + \frac{1}{4}\,e^t$.

§56, pages 117–119

1. 5 ft., $\frac{1}{6}$ sec., 6 cycles/sec., $\frac{5\pi}{72}$ sec., $\frac{11\pi}{72}$ sec. **2.** $\frac{\pi}{16}$ sec., $\frac{16}{\pi}$
cycles/sec., 13 ft. **3.** $y = 5 \sin 10t + 10 \cos 10t$, $\frac{5}{\pi}$ cycles/sec.,
$\frac{\pi}{5}$ sec., $\sqrt{125}$ ft. **4.** 2π sec., $\frac{1}{2\pi}$ cycle/sec., 5 ft. **5.** $\frac{1}{60}$ sec., 60
cycles/sec. **6.** $k^2 < 120$. **7.** 1.99 sec., $e^{-0.05t}$, 13.9 sec. **8.** $x = 2e^{-t/2}$
$\sin 3t$, 2.09 sec., 0.223. **9.** $a = 2$, $x = 2e^{-t/3} \sin 3t$, 2.09 sec. **10.** $b = \frac{1}{5}$,
$c = (120\pi)^2$ nearly. **11.** $b = 0.046$, $c = 400\pi^2$ nearly.

§59, pages 125–128

1. $x = -\frac{1}{6} \cos \sqrt{6g}t$, 0.452 sec., $\frac{1}{6}$ ft., 2.21. **2.** 0.319 sec., $e^{-0.0644t}$,
10.8 sec. **4.** $x = -a \cos (\sqrt{g/h}t)$, $h + \sqrt{h^2 + 2bh}$. **5.** $x = 4 \sin (\sqrt{3g}t)$
$- 3.46 \sin (2\sqrt{g}t)$. **6.** $x = \frac{1}{2} \sin (2\sqrt{g}t) - \sqrt{g}t \cos (2\sqrt{g}t)$, 157 ft.
below initial position. **7.** $2\pi\frac{\sqrt{I}}{k}$. **8.** $I = \frac{g}{16\pi^2}$ lb. / ft.² **9.** $\theta =$
$e^{-0.693t} (c_1 \sin 12.5t + c_2 \cos 12.5t)$, 0.501 sec. **10.** 656 lb. **11.** 0.886 sec.,
0.886 $\rho^{-\frac{1}{2}}$. **12.** $2\pi\sqrt{l/g}$. **13.** $x = -e^{-1.08t} (0.111 \sin 9.77t + \cos 9.77t)$,
0.643 sec. **14.** 21.1 min. **15.** $w/20$, 93.7 ft. **16.** Rises 2.02 sec. then
falls. Speed approaches 80.5 ft./sec. downward.

§60, pages 130–132

1. $x = v_0 \cos \varphi \cdot t$, $y = v_0 \sin \varphi \cdot t - \frac{1}{2}gt^2$. **2.** $x = 130,000(1 - e^{-0.02t})$,
$y = 155,500 (1 - e^{-0.02t}) - 1610t$, max. $y = 22,000$ ft. **3.** (a) $x =$
$49,800 (1 - e^{-0.04t})$, $y = 174.3t - 16.1t^2$. **4.** $x = 347t$, $y = 118,000$
$(1 - e^{-0.0268t}) - 1200t$, 30,000 ft., 27,000 ft. **5.** $x = a \cos (\sqrt{k/mt})$,
$y = v_0\sqrt{m/k} \sin (\sqrt{k/mt})$. **6.** (a) $x = 3 \sin t$, $y = 2 \cos t - 2$, (b) $x =$
$2.12 \sin t$, $y = 2.12 \sin t + 2 \cos t - 2$. **7.** 2120 ft. **8.** 300 ft./sec.,
10,600 ft.

§62, pages 137, 138

1. $q = \dfrac{e^{-5t}}{1600}$ $(-\sin 200t - 40 \cos 200 \ t) + \frac{1}{40}$, $i = 5.00e^{-5t}$
$\sin 200 \ t$, 0.460 sec., $\frac{1}{40}$, 0. **2.** $q = 200e^{-\frac{1}{2}t}(-2 - t) + 400$, $i = 100te^{-\frac{1}{2}t}$.
3. $q = 0.05 \cos 200t$, $i = e^{-5t}(-10 \sin 200t - 0.25 \cos 200t)$, $\pi/100$, 0, 0.
4. $q = q_0 \cos \left(\dfrac{t}{\sqrt{LC}} \right)$, $i = \dfrac{dq}{dt}$. **5.** $q = -CE \cos \left(\dfrac{t}{\sqrt{LC}} \right) + CE$,
$i = E\sqrt{\dfrac{C}{L}} \sin \left(\dfrac{t}{\sqrt{LC}} \right)$. **6.** $q = \left(\dfrac{q_0}{\omega_1} \right)e^{-at}(\omega_1 \cos \omega_1 t + a \sin \omega_1 t)$,
$i = \dfrac{dq}{dt}$. **7.** $q = 0.05e^{-2.5t}(\cos 50t + 0.05 \sin 50t)$, $i = \dfrac{dq}{dt}$.

§64, pages 140, 141

2. $i = -\left(\dfrac{E}{Z^2} \right)(X \cos \omega t - R \sin \omega t)$ **3.** (a) $q = 0.00275(3 \sin 400t + \cos 400t)$, $i = 1.10(\sin 400t - 3 \cos 400t)$. (b) 0.0087 coulombs, 3.48
amperes. **4.** (a) $i = -\left(\dfrac{E}{L\omega} \right) \cos \omega t$. (b) $i = \dfrac{E}{R} \sin \omega t$. (c) $q = CE$
$\sin \omega t$. (d) $q = \left(\dfrac{EC}{1 + R^2C^2\omega^2} \right) (\sin \omega t - RC\omega \cos \omega t)$, $i = $
$\left(\dfrac{EC\omega}{1 + R^2C^2\omega^2} \right) (\cos \omega t + RC\omega \sin \omega t)$. (e) $i = \left(\dfrac{E}{R^2 + L^2\omega^2} \right)$
$(R \sin \omega t - L\omega \cos \omega t)$. (f) $q = \left(\dfrac{CE}{1 - LC\omega^2} \right) \sin \omega t$, $i = \left(\dfrac{CE\omega}{1 - LC\omega^2} \right)$
$\cos \omega t$. **5.** $i = 10 \sin 500t \ (1 - e^{-5t})$, 0.0067 sec. **6.** 4.2×10^{-7} farad,
1.00007.

§65, pages 145–148

1. $i_2 = \dfrac{E}{R} \sin \omega t$, $i_1 = \dfrac{E}{L\omega} (1 - \cos \omega t)$, $i = i_1 + i_2$. **2.** $i_1 = $
$\dfrac{E}{R} \sin \omega t$, $q = CE \sin \omega t$, $i_2 = CE \ \omega \cos \omega t$, $i = i_1 + i_2$. **4.** $i_2 = 2 \sin 400t$.
$160100q = 40e^{-10t} + \sin 400t - 40 \cos 400t$, $i_1 = dq/dt$. **6.** $i = e^{-50t}$
$(3.06 \sin 312t - \cos 312t) + 1$. **7.** $i = \frac{1}{12}(1 - \cos 300t) + 10t$
$\sin 300t$. **8.** $i = \left(\dfrac{(C_1E_1 + C_2E_2)\omega}{1 - L(C_1 + C_2)\omega^2} \right)\left[\cos \omega t - \cos \left(\dfrac{t}{\sqrt{L(C_1 + C_2)}} \right) \right]$.
10. (a) 100 per cent nearly. (b) 100 per cent nearly. (c) 89 per cent.
(d) Less than 20 per cent.

§67, pages 151

1. $y = \log \sqrt{x} + c_1x^2 + c_2x + c_3$. **2.** $y = x^4 + c_1 \log x + c_2$. **3.** $y = c_1xe^x + c_2$. **4.** $4y = 5[\log (3 \tan x/2 + 1) - \log (\tan x/2 + 3)]$.

5. $5y = 3x^5 - 5x^4 + 10x - 8$. **6.** $ay = ae^{x/a} - x$. **7.** $y = a^2 \sinh x/a -$ $2ax$. **8.** $y = 1, 3y + x^3 = 3$.

§68, page 153

1. $y^2 = c_1 x + c_2$. **2.** $x = c_1 y + c_2 - \log y$. **3.** $x = \log\sqrt{3(2+y)} -$ $\log \sqrt{2-y}$. **4.** $y = 1 + \sin \sqrt{8}x$. **5.** $2y + a^2 x = 6a \tan^{-1} \dfrac{y - 3a}{3a + y}$.

6. $\sqrt{2ay - y^2} + a \sin^{-1}\left(\dfrac{1}{a}\sqrt{2ay - y^2}\right) = \pm x$. **7.** $e^{-y/2} = \cos \dfrac{x}{2}$.

§69, pages 154, 155

1. $y = c_1 x^{-1} + c_2 x^{-2} + c_3 x^3$. **2.** $y = c_1 x^3 + c_2 x^{-3} + \dfrac{1}{n^2 - 9} x^n$.
3. $y = c_1(x - 1) + c_2(x - 1)^2 + c_3(x - 1)^{-2} + \log[e(x - 1)]$. **4.** $y = c_1 + c_2 x + c_3 \log x$.

§70, page 156

1. $y = c_1 x + c_2\sqrt{x^2 - 1}$. **2.** $xy = c_1 e^{-x}(x^2 + 2x + 2) + c_2$. **3.** $y = c_1(x^2 - 1) + c_2 x + 3x^2 + x^4$. **4.** $y = (x^4 + c_2)e^x + c_1(x^3 + 3x^2 + 6x + 6)$. **5.** $y = \sin x \log [c_1 \sin x(\csc x - \cot x)^c]$.

§71, pages 158, 159

1. $p_2 - p_1' + p_0'' = 0$, $p_2\mu - (p_1\mu)' + (p_0\mu)'' = 0$. **2.** $p_n - (p_{n-1})' + (p_{n-2})'' - \cdots + (-1)^n p_0^{(n)} = 0$, $p_n\mu - (p_{n-1}\mu)' + (p_{n-2}\mu)'' + \cdots + (-1)^n(p_0\mu)^{(n)} = 0$. **5.** $y = x^2 + c_1 x + \dfrac{c_2}{x^2}$.

§72, pages 159, 160

1. $y = c_1 e^x(x - 1) + c_2 x + c_3$. **2.** $4y = c_1 + c_2 \log x - x^2$. **3.** $(x + c_1)^2 - y^2 = c_2$. **4.** $(y - c_2)^2 = c_1 x^2 - c_1^2$. **5.** $\log y = c_1 e^x + c_2 e^{-x}$. **6.** $y = (x + 1)[c_1(x + 2)e^{-x} + c_2]$. **7.** $y = c_1 e^x(x - 2) + c_2$. **8.** $y = x(c_1 x^{\sqrt{10}} + c_2 x^{-\sqrt{10}}) - 2x^3$. **9.** $y = x[c_1 \sin (\log x) + c_2 \cos (\log x)] + x \log x$. **10.** $y(x^2 + x - 3) = c_1 x^2 + c_2 x + c_3$. **11.** $(x^2 + 1)y = c_1(x \log x - x) + c_2 x + c_3$. **12.** $12y = c_1 + c_2 x + c_3 \log x + 3x^2 - x^{-2}$. **13.** $\pm 3x = \sqrt{4ay^{\frac{1}{2}} + 2a^2 c_1}\,(y^{\frac{1}{2}} - ac_1) + c_2$. **14.** $6x^2 y = c_1 x + c_2 - 6 \cos x + x^3$. **15.** $y = c_2 x_1^c$. **16.** $\pm 2y = -x\sqrt{c_1^2 - x^2} + c_1^2 \sin^{-1}\left(\dfrac{x}{c_1}\right) + c_2$. **17.** $30y = (x + 1)^2[10 (x + 1) + 24c_1\sqrt{x + 1} + 15c_1^2] + c_2$.

§77, pages 170–174

1. (a) $(x - c_1)^2 + y^2 = c_2^2$. (b) $y = c_1 \cosh \left(\dfrac{x}{c_1} + c_2\right)$. (c) $(c_1 x + c_2)^2 = k(c_1 y^2 - 1)$. (d) $c_1 x = \cosh (c_1 y + c_2)$. (e) $x^2 + (y - c_1)^2 = c_2^2$.

(f) $(y - c_1)^2 = 4c_2(x - c_2)$. (g) $c_1 \pm y = \sqrt{k^2 - (x + c_2)^2} + k$ $\log \dfrac{\sqrt{k^2 - (x + c_2)^2} - k}{x + c_2}$. **2.** $(x - c_1)^2 + (y - c_2)^2 = a^2$. **3.** $e^{x/a} = c_1$ $\sin\left(\dfrac{y}{a} + c_2\right)$. **4.** (a) same as 1(a) and 1(b). (b) $c_1 - x = \sqrt{c_2^{\frac{2}{3}} - y^{\frac{2}{3}}}$ $(2c_2^{\frac{2}{3}} + y^{\frac{2}{3}})$. **5.** $2Hy = wx^2$. **6.** $H\dfrac{d^2y}{dx^2} = w_1 + w_2\sqrt{1 + \left(\dfrac{dy}{dx}\right)^2}$.

7. $y = c \cosh\sqrt{\dfrac{w}{H}}x$. **8.** $2Hy = wlx^2$. **10.** $y = a \cosh\sqrt{\dfrac{w}{H}}x$. **11.*** $y = (c + kt) \cosh\left(\sqrt{\dfrac{w}{H}}x\right) - kt$. **12.*** $x = w\displaystyle\int_c^y \dfrac{(c^2 + 2H/w - y^2)dy}{\sqrt{4H^2 - w^2(c^2 + 2H/w - y^2)^2}}$.

13.* Like Ans. (12) with y replaced by $y + kt$. **14.** $y = \dfrac{w}{24EI}(2lx^3 - x^4 - l^3x)$. Max. defl. $= \dfrac{5wl^4}{384EI}$. **15.** $y = \dfrac{P}{EI}\left(\dfrac{x^3}{12} - \dfrac{l^2x}{16}\right)$. **16.** $\dfrac{Pl^3}{192EI}$.

17. (b) $y = \dfrac{-w}{24EI}(x^4 - 4l^3x + 3l^4)$. **18.** $0.578l$. **19.** $\dfrac{kl^5}{30EI}$. **20.** $\dfrac{v - v_1}{v - v_0} = \dfrac{r_0(r - r_1)}{r_1(r - r_0)}$. **21.** $\dfrac{1}{3}a^{\frac{3}{2}}\left(2 - \dfrac{1}{\sqrt{2}}\right)$. **22.** $\dfrac{a^2}{\sqrt{k}}$. **24.** $\rho \cosh(\sqrt{n - 1}\,\theta) = b, n \geqq 1, \rho \cos(\sqrt{1 - n}\,\theta) = b, 0 \leqq n \leqq 1$. **25.** $\rho = \dfrac{b}{n - (n - 1)\cos\theta}$.

27. $\rho^{n+1}\cos[(n + 1)\theta + c_1] = c_2$. **29.** (a) $x = \dfrac{30{,}000}{g} \times \log\left(\dfrac{154g}{30{,}000}t + 1\right)$, $y = -\dfrac{30{,}000}{g} \times \log\cosh\left(\dfrac{g}{\sqrt{30{,}000}}t\right)$. (b) 15.3 sec. (c) 1170 ft.

30. $y = \dfrac{Pb^2x^2}{6l^3EI}[(3a + b)x - 3al], x \leqq a$. **31.** $x_0 = a\tanh^{-1}\dfrac{b}{l}, y_0 = l\coth\dfrac{c}{a} - a$, where a satisfies $l^2 - b^2 = a^2\sinh^2\dfrac{c}{a}$.

§79, pages 178, 179

1. $x^2 - y^2 = c_1, x + y = c_2z$. **2.** $bx^2 - ay^2 = c_1, cy^2 - bz^2 = c_2$. **3.** $y = c_1x, 2x - 2y = z^2 + c_2$. **4.** $y^2 + z^2 = c_1, \log c_2x = \tan^{-1}\left(\dfrac{y}{z}\right)$. **5.** $x - y = c_1(x - z) = c_2(y - z)$. **6.** $3xz^2 = z^3 + c_1, x + y = c_2e^z$. **7.** $x^2 - y^2 = c_1, (x + y)(z - 1) = c_2(z + 1)$. **8.** $x^2 + y^2 + z^2 = c_1y, y = c_2z$. **9.** $x + y + z = c_1, xyz = c_2$. **10.** $x - y - z = c_1, x^2 - y^2 = cz^2$. **11.** $lx + my + nz = c_1, x^2 + y^2 + z^2 = c_2$. **12.** $x + y - z = c_1$,

* c is the depth of material over the highest point of the arch, and t is the thickness of the top layer.

$xy - z^{-1} = c_2$. **13.** $x^2 - y^2 = c_1$, $z^2 - w^2 = c_2$, $x + y = c_3(z + w)$.
14. $x - y = c_1$, $x + y + z + w = c_2$, $x^2 + y^2 + z^2 + w^2 = c_3$.
15. (I) $y = c_1 \sin 2x + c_2 \cos 2x + \frac{5}{2}$, $5z = (2c_1 + c_2) \cos 2x + (c_1 - 2c_2)$
$\sin 2x - 10x + \frac{5}{2}$.   (II) $y = c_1 + c_2 e^{2x} - 4e^x$, $z = -c_1 + c_2 e^{2x} - 2e^x$.
(III) $y = c_1 e^{2x} + c_2 e^{-2x} - 3x$, $3z = 3c_1 e^{2x} - c_2 e^{-2x} - 3 - 3x - 6x^2$.

(IV) $y = c_1 \sin x + c_2 \cos x - \dfrac{a}{3} \sin 2x$, $2z = (c_1 - c_2) \cos x - (c_1 +$

$c_2) \sin x - \dfrac{2a}{3} (\cos 2x + \sin 2x)$.

§80, page 181

1. (a) $y_1 = \dfrac{dy}{dx}$, $y_2 = \dfrac{dy_1}{dx}$, $x^2 \dfrac{dy_2}{dx} = xyy_2 - y^2 y_1 - y + x$.   (b) $x_1 =$

$\dfrac{dx}{dt}$, $y_1 = \dfrac{dy}{dt}$, $y_2 = \dfrac{dy_1}{dt}$, $\dfrac{dy_2}{dt} = 3x - y_2$, $\dfrac{dx_1}{dt} = 3x - 3y - 2y_2$.   (c) $\dfrac{dy}{dt} =$

y_1, $\dfrac{dy_i}{dt} + y_{i+1}$, $i = 1, 2, \cdots (n - 2)$; $\dfrac{dx}{dt} = x_1$, $\dfrac{dx_i}{dt} = x_{i+1}$, $i = 1, 2, \cdots$

$(k - 2)$; $\dfrac{dx_{k-1}}{dt} = y + y_{n-1}$, $\dfrac{dy_{n-1}}{dt} = x + y + y_{n-1}$.   **2.** $y = Ae^x +$

$Be^{-x} - x$.   **4.** $\dfrac{dy}{dx} = y_1$, $\dfrac{dy_i}{dx} = y_{i+1}$, $i = 1, 2, \cdots (n - 2)$; $\dfrac{dy_{n-1}}{dx} =$

$A_0 \dfrac{dy_{n-1}}{dx} + A_1 y_{n-2} + \cdots + A_n y = 0$; n constants.

§81, pages 186, 187

1. $y = x(c - z^2)$.   **2.** $x + \log (y - z) = c$.   **3.** $xy = c(z - a)$.   **4.** $(x^2 + y^2) e^z + z = c$.   **5.** $y(1 + zx^2y) = c$.   **6.** $xy^2 = z(c - z)$.   **7.** $z = (y + c)$ $(x + a)$.   **8.** $z = x^3 + y^3 + xy^2 + c$.   **9.** $x^2 + y^2 - z(x + y) = c$.
10. $ax - cz = c_1(ay - bz)$.   **11.** $xy + xz + yz = cx$.   **13.** $ax^2 + 2(a + 2b)xy + 2by^2 - 2cx = c_1$.

§82, page 188

1. $x^2 + xy + yz = c$.   **2.** (a) $x = c_1 y = c_2(z - c)$.   (b) $x^{a^2} = c_1 y^{b^2} =$ $c_2 z^{c^2}$.   **3.** Yes, provided the functions $f_1 = \dfrac{\partial f}{\partial x}$, $f_2 = \dfrac{\partial f}{\partial y}$, $f_3 = \dfrac{\partial f}{\partial z}$ satisfy the conditions of Theorem II §83.   **4.** $x^2 + y^2 - z^2 = c$.   **5.** $y = cx$.
6. $P = ay + b$, $Q = -ax + c$.

§83, pages 191, 192

1. Yes. $y = 2x + 5$, $z = -3x - 8 - 2e^x$.   **2.** No. Because $y' = \dfrac{y}{x}$ is not continuous when $x = 0$.   **3.** No. Yes.   **4.** $a = 0$, $a = 1$.

§85, pages 196, 197

1. $y = c_0\left(1 + x + \dfrac{x^2}{2!} + \dfrac{x^3}{3!} + \cdots + \dfrac{x^n}{n!} + \cdots\right).$

2. $y = c_0\left(1 + x^2 + \dfrac{x^4}{2!} + \cdots + \dfrac{x^{2n}}{n!} + \cdots\right).$

3. $y = c_0 + c_1 x + c_0 \displaystyle\sum_{n=0}^{\infty} \dfrac{1 \cdot 4 \cdot 7 \cdots (3n-2)}{(3n)!} x^{3n} +$

$$c_1 \sum_{n=0}^{\infty} \dfrac{2 \cdot 5 \cdot 8 \cdots (3n-1)}{(3n+1)!} x^{3n+1}.$$

4. $y = c_0 \displaystyle\sum_{n=0}^{\infty} (-1)^n (2n+1) x^{2n} + c_1 \displaystyle\sum_{n=0}^{\infty} (-1)^n (2n+2) x^{2n+1}.$

5. $y = c_0 \displaystyle\sum_{n=0}^{\infty} (2n+1)(x-1)^{2n}$

$$+ c_1 \sum_{n=0}^{\infty} (n+1)(x-1)^{2n+1}.$$

6. $y = c_0 \displaystyle\sum_{n=0}^{\infty} (n+1)(2n+1)(x+1)^{2n} +$

$$c_1 \sum_{n=0}^{\infty} (n+1)(2n+3)(x+1)^{2n+1}.$$

7. $y = c_1(x - x^3) + c_2 \displaystyle\sum_{n=0}^{\infty} \dfrac{3}{(2n-1)(2n-3)} x^{2n}.$

8. $y = -x^{-3} - x^{-4} + 24 \displaystyle\sum_{n=5}^{\infty} (-1)^{n-1} \dfrac{x^{-n}}{n!}.$

9. $y = x + \frac{1}{3}x^3 + \frac{2}{15}x^5 + \frac{17}{315}x^7 + \cdots.$

§86, pages 199, 200

1. $y = A\left(1 + \dfrac{2x}{1!1} + \dfrac{2^2 x^2}{2!(1 \cdot 3)} + \cdots\right) +$

$$Bx^{\frac{1}{2}}\left(1 + \dfrac{2x}{1!3} + \dfrac{2^2 x^2}{2!3 \cdot 5} + \cdots\right).$$

2. $y = A(1 + 2x^2 + 3x^4 + 4x^6 + \cdots) +$

$$Bx^{-1}(1 + 3x^2 + 5x^4 + 7x^6 + \cdots).$$

3. $y = A\left(\dfrac{1}{2} + \dfrac{1\cdot4}{5!}x^3 + \dfrac{1\cdot4\cdot7}{8!}x^6 + \cdots\right) +$
$$Bx^{-2}\left(1 + \dfrac{2x^3}{3!} + \dfrac{2\cdot5}{6!}x^6 + \cdots\right).$$

4. $y = Ax^2\left(1 - \dfrac{2\cdot2}{5}x + \dfrac{3\cdot2^2}{5\cdot6}x^2 - \cdots\right) +$
$$B\left(\dfrac{1}{x^2} - \dfrac{4}{3x} + \dfrac{2}{3}\right).$$

6. $y = Ax^{-1} + B\left(1 + \dfrac{x^2}{3} + \dfrac{x^4}{5} + \cdots\right).$

7. $y = A(x+1) + B(x^2 + x^3 + x^4 + \cdots).$

8. $y = A\left(1 - \dfrac{x^{-2}}{3!} - \dfrac{x^{-4}}{5!} - \dfrac{3x^{-6}}{7!} - \cdots\right) + B(x - x^{-1}).$

12. $y = A\left(1 - \dfrac{2a^3x^3}{5!} + \dfrac{2a^6x^6}{8!} - \cdots\right) +$
$$Bx^{-1}\left(1 - \dfrac{a^3x^3}{4!} + \dfrac{a^6x^6}{7!} - \cdots\right) +$$
$$cx^{-2}\left(1 - \dfrac{a^3x^3}{3!} + \dfrac{a^6x^6}{6!} + \cdots\right).$$

§87, page 201

1. $y = 16x^{\frac{3}{2}}\left(1 + \dfrac{4}{5\cdot7}x^2 + \dfrac{4^2x^4}{5\cdot7\cdot9\cdot11} + \cdots\right).$

2. $y = 4x^{-\frac{1}{2}}\left(1 - 4x - \dfrac{4^2x^2}{1\cdot3} - \dfrac{4^3x^3}{1\cdot3^2\cdot5} - \dfrac{4^4x^4}{1\cdot3^2\cdot5^2\cdot7} - \cdots\right).$

3. $y = 8x^{-\frac{5}{2}}\left(1 + \dfrac{4x^4}{11\cdot13} + \dfrac{4^2x^3}{11\cdot13\cdot19\cdot21} + \cdots\right).$

4. $y = 4x^{-\frac{3}{2}}\left(1 - \dfrac{4x^{-3}}{9^2} + \dfrac{4^2x^{-6}}{9^2\cdot15^2} - \dfrac{4^3x^{-9}}{9^2\cdot15^2\cdot21^2} - \cdots\right).$

§88, pages 205, 206

1. $y = (c_0 + c_1 \log x)\left[1 + \dfrac{x^2}{2^2} + \dfrac{x^4}{2^2\,4^2} + \dfrac{x^6}{2^2\,4^2\,6^2} + \cdots\right]$
$$+ c_1\left[\dfrac{x^2\left(\frac{-2}{2}\right)}{2^2} + \dfrac{x^4\left(\frac{-2}{2} - \frac{2}{4}\right)}{2^2\cdot4^2} + \dfrac{x^6\left(\frac{-2}{2} - \frac{2}{4} - \frac{2}{6}\right)}{2^2\cdot4^2\cdot6^2} + \cdots\right].$$

2. $y = (c_0x + c_1x \log x)\left[1 + \dfrac{x}{2(1!)^2} + \dfrac{x^2}{3(2!)^2} + \dfrac{x^3}{4(3!)^2} + \cdots\right] +$
$$c_1\left[1 + \dfrac{x\left(\frac{-1}{1}\right)}{(1!)^2} + x^2\dfrac{\left(\frac{-2}{1} - \frac{1}{2}\right)}{(1!)^2\cdot2} + x^3\dfrac{\left(\frac{-2}{1} - \frac{2}{2} - \frac{1}{3}\right)}{(2!)^2\cdot3} + \cdots\right].$$

3. $y = (c_0 + c_1 \log x)\left[1 - \dfrac{x}{(1!)^2} + \dfrac{x^2}{(2!)^2} - \dfrac{x^3}{(3!)^2} + \cdots\right]$

$$+ c_1\left[\frac{x(\frac{2}{1})}{(1!)^2} - \frac{x^2(\frac{2}{1} + \frac{2}{2})}{(2!)^2} + \frac{x^3(\frac{2}{1} + \frac{2}{2} + \frac{2}{3})}{(3!)^2} - \cdots\right].$$

4. $y = c_0\left[1 + \frac{x^2}{1^2 \cdot 2} + \frac{x^4}{1^2 \cdot 2 \cdot 3^2 \cdot 4} + \frac{x^6}{1^2 \cdot 2 \cdot 3^2 \cdot 4 \cdot 5^2 \cdot 6} + \cdots\right]$

$$+ x(c_1 + c_2 \log x)\left[1 + \frac{x^2}{2^2 \cdot 3} + \frac{x^4}{2^2 \cdot 3 \cdot 4^2 \cdot 5} + \cdots\right]$$

$$+ c_2 x\left[\frac{x^2(\frac{-2}{2} - \frac{1}{3})}{2^2 \cdot 3} + \frac{x^4(\frac{-2}{2} - \frac{1}{3} - \frac{2}{4} - \frac{1}{5})}{2^2 \cdot 3 \cdot 4^2 \cdot 5} + \cdots\right].$$

5. $y = (A + B \log x)\left(1 + \frac{a^3 x^3}{3^2} + \frac{a^6 x^6}{3^2 \cdot 6^2} + \cdots\right) -$

$$2B\left(\frac{\frac{1}{3} a^3 x^3}{3^2} + \frac{(\frac{1}{3} + \frac{1}{6}) a^6 x^6}{3^2 \cdot 6^2} + \cdots\right).$$

6. $y = \left(A - \frac{B}{4} a^2 \log x\right)\left(2 - \frac{a^2 x^2}{4} + \cdots\right) +$

$$B x^{-2}\left[1 + \frac{1}{4} a^2 x^2 - \left(\frac{2}{2} + \frac{1}{4}\right)\frac{a^4 x^4}{2^2 \cdot 4} + \cdots\right].$$

7. $y = x(A - B \log x) + B(1 + x - x^2 - \frac{1}{2} x^3 - \cdots).$

8. $y = (A - B \log x)(1 + \frac{1}{2} x^{-1} + \frac{1}{2^2 \cdot 3} x^{-2} + \cdots) +$

$$B x\left[1 - x^{-1} - \left(\frac{2}{1} + \frac{1}{2}\right)\frac{x^{-2}}{1^2 \cdot 2} - \cdots\right].$$

9. $y = (A + B \log x + 3c \log x)(1 + x)^2 + B(1 - x - 2x^2 - \cdots) + cx^{-1}(1 - x - 11x^2 - \cdots).$

§89, page 209

2. $\frac{21}{16}(11x^6 - 15x^4 + 5x^2 - \frac{5}{24})$. **5.** $x^4 = \frac{1}{5}P_0(x) + \frac{4}{7}P_2(x) + \frac{8}{35}P_4(x)$.

6. $1.175 P_0(x) + 1.104 P_1(x) + 0.357 P_2(x) + 0.077 P_3(x) + \cdots$.

§90, page 211

1. (a) $y = c_1 x^{\frac{1}{2}}\left(1 - \frac{x^2}{3!} + \frac{x^4}{5!} - \cdots\right) + c_2 x^{-\frac{1}{2}}\left(1 - \frac{x^2}{2!} + \frac{x^4}{4!} - \cdots\right).$

(b) $y = c_1 x^3 \sum_{r=0}^{\infty} \frac{(-1)^r (x/2)^{2r} 3!}{r!(r-3)!} +$

$$c_2\left[x^{-3} \log x \sum_{r=3}^{\infty} 2\frac{(x/2)^{2r}(-1)^r}{r!(r-3)!} + 2x^{-3} + \frac{x^{-1}}{4} + \frac{x}{32}\right.$$

$$\left. + x^{-3} \sum_{r=3}^{\infty} \left\{ 2\frac{(-1)^{r+1}(x/2)^{2r}}{r!(r-3)!} \sum_{n=1}^{r} \left(\frac{1}{2n} + \frac{1}{2(\bar{n} - 3)}\right)\right\}\right],$$

where $\bar{n}$ does not take the value 3 but takes all the other values from 1 to r.

2. $y = c_1 \sum_{r=0}^{\infty} \frac{(x/2)^{2r}(-1)^r}{(r!)^2} +$

$$c_2\left(\log x \sum_{r=0}^{\infty} \frac{(x/2)^{2r}(-1)^r}{(r!)^2} + \sum_{r=1}^{\infty} \frac{(x/2)^{2r}(-1)^{r+1}}{(r!)^2} \sum_{n=1}^{r} \frac{1}{n} \right).$$

§92, page 214

1. $y = 1 + x + x^2 + 2\left(\dfrac{x^3}{3!} + \dfrac{x^4}{4!} + \cdots \right).$

2. $y = 1 + x + \dfrac{x^2}{2} + \dfrac{x^3}{3} + \dfrac{x^4}{2\cdot 4} + \dfrac{x^5}{3\cdot 5} + \dfrac{x^6}{2\cdot 4\cdot 6} + \dfrac{x^7}{3\cdot 5\cdot 7} + \cdots.$

3. $x = 1 - t + \dfrac{t^2}{2!} + \dfrac{t^4}{4!} + \dfrac{t^6}{6!} + \cdots,$

$$y = -1 + t + \frac{t^3}{3!} + \frac{t^5}{5!} + \cdots.$$

4. $y = 1 + \dfrac{1x^3}{3!} + \dfrac{1\cdot 4x^6}{6!} + \dfrac{1\cdot 4\cdot 7x^9}{9!} + \cdots.$

§93, page 216

1. $x = 0.4$, $y = 2.8918$. **2.** $(0,1)$ $(0.1, 1.1053)$ $(0.2, 1.2229)$. **3.** $t = 0.1$, $x = 1.1003$, $y = 1.1100$; $t = 0.2$, $x = 1.2026$, $y = 1.2401$; $t = 0.3$; $x = 1.3090$, $y = 1.3906$.

§95, pages 220, 221

1. (a) $z = px + qy$. (b) $p = q^2$. (c) $z = xp + yq$. (d) $q = f(p)$. **2.** (a) $z = px + qy$. (b) $z = px + qy - pq/(p + q - pq)$. (c) $y^2(1 + p^2 + q^2) = q^2$. (d) $(1 + q)(x + zp) - (1 + p)(y + zq) = 0$. (e) $py = qx$. (f) $x^2 + y^2 + 2z(xp + yq) = z^2$. **3.** (a) $p = q$. (b) $x(p - q) = z$. (c) $y(q - p) = z$. (d) $pt = qs$. (e) $s = 0$. (f) $q(r - s) + p(t - s) = 0$. (g) $2r + s - t = 0$. (h) $x(rx + p) = y(ty + q)$. **5.** $z = px + qy$. **6.** $py - qx = 0$.

§96, page 223

1. $z = x^3 + xy^2 + \varphi(y)$. **2.** $yz = x^2y + \varphi(x)$. **3.** $yz = x^2y + \varphi(x) + \psi(y)$. **4.** $z = \iint f(x,y)dx^2 + x\varphi(y) + \psi(y)$. **5.** $2z = x^2 \log y + 2axy + \varphi(x) + \psi(y)$. **6.** $z = -ye^x + e^y[y + \varphi(x)] + \psi(x)$. **7.** $2z = x^2y - 2xy + \varphi(y) + e^{-x}\psi(y)$. **8.** $4z = x^2y + \varphi(y) \log x + \psi(y)$. **9.** $z = \log [e^{xy}\varphi(y) - e^{-xy}] + \psi(y)$. **10.** $2z^2 = (2x - 1)y^2 + \varphi(y)2^{-2x}$. **11.** $\pm z = \sqrt{a - \varphi(y)e^{-2x}} + \sqrt{a} \log [\sqrt{ae^{2x} - \varphi(y)} - \sqrt{a}e^x] + \psi(y)$. **12.** $z = 6x^2 + e^{-y}\varphi(x) + x\psi(y) + \theta(y)$. **13.** $z = x^2y^3 + y^{-1}\varphi(x) + \psi(x)$.

§97, pages 227, 228

1. $z = e^x \varphi(x - y)$. **2.** $z = x^2 \varphi\left(\dfrac{y}{x}\right)$. **3.** $y + z = x\varphi[x(y - z)]$. **4.** $az =$

$cx + \varphi(bx - ay)$. **5.** $\tan^{-1}\left(\dfrac{y}{z}\right) = \log x + \varphi(x^2 + y^2)$. **6.** $3xz = y^2 +$

$\varphi(xy)$. **7.** $z(y - x) = axy \log\left(\dfrac{y}{x}\right) + (y - x) \varphi\left(\dfrac{x - y}{xy}\right)$. **8.** $x^2 - y^2 =$

$\varphi(z^2 + 2y^2)$. **9.** $3y^2 \log z + ax = 3y^2 \varphi(xy)$. **10.** $(x + y) \log z - x =$

$\varphi(x + y)$. **11.** $y = x\varphi(z)$. **12.** $y^2 = z^2 + \varphi(x)$. **13.** $x^2 = 2xz + 2yz +$

$\varphi(y)$. **14.** $x^2 = y^2 + 2xy + \varphi(z)$. **15.** $(x + y)(x^2 - y^2 - z) = \varphi(x^2 - y^2)$.

16. $3z = 2x^3 + \varphi(ye^{-x}) + \psi(y)$. **17.** $2z = x^2 + xy + \varphi(y/x) + \psi(y)$.

19. (b) ∞ generally. For $\varphi(a^2 + b^2, c - a) = 0$ may be written

$c = a + \psi(a^2 + b^2)$ and a and b may be chosen arbitrarily. **20.** $z =$

$y^3 \varphi(x^5/y^3)$. **21.** (a) $x^2 + x = c(x + 1) + y + 1$. (b) $y^2 + 2x^3 = cx$.

(c) $x^3 - y^2 = cxy$. **22.** $(y + y^2)^{-2}$. **23.** (a) $e^{\int f(y)\, dy}$. (b) $e^{-\int f(x)\, dx}$.

(c) $(xy)^k$. (d) $1/(x^2 + y^2)$. (e) $x^a y^b$. **24.** $\dfrac{e^x}{y}$.

§98, page 230

2. $az = x \sin\left(\dfrac{ay}{x}\right)$. **3.** (a) $z = e^y \sin(x - y)$. (b) $z = [a^2 - 2a$

$(x - y) + (x - y)^2]e^{x - 1}$. (c) $z^2 = [a^2 - (x - y)^2]e^{2y}$. **4.** (a) $z = x^2 y^2 +$

$3x^3 y^3 + \dfrac{y^2}{3x} + c$. (b) $z = \dfrac{y^2}{3x} + \dfrac{x^2 y^2}{6} + xy + \log(xy - 1) + c$. **5.** $10z$

$= 10x - xy^3 + 10y^2$.

§99, page 234

2. $z = ax + \psi(a)y, x + \psi(a) + \psi'(a) (y + a) = 0$. $2z + (x + y)^2 = 0$.

3. $z = ax + \psi(a)y, x = \psi'(a)y$. **4.** $2(x - a)^2 + 2[y - \psi(a)]^2 + 2z^2 =$

$a^2 + \psi^2(a), 2(x - a) + 2[y - \psi(a)] \psi'(a) + 2a + 2\psi(a)\psi'(a) = 0$.

The complete solution represents spheres with centers in the xy-plane

and tangent to the cone $z^2 = x^2 + y^2$. The general solution represents

envelopes of families of the spheres. **5.** $4(x - a)^2 + 4[y - \psi(a)]^2 + z^2 =$

$[\psi(a) - a]^2, 4(x - a) + 4[y - \psi(a)]\psi'(a) + 2[\psi(a) - a][\psi'(a) - 1] = 0$.

The complete solution represents ellipsoids having centers in the xy-plane

and tangent to the cone $z^2 = (x - y)^2$. The general solution represents

envelopes of families of these ellipsoids.

§100, pages 237, 238

2. (a) $(5a - 6) \log z = ax + y + b$. (b) $2\sqrt{z} = ax + \dfrac{y}{a} + b$.

3. $z = e^{x^2}(-ax + ay + b)$. **4.** $z = a \log\left(\dfrac{x}{y}\right) + b$. **5.** (a) $z(ax + y + b)$

$+ a + 1 = 0.$ (b) $2\sqrt{z} = ax + \sqrt{1 - a^2}\, y + b.$ (c) $(a^2 + 1)(c^2 - z^2)$ $= (x + ay + b)^2.$ (d) $2(a^2 z^n + a)^{\frac{3}{2}} = 3a^2 nR(ax + y + b).$ **6.** (a) $z = ax + by + ab.$ (b) $z = ax + by - na^{1/n}b^{1/n}.$ (c) $z = ax + by.$ (d) $f(z - ax - by, a, b) = 0.$ **7.** (a) $2z = (a + y)^2 - (a - x)^2 + b.$ (b) $3z = 2(a + x)^{\frac{3}{2}} + 2(a + y)^{\frac{3}{2}} + b.$ (c) $3z = 2(ax)^{\frac{3}{2}} + 2(ay)^{\frac{3}{2}} + b.$

(d) $z = ax + f(x) + ay - F(y) + b.$ **8.** (a) $z = ax + \dfrac{y}{a} + b.$

(b) $z = a(x + y) + b,\ 2z = a(2x - 3y) + b.$ (c) $z = e^{ax} + ay + b.$ (d) $z = ay + (6 - a^2 - 5a)x + b.$ **9.** (a) $z = a^2 x^2 + ay + b.$ (b) $z^2 =$

$a^2 x^2 + (ay + b)^2.$ (c) $2\sqrt{z} = \sqrt{ax} + (y - ay^2)^{\frac{1}{2}} + \dfrac{a^{-\frac{1}{2}}}{2}\,\sin^{-1}(2ay$

$- 1) + b.$ (d) $z^{\frac{3}{2}} = (x + a)^{\frac{3}{2}} + (y + a)^{\frac{3}{2}} + b.$ (e) $(x + a)z = y + 2(x + a)$ $\log(x + a) + 2a + b(x + a).$

§105, page 245

1. $z = \varphi_1(y) + \varphi_2(y - x) + \varphi_3(y + 2x).$ **2.** $z = \varphi_1(y) + x\varphi_2(y) + x^2\varphi_3(y) + \varphi_4(y - x).$ **3.** $z = \varphi(y - 2x) + \varphi(x) + y\psi(x).$ **4.** $z = \varphi_1(y) + x\varphi_2(y) + \varphi_3(x) + y\varphi_4(x).$ **5.** $y = \sum^{n} e^{n(y+2x)}(a_n \cos 3nx + b_n \sin 3nx).$ **6.** $\varphi(y + axi) + \varphi(y - axi) + i[\psi(y + axi) - \psi(y - axi)].$ Or $z = \sum^{n} e^{ny}[a_n \cos nax + b_n \sin nax].$ **7.** $z = \varphi(y - ax) + \psi(y + ax).$ **8.** $z = \varphi(y + ax) + \psi(y - ax) + \sum^{n} e^{ny}(a_n \cos anx + b_n \sin anx).$ **9.** $z = \varphi(y + 2x) + \sum^{n} e^{n(y-x)}(a_n \sin\sqrt{3}nx + b_n \cos\sqrt{3}nx).$ **10.** $z = \varphi_1(y) + x\varphi_2(y) + x^2\varphi_3(y) + \cdots + x^{n-1}\varphi_n(y).$ **11.** $z = (x + y + 1)^3 - (x - y - 1)^3 - 2.$ **12.** $z = 6y^2 + (y + 2x)^2 + (y - 2x)^2.$

§107, pages 248, 249

2. $z = \varphi(y + x) + e^{-3x}\psi(y - x).$ **3.** $z = e^{-2x}\varphi(y) + e^{3x}\varphi(y + x).$ **4.** $z = e^{-4y}\varphi(x) + e^{3x/2}\psi(y - \tfrac{3}{2}x)$ **5.** $z = e^{-x}[\varphi_1(y - x) + x\varphi_2(y - x) + x^2\varphi_3(y - x).$ **6.** $z = \varphi(y) + e^{3y}[\varphi_1(x - 2y) + x\varphi_2(x - 2y)].$ **7.** $z = e^{4y}\varphi(x) + e^{-y}\psi(x - y).$ **8.** $z = e^{4y}\varphi(x) + e^{-1y}\psi(x).$ **9.** $z = e^{-ax}\varphi(y) + e^{ay}\varphi_1(x) + e^{-ay}\varphi_2(x).$ **10.** $z = \sum^{h} e^{hx - h^3 y}$ **11.** $z = \sum^{h} a_h e^{hx - h^3 y} + \sum^{h} b_h e^{hy - h^2 x}.$ **12.** $z = e^x\varphi(y) + e^{-x}\psi(x + y).$ **13.** $z = e^{-bx}\varphi(y) + e^{-ay}\psi(x).$ **14.** $z = e^{-y}\varphi(x) + e^x\psi(y - x).$ **15.** $z = e^{-y}\varphi(x + 2y) + \psi(x + y).$ **18.** $z = e^{-mx}[\varphi(y - ax)\cos nx + \psi(y - ax)\sin nx].$ **19.** $z = e^{-2x}[\varphi(y - x) +$

$x\psi(y - x)]$. **20.** $z = \varphi(y - x) \cos x + \psi(y - x) \sin x$. **21.** $z =$
$\sum_k a_k e^{ky+2k^{\frac{3}{2}}x}$.

§108, page 252

1. $z = \frac{1}{3}e^{2x-y}$. **2.** (a) $5a^2z = -\sin 2ay$. (b) $z = \cos x - \sin x$. **3.** $z = e^{-2y}(y - 2xy - y^2)$. **4.** $4z = 12xy^2 - 4y^3 - 3y^2$. **5.** $3z = x^3$. **6.** $z + y \log x = 0$. **7.** $z = xy - 2y - 2e^{x-2y}$. **8.** $z = x^2y - 2x^3 + 2 \sin (x + 2y)$. **9.** $z = y^2e^{x-y}$. **10.** $z = -(1/2a^2) \sin (y - ax)$. **11.** $z = (-\frac{1}{2}x - \frac{1}{4})e^{x-y}$.

§109, pages 254, 255

1. (a) $z = 2xy^3 + y\varphi(x) + \psi(x)$. (b) $z = -x^2e^{-3y} + \varphi(x) + \psi(y)$. **2.** (a) $z = \varphi_1(y)e^{-3x} + \varphi_2(y)e^{2x}$. (b) $z = \varphi_1(x)e^{-2y} + \varphi_2(x)e^y$. (c) $z = \varphi_1(x) \sin 2y + \varphi_2(x) \cos 2y + \frac{1}{4}x^2$. (d) $z = \varphi_1(y)e^{2xy} + \varphi_2(y)e^{-xy} - x + \frac{1}{2y}$. **3.** (a) $yz + 2xy^2 = \varphi(xy) + \psi(y)$. (b) $z = y\varphi\left(\frac{x}{y}\right) + \psi(y)$. (c) $xz - 2x^2y = \varphi(xy) + \psi(x)$. (d) $z + 3x^2 = \varphi(x)e^y + \psi(y)$. (e) $x^2z - 6x^3y^2 = \varphi(xy) + \psi(x)$. (f) $z = x\varphi(y + x^2) + \psi(x)$. **4.** (a) $\pm 2zy = xy\sqrt{x^2y^2 + \varphi(y)} + \varphi(y) \log [xy + \sqrt{x^2y^2 + \varphi(y)}] + \psi(y)$. (b) $z = \varphi(ye^x) + \psi(y)$. (c) $4z = 2x^2 \log x - x^2 + y\varphi\left(\frac{y}{x^2}\right) + \psi(y)$. (d) $z = \varphi(y)e^x + \psi(y)e^{-5x/2} - y(5x + 3)$. (e) $z + xy = \varphi(x^2y) + \psi(x)$. (f) $2z + 3x^2y = \varphi(x)e^{2y} + \psi(x)$. (g) $z = y\varphi\left(\frac{e^x}{y}\right) + \psi(y)$. (h) $z = \varphi\left(\frac{e^y}{x}\right) + \psi(y)$. (i) $2z = \varphi(y) \cos (\log x) + \psi(y) \sin (\log x) + xy$. (j) $y = \varphi(x) + \psi(z)$.

§110, pages 258, 259

1. $z = x^2\varphi(x - y) + \psi(x - y)$. **2.** $z = y^{1-x-y}\varphi(x + y) + \psi(x + y)$. **3.** $z = \varphi\left(\frac{y}{x}\right) + x\psi\left(\frac{y}{x}\right)$. **4.** $z = x\varphi(y) + \psi(xy)$. **5.** $\log x = \varphi(z) + \psi\left(\frac{y}{x}\right)$. **6.** $z = \varphi(xy) + \psi\left(\frac{x}{y}\right)$. **7.** $z = y\varphi(xy) + \psi(xy)$. **8.** $z = \varphi(ye^{-2x}) + \psi(ye^x)$. **9.** $z = \varphi(x - y) + \psi(ye^x)$. **10.** $z = x^2\varphi(x + y) + \psi(x + y)$. **11.** $z = \varphi(x - y) + \psi(xy)$. **12.** $z = \varphi(xy) + \psi(x + y)$. **13.** $z = \varphi\left(\frac{x}{y}\right) + \psi(xy)$. **14.** $z = y^3 + y\varphi(2x + y^2) + \psi(2x + y^2)$. **15.** $y = x\varphi(z) + \psi(z)$. **16.** $x = \varphi(z) + \psi(y)$. **17.** $y = x\varphi(ex + ay + fz) + \psi(ex + ay + fz)$.

§111, pages 263, 264

2. $x = 2\left(\dfrac{\sin x}{1} - \dfrac{\sin 2x}{2} + \dfrac{\sin 3x}{3} - \cdots\right).$

3. $x = \tfrac{1}{2} + \dfrac{2}{\pi}\left(\dfrac{\sin x}{1} + \dfrac{\sin 3x}{3} + \dfrac{\sin 5x}{5} + \cdots\right).$

4. $x = \tfrac{1}{2} - \dfrac{2}{\pi^2}\left(\dfrac{\cos x}{1^2} + \dfrac{\cos 3x}{3^2} + \dfrac{\cos 5x}{5^2} + \cdots\right) -$

$$\dfrac{1}{\pi}\left(\dfrac{\sin 2x}{2} + \dfrac{\sin 4x}{4} + \dfrac{\sin 6x}{6} + \cdots\right).$$

§112, page 266

1. (a) $x = \dfrac{2c}{\pi}\left(\sin\dfrac{\pi x}{c} - \tfrac{1}{2}\sin\dfrac{2\pi x}{c} + \tfrac{1}{3}\sin\dfrac{3\pi x}{c} - \tfrac{1}{4}\sin\dfrac{4\pi x}{c} + \cdots\right).$

  (b) $x^2 = \dfrac{c^2}{3} - \dfrac{4c^2}{\pi^2}\left(\dfrac{1}{1^2}\cos\dfrac{\pi x}{c} - \dfrac{1}{2^2}\cos\dfrac{2\pi x}{c} + \dfrac{1}{3^2}\cos\dfrac{3\pi x}{c} - \cdots\right).$

2. Same as 1 (a).

3. $x = \dfrac{\pi}{2} - \dfrac{4}{\pi}\left(\dfrac{\cos x}{1^2} + \dfrac{\cos 3x}{3^2} + \dfrac{\cos 5x}{5^2} + \cdots\right).$

5. $x^2 = \dfrac{2c^2}{\pi^3}\left[\left(\dfrac{\pi^2}{1} - \dfrac{4}{1^3}\right)\sin\dfrac{\pi x}{c} - \dfrac{\pi^2}{2}\sin\dfrac{2\pi x}{c} + \right.$

$$\left.\left(\dfrac{\pi^2}{3} - \dfrac{4}{3^3}\right)\sin\dfrac{3\pi x}{c} - \dfrac{\pi^2}{4}\sin\dfrac{4\pi x}{c} + \cdots\right].$$

6. $h + kx = \dfrac{2}{\pi}\left(\dfrac{2h + kc}{1}\sin\dfrac{\pi x}{c} - \dfrac{kc}{2}\sin\dfrac{2\pi x}{c} + \right.$

$$\left.\dfrac{2h + kc}{3}\sin\dfrac{3\pi x}{c} - \dfrac{kc}{4}\sin\dfrac{4\pi x}{c} + \cdots\right).$$

§113, pages 268, 269

1. $y = 0.0232\left(\cos 178t\,\sin\dfrac{\pi x}{3} + \dfrac{1}{3^3}\cos\dfrac{3\cdot178t}{3}\sin\dfrac{3\pi x}{3} + \cdots\right).$

About 28 vibrations per second.

2. $y = A\cos\dfrac{2a\pi t}{L}\sin\dfrac{2\pi x}{L}.$

3. $y = \dfrac{LA}{na\pi}\sin\dfrac{an\pi t}{L}\sin\dfrac{n\pi x}{L}.$

4. $y = \dfrac{8L^3 m}{a\pi^4}\left(\dfrac{1}{1^4}\sin\dfrac{a\pi t}{L}\sin\dfrac{\pi x}{L} + \dfrac{1}{3^4}\sin\dfrac{3a\pi t}{L}\sin\dfrac{3\pi x}{L} + \right.$

$$\left.\dfrac{1}{5^4}\sin\dfrac{5a\pi t}{L}\sin\dfrac{5\pi x}{L} + \cdots\right)$$

§114, page 270

1. (a) $y(x,t) = A \sin \dfrac{2\pi x}{L} \cos \dfrac{2\pi a t}{L}$.

(b) $y(x,t) = A \sin \dfrac{m\pi x}{L} \cos \dfrac{m\pi a t}{L} + B \sin \dfrac{n\pi x}{L} \cos \dfrac{n\pi a t}{L}$.

(c) $y(x,t) = \dfrac{8AL^3}{\pi^3}\Big(\dfrac{1}{1^3} \cos \dfrac{\pi a t}{L} \sin \dfrac{\pi x}{L} + \dfrac{1}{3^3} \cos \dfrac{3\pi a t}{L} \sin \dfrac{3\pi x}{L} +$
$\dfrac{1}{5^3} \cos \dfrac{5\pi a t}{L} \sin \dfrac{5\pi x}{L} + \cdots\Big)$.

2. Same as 1 (c) with $L = 3$ ft., $A = 0.001$, and $a = 17{,}000$. Frequency 2800 oscillations per second.

§115, pages 273, 274

1. (I) $\theta(x,y) = Ae^{-3y} \sin 3x$. (II) $\theta(x,y) = 2A \displaystyle\sum_{n=1}^{\infty} (-1)^{n+1}\dfrac{e^{-ny}}{n} \sin nx$.

2. $\theta = m + me^{-3y} \sin 3x$.

3. $\theta = m + (1 - m) \dfrac{4}{\pi}(e^{-y} \sin x + \tfrac{1}{3}e^{-3y} \sin 3x + \cdots)$.

4. $y = \dfrac{4cg}{\pi^2} \displaystyle\sum_{m=1}^{\infty} \left(\dfrac{1}{m^2} \sin \dfrac{m\pi}{2} \sin \dfrac{m\pi x}{c} \cos \dfrac{m\pi a t}{c}\right)$.

5. $\theta(x,y) = 10 + 90x/\pi - (20/\pi)(3e^{-y} \sin x - \tfrac{9}{2}e^{-2y} \sin 2x +$
$\tfrac{3}{3}e^{-3y} \sin 3x - \tfrac{3}{4}e^{-4y} \sin 4x + \cdots)$.

§116, page 276

1. $\theta = 10 + \dfrac{90x}{L}$.

2. $\theta(x,t) = \dfrac{100x}{L} - \dfrac{200}{\pi}\Big(e^{-a^2\pi^2 t/L^2} \sin \dfrac{\pi x}{L} - \tfrac{1}{2}e^{-4a^2\pi^2 t/L^2} \sin \dfrac{2\pi x}{L} +$
$\tfrac{1}{3}e^{-9a^2\pi^2 t/L^2} \sin \dfrac{3\pi x}{L} - \cdots\Big)$.

§117, pages 278, 279

2. $e = -A\sqrt{\dfrac{L}{C}} \sin \omega\sqrt{LC}x \cos \omega t + B$.

4. (a) $i = \dfrac{A\omega}{R}e^{\frac{-\omega^2}{RC}t} \sin \omega x$. (b) $e = \dfrac{AR}{\omega}e^{\frac{-\omega^2}{RC}t} \cos \omega x + B$.

5. $e = Ax + B, \ i = -\dfrac{A}{R}$.

6. $e = -\dfrac{2}{\pi}\Big(7e^{-at}\sin\dfrac{\pi x}{L} - \tfrac{3}{2}e^{-4at}\sin\dfrac{2\pi x}{L} + \tfrac{7}{3}e^{-9at}\sin\dfrac{3\pi x}{L} -$

$$\tfrac{3}{4}e^{-16at}\,s\dot{}n\,\dfrac{4\pi x}{L} + \cdots\Big)$$

$i = \dfrac{2}{RL}\Big(7e^{-at}\cos\dfrac{\pi x}{L} - 3e^{-4at}\cos\dfrac{2\pi x}{L} + 7e^{-9at}\cos\dfrac{3\pi x}{L} -$

$$3e^{-16at}\cos\dfrac{4\pi x}{L} + \cdots\Big)$$

where $a = \dfrac{\pi^2}{L^2 RC}$, $t > 0$.

8. $i = -A\sqrt{\dfrac{C}{L}}\,e^{-\frac{G}{C}t}\,\cos\omega\sqrt{LC}\,x\,\sin\omega t$.

§118, pages 283, 284

3. (a) $x^3 - 3xy^2 = c$, $3x^2y - y^3 = c$, $p = \dfrac{\rho}{g}\Big[c - gy - \tfrac{1}{2}(x^2+y^2)^2\Big]$.

(b) $x^2 + y^2 = c$, $y = cx$, $p = \dfrac{\rho}{g}\Big[c - gy - \tfrac{1}{2}(x^2 + y^2)^{-1}\Big]$.